W9-DEA-103

St. Louis Community College

Library

5801 Wilson Avenue
St. Louis, Missouri 63110

Machine
Tool
Operations

Machine
Tool
Operations

William J. Patton

Red River Community College
Manitoba, Canada

RESTON PUBLISHING COMPANY, INC.
Reston, Virginia 22090
A Prentice-Hall Company

Library of Congress Cataloging in Publication Data

Patton, W   J
    Machine tool operations.

    1. Machine-shop practice.   I. Title
TJ1160.P373   621.7′5   73-13943
ISBN 0-87909-465-6

© 1974 by
Reston Publishing Company, Inc.
A Prentice-Hall Company
Box 547
Reston, Virginia 22090

10 9 8 7 6 5 4 3 2 1

Printed in the United States of America.

Preface

This book is intended as a text for students in technical institutes, junior colleges, and other such institutions which offer courses in machine tool operations, manufacturing processes, or machine tool technology. Machine shop training has seen some changes in the last decade. Electric discharge machines, numerically controlled machines, and other newer types of machines are found in most training shops, which have adopted these new techniques as fast as industry has. The machine shop trainee must still know the standard machine tools and techniques, but his training must now be somewhat broader. In addition to new tools and methods, a much wider range of materials must be machined nowadays: alloy steels, light metals, rubbers, and plastics.

Few institutional training courses for machinists are longer than two years. This is barely time enough to develop basic skills. It is not time enough for much learning or experience in this demanding skilled trade. In this book, therefore, background subjects such as metallurgy, heat treating, and power transmission are offered with a definite machine shop bias rather than the usual broader treatment.

Skilled trades and professions are not learned from books, but from skilled instructors. The student can look up information such as tool angles, mathematical formulas, or basic principles in a book, but he cannot learn such skills as proper setup operations on machine tools from a book. This book does not pretend to replace the instructor in those demonstrations that only a skilled instructor can supply.

Fortunately any machinist can learn the methods of numerical control from a book. The two chapters devoted to this subject should make the student familiar with the standard programming and operating methods that apply to all NC machine tools. These chapters carry the student as far as contouring operations on two-axis positioning mills. A short treatment of the programming of NC lathes is also included.

William J. Patton

Contents

Part I

Benchwork

Chapter 1

The Machine Shop Occupations

The methods, and especially the attitudes, with which you approach a new skill, subject, or occupation will decide your success or failure. Machining skills, applications, and knowledge cover an impressively large range and are in a constant state of change. This opening chapter discusses successful approaches to machine tool operations.

1.1 INSTRUCTORS—AND BOOKS

The competence possessed by any machinist of broad experience is impressive indeed. He knows how to operate a greater range of machinery than is used in any other skilled trade, using a range of cutters that include single-point lathe cutters, taps, dies, drills, reamers, and milling cutters, all of which come in many types. Some of these cutters are made of high-speed steel, and some are made of carbides; the methods of cutting with these two materials may be entirely different. The material of his workpiece may be a soft steel, a machinery steel, a tool steel, a cast iron, a stainless steel, brass, aluminum, plastic, rubber, or any other familiar or unfamiliar material, and each of these materials has its own peculiar machining requirements.

This book discusses all these matters, and perhaps some reader may suspect that he can learn the machinist's trade by reading this book and practicing a little on a few machine tools. He cannot. No doubt the book can explain the bare bones of a machining procedure, but to see that same procedure executed by an experienced man is something quite different. The experienced machinist can bring to these operations a style that no book can suggest, and certain twists of operation that must be learned by watching, not reading.

It is unwise for the student to undertake most of the machining operations discussed in this book until the procedure has been demonstrated to him by his instructor. Nevertheless, such a book as this has a place in the student's training program. The machinist must process more information— measurements, angles, speeds, feeds, etc.—than does any other skilled trade. You cannot store in your mind all the information you may possibly require, and if you could, you could not be sure that you would remember it correctly. Much of this information must be stored in books, and the more complex your technical work becomes, the more dependent you become on information stored in books.

The training programs of the United States Navy are among the best in the world. Before getting into this book, take a word of advice from one of the Navy's rate training manuals:

> "Before you begin to study any part of the training manual intensively, become familiar with the entire manual. Read the preface and the table of contents. Check through the index. Look at the appendixes. Thumb through the manual without any particular plan, looking at the illustrations and reading bits here and there as you see things that interest you.
>
> ". . . Ask yourself some questions: What do I need to learn about this? What do I already know about this? How is this information related to information given in other chapters? How is this information related to the qualifications for advancement?"

The information in this book is meant to serve in the way best suited to your own interests. To that purpose you must digest it, question it, add to it, modify it, and twist it about to serve your own unique needs and purposes. Your instructor may have opinions that do not agree with those expressed in this book. If so, he is probably right—after all, he practices his trade every day. Certainly there is a diversity of opinion on many topics in machine shop practice. Only when you have heard them all can you safely decide your own opinion.

1.2 THE MACHINE SHOP OCCUPATIONS

The machine shop trades and occupations are employed in the shaping of parts by the removal of metal on machine tools.

The complete practitioner of any of the machine shop trades requires three broad skills:

1. The manual skills of the trade.
2. .Speed and certainty of execution in these manual skills.
3. The knowledge and mental skills required in these operations.

A characteristic of the machine shop operations that has been little noted is that no other trade processes so much information as the machinist. The quantity of information processing that goes on in the machinist's mind when he sets up a job on a lathe cannot be noticed, but the first time anyone programs a numerically controlled lathe operated by information punched into tape, he gains a new respect for the thinking that the machinist does more or less by instinct. This matter of information processing is dealt with in the chapters on numerical control.

The second requirement, speed of execution, must be noted. It is easy enough to learn many operations on a lathe, for example. But only an experienced machinist can execute such operations with the speed, the flair, and the certainty of touch expected of a skilled man.

There are several machine shop occupations, and several other occupations that require machine shop knowledge. Occupations are usually classified as unskilled, semiskilled, skilled, and professional, but such labels are rather meaningless. Is there a truly unskilled occupation? Probably not.

An unskilled job is really a job that is sufficiently simple that the worker can learn the skills on the job in a few days. There are no such jobs among the machine shop operations.

There are, however, a number of semiskilled machine shop occupations, including *machine operator*. The machine operator is not really semiskilled, whatever that means; rather, his skills and responsibilities are restricted to the operation of a single machine, such as a radial drill or an automatic lathe, and he is more closely supervised than the all-around machinist.

The all-around *machinist* is a broadly skilled man who can set up and operate most types of machine tools. He may be employed as a machinist producing parts, or as that variant of the machinist trade, the *millwright*, who repairs and maintains equipment.

The *set-up man* sets up such machine tools as the automatic lathe, checks the first parts off, then turns the operation over to the machine operator.

The *toolmaker* and *die maker* may be required to work to closer tolerances than the machinist. These are all-around machinists with extra skills. Tool and die makers do not produce production parts; they produce the tooling, dies, and fixtures on which such parts are produced. Usually the production equipment they make is operated by semiskilled men and women.

Draftsmen and machine designers do not operate machine tools but must have a sufficiently close acquaintance with the machine shop operations to design parts that do not call for unrealistic operations in the machine shop. It is not uncommon for the machinist to point out improvements to such design work, and no production man likes to work with a draftsman or designer who is indifferent to manufacturing difficulties.

Mechanical engineers, mechanical technologists, industrial engineers, and other engineering occupations require a broad general knowledge of machining operations for the same reason as do designers and draftsmen, because how a part is made partly decides how it should be designed. The machinist's knowledge, therefore, is one component in the broad range of engineering sciences.

The development of numerically controlled machining, which is discussed at the end of this book, has produced two new job classifications: *numerical control programmer* and *numerical control machine operator.*

The programmer lays out the sequence of numerically controlled machining for punching into the control tape. He too requires a competent knowledge of machining operations, since he must plan the machining sequence without being the operator of the machine. In addition, NC programming requires ability in geometry and trigonometry and the management of calculations. The programming of contouring operations requires also the ability to manipulate one or more of the special computer languages used in machining work such as AUTOSPOT or APT.

The machine operator of a numerically controlled machine tool uses little manipulative skill other than that required to make his machine setups, but he must be knowledgeable in machining practice, with an understanding of numerical control programming.

It may be noted here that it is considerably more difficult, and requires much more time to train to be a machinist than to learn the techniques of numerical control, though numerical control methods cannot be applied by personnel who have not learned their basic machining practices first.

1.3 OCCUPATIONAL OBSOLESCENCE

There is nowadays an awareness that occupations change rapidly over the lifetime of the practitioner of the occupation. Indeed, some occupations become obsolete and disappear. Automatic methods of production, such as numerical control, may not reduce the number of jobs, but they certainly alter the types of jobs and their characteristics. What are the long-term prospects for machining?

The machining occupations appear to have survived the 70 years of rapid technical advance of this century. Actually, the most serious threats to employment in the machining trades came at a relatively early stage. The automatic lathe and other automatic machining methods no doubt greatly reduced the demand for machinists. But these inventions are past history. The most recent technical innovation has been numerical control, the control of machining operations by punched tape. But numerical control appears not to have reduced the demand for machining jobs, since it has extended the scope of machining operations. Numerical control, though it reduces the need for the machinist's skills, makes heavy demands on the machinist's knowledge.

What sustains the demand for machinists is that only machining operations can provide the final surface finish and accuracy for parts that sometimes can be produced by methods other than machining. Many production parts can be cast or forged more cheaply than they can be machined, but accuracy requirements may require final machining operations on such cast or forged parts.

The machinist need not look upon technical change as a threat to his security. However, if he intends to maintain his status as a competent machinist, he must keep up to date. He must read technical articles, go to technical meetings, and learn new techniques and new machining materials. If he assumes his learning to be complete at any time, he has sentenced himself to be out-of-date.

1.4 TO LEARN, ASK QUESTIONS

As a learner, your position is not enviable. You frequently do not understand explanations given to you, you make mistakes, and put yourself in embarrassing positions.

You must remember that everything is difficult when you are learning, and everything that has already been learned is easy. Perhaps nobody is stupid except those unfortunate people who think they are. Do not be disturbed if you do not understand something on first acquaintance; few people do, including those who claim they do: Ask questions. Ask stupid questions if you need to. You would not ask questions if you did not need to know. Since you want to learn, get yourself a bargain and learn as much as you can.

Everyone wants to learn only that information that will be useful to him. Do not be too hasty in your judgment of what is useful and useless information. Useful information sometimes becomes out-of-date; some apparently useless information may become very handy at a later date. The author had to learn the theory of optical lenses in high school physics, and thought it uninteresting and unimportant to his future career. His first job after he completed his technical training was to design and make a simple instrument based on the theory of optical lenses, and he had to learn this "useless" theory all over again.

Be interested. Take pride in your work—it is your personal advertising. Whether it turns out good or bad, be sure that anything you do represents your best effort.

1.5 HOUSEKEEPING

Housekeeping is the activity of keeping order, cleanliness, and tidiness in a shop. It is true that a disorderly shop can put out production in not too inefficient a manner. Nevertheless, there are strong reasons for a high standard of housekeeping.

Safety is one reason. A disorderly shop is certain to be accident-prone, if only because unexpected things happen to be in unexpected places.

Ease of working is a second reason. In a disorderly shop you can never find the small tools you need. You make aimless searches for the crescent wrench, first looking in the likely places, where you never find it, then in the unlikely places. After a few minutes of hopeless search, you begin to interrupt the work of others by getting them involved in the search. If you are lucky, you find the tool. If it's a small tool, such as an Allen wrench, it can be buried under a pile of chips to be thrown into the trash can. With good housekeeping, such irritations are rare.

Pride of workmanship is another. If you are a disorderly worker, you will not even look competent to anyone else. A clean shop is a pleasant place to work and a pleasant place to visit.

Housekeeping is a simple matter of forming the required habits. In a spare moment put a tool away. Sweep the chips from under your feet. Clean a thread. Oil a tool. You always have time for these small chores, which make life easy, simple, and trouble free.

Your objective should not be the least housekeeping that is acceptable, but a thorough effort. The best shops in this country set very high standards for housekeeping, and you are expected to measure up to such standards.

1.6 RIGIDITY IN SETUPS

The beginner in machining operations may or may not be an acceptable housekeeper, but he is almost certain to make setups of workpiece and tools that lack the required rigidity. Drill bits, centers, cutters, toolholders, and other components must always be set up with the least possible overhang

Fig. 1 (a) An exaggeration of common beginner's mistakes in setting up work. The bar to be machined should have the shortest possible projection, or should be supported at both ends. Similarly the tool should have the shortest possible projection from its holder. (b) A better arrangement. The bar has the shortest possible projection from the chuck and also the cutter from the toolpost. Note the use of a heavy style of toolpost in both photographs; light toolposts are sources of trouble.

and the least possible projection from the holder. A cutter that projects twice as far out of its holder will deflect eight times as much.

Lack of rigidity produces a number of unfavorable effects. These include tool chatter, damage to tool or workpiece, loss of accuracy, and other effects.

Rigidity is ensured by using the largest possible cutters and toolholders. If you have a choice, pick a big one over a smaller one, especially in the case of boring bars. When machining, think rigidity. More extended discussions of this important matter will be made in this book as required.

1.7 SAFETY

Of all the aspects of machining, safety and accident prevention are least likely to be learned from a book, in part because reading a book is just about the safest thing you can do. Nevertheless, even a book can make some useful remarks about safety, though safe procedures must be learned on the shop floor and developed into rigid habits.

Safety considerations should begin by considering first two characteristics of a machining operation:

1. A motor is supplying a high torque and horsepower to a rotating spindle, chuck, or tool.
2. A hot, sharp chip is being produced at high speed.

The rotating spindle or drill can capture such personal articles as sweaters, ties, rings, or long hair, and wind the operator into the machinery in a few revolutions. Therefore, loose or dangerous jewelry and clothing must be removed or controlled, sleeves should be rolled up, and hair protected. If your housekeeping is imperfect, long loose chips may pile up until they tangle with rotating parts, creating a hazardous condition.

Machining chips can be razor-sharp and may have a high temperature. Under conditions of heavy cutting, machining chips can burn holes in clothing. Since they come off the workpiece at high velocities, machining chips are in effect a hot travelling knife. Chip velocities of 1000 feet per minute are not unusual when carbide cutters are used; this is a speed of 15 miles per hour. Flying chips are a frequent cause of eye accidents—hence the required use of approved types of safety glasses and face shields. Grinding chips are especially dangerous because of their small size and their abrasiveness.

Any accident is some occurrence that could not possibly happen, but did. No one is so foolish as to leave a chuck key in a chuck when he turns on the lathe. And yet otherwise sensible people do this. The operator intends to remove the chuck key, but perhaps someone talks to him, thus interrupting his train of thought; in the end the chuck key is thrown across the shop when the chuck begins to rotate. Distractions are one of the major causes of accidents.

Compressed air is especially dangerous. The cleaning of chips from machine beds with compressed air has been a frequent cause of eye injuries, since high-pressure air can throw chips a considerable distance. Even the sharp hiss of escaping air can startle a preoccupied operator and cause an accident.

All skilled operations call for a final checkout before the operation begins. A competent pilot of a light plane, before he starts up the engine, makes a "walk-around" of his plane, checking all parts and control surfaces, looking for nicks in the propeller, and so on. The plane may well be ready for takeoff, but the pilot must actually see and know with absolute certainty that the plane is ready. Similarly, a competent horseman does not take the horse out of the stall and climb aboard for a ride. Only beginners make assumptions. The experienced horseman checks the condition of the horse's feet, even making sure that there is a shoe on each foot.

The same care goes with machining. When you are ready to begin a job, make a final checkout of the machine. Sure, you clamped the tool. But before you begin, check it out. To repeat, only beginners make assumptions. Do not turn any machine on until you have checked out everything— tool, toolholder, centers, workpiece, and chuck. Be sure that floor conditions give you a safe footing. Remove patches of oil on the floor, which are especially dangerous, and periodically sweep the chips from under your feet; these make a treacherous footing, too.

Safety, like good housekeeping, is a state of mind and a habit. The best way to prevent accidents is to assume that they will happen.

1.8 MISTAKES

Only beginners make assumptions, but everybody makes mistakes. Suppose you must saw off a length of bar stock roughly 9 in. long. If you think you could not be so foolish as to measure 8 in., you have much to learn about yourself. That silly mistake has been made by every person, skilled or inexperienced. Experienced machinists know how easy it is to make a mistake, beginners do not. Old-timers have a rule: "Measure twice, and cut once." Do not measure once and then find you have to cut twice.

When making measurements, measure twice. Always. When making precision measurements, it may be wise to measure three times. Or four times. This book offers you an ironclad guarantee that you will make mistakes, because you too have all the human weaknesses. The only protection against mistakes is the same protection as against accidents: the realization that the next possibility for a mistake is available at all times. Never trust yourself, and keep checking.

Your best opportunities for error lie in shop mathematics, and it is here that mistakes can have serious consequences. Do not trust your calculations or anyone else's.

A great many formulas are used to calculate depths of cut on machine tools. Even if your calculations by formula are correct, you may find that they do not come out quite right on the machine tool and that some final slight adjustments are required. Mathematics is useful, provided that your faith in it is not boundless.

1.9 MATHEMATICS

In every course of study for machining, a mathematics course is included, and of course some student raises the question: What has mathematics to do with this skilled trade? What indeed? Look through the later chapters of this book on advanced milling operations or numerical control. Decide then how an attitude of antimathematics will influence your career prospects. A machinist does precision work, and the word "precision" implies mathematics. Remember that the history of technical development shows a constant trend from muscle power toward increasing mental power, and as the decades go by, more and more mathematics is applied to machining operations.

A machinist is continually converting from 64ths of an inch to thousandths of an inch. To make these conversions quick and easy for you, there is a little fact that you should memorize:

$$\tfrac{1}{64} = 0.015625, \text{ or approximately } \tfrac{15}{1000}$$

Similarly, a 32nd equals 0.03125, or almost 32 thousandths in a 32nd of an inch.

Do not, however, try to memorize too much information, for then you will make the serious error of relying on your memory. Your memory is the most unreliable of your abilities. Look up numbers and facts just to be sure. Look them up even when you think you know them. It is not your business to be a walking encyclopedia, but to get things right. If you do not have the time to make sure, then you do not have the time to correct the mistake you are going to make.

1.10 DRAWINGS, CONTROL TAPES, AND COMMUNICATION

Except in unusual circumstances, every component that must be machined requires a drawing to control its manufacture. The part drawing, like speech or written communication, is a communication given in a certain code, this code being a graphic language. Both the person who made the drawing and the person who uses the drawing must understand the drawing code if they are to communicate effectively. The machinist must be able to read the drawing in such a way that he can lay out in his mind the sequence of machining steps to produce the part successfully, and select the proper tools and equipment.

The part drawing specifies requirements and dimensions of the finished product, but does not tell the machinist how to make the part. In the last decade, the use of numerically controlled machining (see Chapters 22 and 23) has developed extensively, and in this method the machinist receives both a drawing and a punched tape. The holes in the punched tape are a series of hole-no hole coded instructions that the tape reader of the numerically controlled machine reads and executes. The punched tape usually contains all the machine instructions to produce the part automatically. Therefore, the tape includes all the information given on the drawing, plus also the planning and the sequence of operations. Since the punched tape does most of what the machinist otherwise could do, including all machine motions and their sequence, it would seem that a machinist is not needed for numerically controlled operations. But this conclusion is too hasty.

The person who plans and programs the numerically controlled operation and the punched tape, unless he is a machinist, will have less knowledge of machining than the operator of the numerically controlled machine. He will need to consult with the machine operator in order to draw upon the latter's experience. Suppose, for example, that the programmer wishes to program a numerically controlled lathe using a button carbide insert (a circular carbide cutting tool). The machinist might consider the operation and recommend against a button insert, because in his experience it will cause chatter. There is always the possibility that the tape program may be wrong, or require modification. The machinist must often make these changes. The machinist must know when the tool is becoming dull, or is not producing an acceptable finish, or he must use his experience when he finds the programmed cutting speed is excessively high. Always the machinist must keep this so-called "automatic" operation under control. To do so, he needs the part drawing, and, of course, all his experience. In tape control, the tape puts the information into the process; in standard machining practice the operator puts the information into the process. The operator, however, has the great advantage that he can correct his errors. The tape can also have errors, which only the operator can correct.

Therefore, to control any machining operation, including a numerically controlled one, the operator must be able to read a part drawing knowledgeably.

We have not yet discussed the most important communication methods: the verbal and written ones. Beginners often take the attitude that ability to speak and write good English is not important to their careers. In all honesty, it must be said that the ability to speak and write is of greater importance to your career than technical competence. Often a mediocre machinist or other craftsman is promoted over a superior craftsman simply because he is a better communicator. Promotions must usually go to those who best communicate. This is not an argument against technical competence, but simply a reminder that the world of men and their activities requires not one, but many abilities in those who are destined to receive preference. You cannot work alone in the world; therefore, you cannot neglect the all-important matter of communicating with others on the industrial team. The way in which you speak, write, and spell is your style by which you are remembered by other people. If everyone knows stories of the incompetent man who talked himself into a good job, does not that prove that the world values the ability to communicate?

1.11 READING A PART DRAWING: A CRANK PULLEY CENTER PIN

Figure 2 shows a crank pulley center pin to be machined from round bar. The part requires turning, threading, parting-off, and chamfering on the lathe, with also a milling operation to produce the flat at the threaded end.

It would be most convenient to do all the lathe operations first, including the cutting of the threads, and then to mill out the flat. This sequence, however, will leave a burr on the threads from the milling operation. Probably, therefore, the milling operation will be done before the threads are cut.

The material is a free-machining steel, the L in the steel designation 12L14 indicating that lead is added to the steel to lubricate the cutting tool. Every steel has a best machining speed. A handbook will suggest a lathe

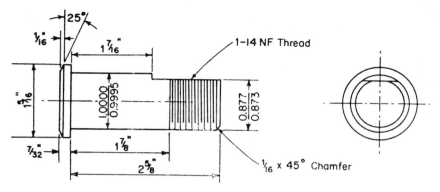

Fig. 2

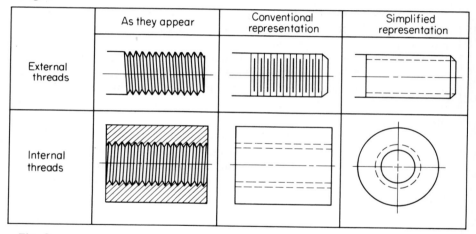

	As they appear	Conventional representation	Simplified representation
External threads			
Internal threads			

Fig. 3

speed of about 550 rpm for this steel in this diameter, using high-speed steel cutters.

The 1″-14 NF (National Fine) thread is cut either with a threading tool or with a special threading head.

Threads may be indicated on drawings in various ways, as shown in Fig. 3.

1.12 READING A PART DRAWING: A PLANETARY PIN

The planetary pin of Fig. 4 seems simple enough, but is a more complicated part than the crank pulley center pin. Both are components for agricultural machines. In its basic shape, the planetary pin has a hole drilled at one end and a groove for an O-ring at the other end.

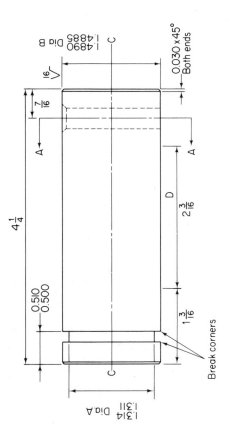

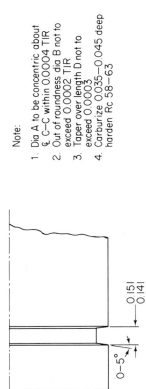

Note:

1. Dia A to be concentric about ℄ C—C within 0.0004 TIR
2. Out of roundness dia B not to exceed 0.0002 TIR
3. Taper over length D not to exceed 0.0003
4. Carburize 0.035—0.045 deep harden Rc 58—63

Groove detail double size

Fig. 4

The line c-c is drawn as a light broken line of long and short dashes, indicating that it is a center line. Two center lines at right angles are used to indicate and dimension hole centers, as in Fig. 5. Center lines are also used as base lines for dimensioning. The drilled hole in Fig. 4 is indicated by the convention for hidden lines, which is a series of short dashes.

The planetary pin is made in large numbers for a large farm tractor. The bar material is 8620 steel, a machinery steel, $1\frac{1}{2}$ in. in diameter, which is ground to size and surface-hardened.

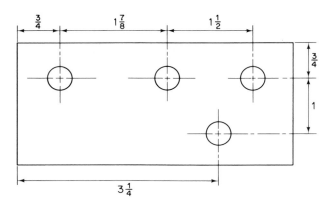

Fig. 5

The drilled hole has a length/diameter ratio of about 5. The hole can be produced without woodpecker drilling (retracting the drill to clear chips) if the drill bit is kept cool by lubrication with a coolant. Deep holes, however, can run off line unless the drilling operation is carefully controlled. The O-ring groove follows the machining rules for such grooves: rounded corners and a slight taper to the sides to avoid cutting the rubber ring that fits into the groove. This groove requires the grinding of a suitable cutter.

Few length dimensions are critical, but note that the outside diameter is allowed a total variation of half a thousandth only. A surface finish of 16 microinches (millionths of an inch) is likewise specified. See Chapter 25 for an explanation of this surface finish. Sixteen microinches is a rather smooth finish. The close dimensional control and the fine finish indicate a final grinding operation. Since the diameter is uniform, and the production quantities are large, the planetary pin will be centerless ground (see Chapter 15). Note also the specification for T.I.R. (total indicator runout, discussed in Chapter 17) and for taper.

The rough turning, the plunge cut for the groove, the cutting-off, and perhaps the cross-drilling of the hole would be done on a multiple-spindle automatic lathe, as discussed in Chapter 21. Induction hardening would follow, and grinding would complete the part.

This pin must be made for less than $1.50, material included, or about one dollar for machining, heat-treating, and grinding. This price is possible only with production techniques.

These are the types of drawings that the machinist must read, interpret, and study. From the drawing he decides the sequence of machining operations, makes up any cutters of special shape, such as the one to cut the O-ring groove of Fig. 4, and notes any operations or dimensions that will give him difficulties.

Make up a list of the things you do not know or understand about Figs. 2 and 4. For example, you do not know what 8620 steel is. Neither do most machinists, but they know where to find out. Do you understand dimension D, which seems to dimension nothing at all? Try to find answers to some or all of these unknown matters.

1.13 MACHINE SURFACES

This topic is deferred to the end of this chapter because of its importance and its unfamiliarity to untrained people in machine shop work. We refer here to the care of critical surfaces of machine tools.

Machine tools generally cost from $3 to $10 a pound, yet are made from steel and gray cast iron which are worth only about 20¢ a pound. The machine tool is worth more than 10 times its raw material.

This great difference in costs is chiefly explained by the critical surfaces of machine tools. Look about you at the machine tools in your own shop. The lathe has accurate ways to align accurately the headstock, tailstock, and carriage so that the turning tool will move exactly at right angles to the workpiece. The small drill press has a ground worktable that must be exactly at right angles to the drill spindle. Taper shank drills have accurately ground taper shanks that are designed to fit with accuracy the accurately ground sockets that mate with them. The hole in a milling cutter must be exactly in the middle of the cutter. The measurements of a micrometer or vernier caliper are only as good as the contact surfaces of these measuring instruments. The list of critical machine surfaces is endless.

The machinist deals in precision. That precision is dependent on his skill, but it is equally dependent on these hundreds of critical surfaces. To give the machinist the precision he needs, these surfaces are machined, hardened, ground, scraped, checked, measured, and inspected with considerable care and expense. These surfaces, so often taken for granted, are the most important of the machinist's tools. They must be guarded and protected from scratches, grit, hammer blows, heat, and other destructive agents (the application of heat to metals invariably causes small distortions, as discussed in Chapters 17 and 18). An untrained operator will not be greatly disturbed if he drills into a worktable or uses the lathe ways as a convenient anvil. The experienced man knows that these are gross errors since these surfaces are what make a machine tool different from a machine; *these surfaces are the most valuable things in the machine shop.*

QUESTIONS

1. The crank pulley center pin of Fig. 2 is made from bar stock 12 feet (144 in.) long. When the part is complete, it is cut off on the lathe with a cutoff tool $\frac{3}{16}$ in. wide. How many of these pins can be obtained from a 144-in. bar, if the last 6 in. of the bar cannot be used?

2. What length of the crank pulley center pin is threaded (include the chamfer on the end of the thread)?

3. What is a chamfer?

4. What does the instruction "break corners" mean in Fig. 4?

5. What is the length of the flat milled at the threads of Fig. 2?

6. The threaded pin of Fig. 2 has 14 threads per inch. How many complete threads are to be cut into the pin (include the chamfer)?

7. In Fig. 2, suppose that the pin of the drawing is to be produced from $1\frac{3}{8}$ ⌀ bar. What depth of cut is required to reduce the bar from $1\frac{3}{8}$ to 1.000 diameter on the lathe?

8. What is the total length of the pin of Fig. 2?

9. How many millimeters are there in an inch?

10. How many centimeters are there in an inch?

11. How many thousandths of an inch are there in the following dimensions (it is preferable to obtain this information from a table rather than to calculate): $\frac{1}{64}, \frac{1}{32}, \frac{1}{16}, \frac{5}{32}, \frac{7}{16}, \frac{5}{8}$?

12. Make a list of all the cutting operations required to produce the pin of Fig. 2. Do not be concerned about the order in which these operations will be performed.

13. Arrange the operations of Question 12 in what you believe to be a suitable order.

14. Make a list of all the cutting operations required to produce the planetary pin of Fig. 4.

15. What is the difference in responsibilities and work between a machine operator and a machinist?

16. What kind of work does a machine shop inspector perform?

17. What is the purpose of a chamfer?

18. Make a list of the types of machine tools in your shop, stating the types

of work that each can perform. Group all machine tools into three general types:

a. Machine tools for producing cylindrical surfaces.
b. Machine tools for producing flat surfaces.
c. Machine tools for interior surfaces such as holes.

Chapter 2

Hand Tools and Fasteners

The machinist's work includes a certain amount of casual benchwork such as assembling, disassembling, fitting, and a variety of other operations with hand tools.

2.1 HAMMERS AND CHISELS

The *ball peen hammer* is the usual machine shop hammer for general purposes. This is a forged hammer with a hardened face. Such hammers are classified by the weight of the head: 2, 4, 8, or 12 ounces, or 1, $1\frac{1}{4}$, $1\frac{1}{2}$, 2, or 3 pounds.

Soft-face hammers have inserted plastic, lead, or polyurethane rubber heads. These must be used when a hammer blow must not mar the work. Such hammers are needed for leveling work on parallels in machine vises preparatory to machining.

Cold chisels are used to cut cold metal, whereas a hot chisel is a blacksmith's tool for cutting hot metal. The cold chisel is held in the left

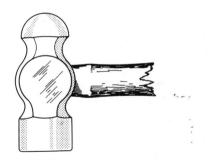

Fig. 6

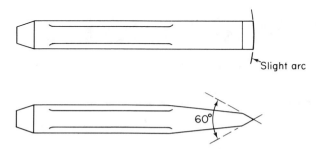

Slight arc

60°

Fig. 7

hand and struck with a ball peen hammer in the other hand. If you miss the chisel with the hammer, you will likely hit the knuckle of your left hand and skin it. Your left hand, however, will be quite safe if the forefinger of the left hand is straight and not curled around the chisel. In this position your finger will not be skinned if hit.

The cold chisel should be sharpened to an angle of approximately 60 deg, and the cutting edge should not be ground straight but very slightly curved. This curvature is used so that the chisel will begin to cut in the middle and not at the corners, which might chip out.

In such operations as cutting rivets with a cold chisel, the rivet head will fly when sheared. Take care for adjacent personnel or equipment, therefore. Also, if the end of the cold chisel is mushroomed from too many hammer blows, grind off the mushroom so that particles do not split off and fly.

2.2 HAND HACKSAWS

Hacksaw blades are made in 10- and 12-in. lengths, with 14, 18, 24, and 32 teeth per inch. Finer teeth are used for thinner material, and coarser teeth for heavier thicknesses and softer materials such as aluminum. More than one tooth of the blade must be cutting the workpiece if the teeth are not to be ripped out of the blade.

When cutting shapes that are open on one side, such as angles or channels, set them up in the vise open-end down. Cut close to the vise so that the workpiece does not vibrate while cutting.

Hacksaw blades and drill bits receive more abuse than is given to other equipment. Most people are impatient to complete a saw cut or to drill a hole, and force the tool. (The same people will run a lathe too slowly!) In both cases, forcing the tool heats and softens it, so that the tool is ruined. If a drill bit is burned, the shop may not have a spare bit of the same size. Usually there are spare hacksaw blades, however. If a hacksaw blade is carefully used, it will cut many square inches of metal (power hacksaw blades have cut as much as 3000 sq in. of steel per blade), but in normal use is good for only about four square inches of steel sawing. Good quality blades should be used if the blades are well cared for, and cheap blades should be used if they are abused.

2.3 WRENCHES

The crescent wrench, with an adjustable jaw, is available in lengths of 4, 6, 8, 10, 12, and 15 in. Each size can be adjusted to fit a range of bolt heads and nuts. But since this wrench fits many sizes, it fits no one bolt size exactly. If bolt heads on lathes and grinders are tightened with crescent wrenches over a period of a few years, the heads become somewhat mangled. For machine tool operations, use the proper size of open-end, box, or socket wrench.

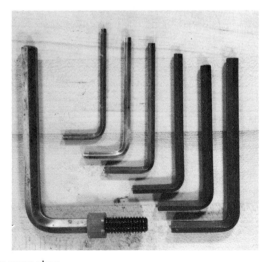

Fig. 8 Allan wrenches.

When one is tightening with the crescent wrench, the movable jaw should lie in the direction of rotation.

The Allan wrench is an excellent type, since the fit between the wrench and the socket in the head of the screw is very close. This wrench has a short right-angle bend in it. If the end of this bend is ground as a lathe cutter, the wrench makes a good temporary boring tool, though it is capable only of light cuts and short service.

2.4 FILES

Files are used for light dressing of parts, deburring and chamfering, and for finishing dies in toolmaking operations. In earlier times, the apprentice machinist was given difficult filing operations to perform, such as filing a block of metal to a perfect cube. Although such operations are better done by machine tools, it is still necessary for the machinist to be able to handle a file with considerable expertise. The file is not an easy tool to learn to handle. It is not even easy to file a flat surface flat.

Filing must be done at about elbow height for best results and ease in filing. The file must be passed across the work without rocking it, as this produces a curved surface. File pressure must be neither too heavy nor too

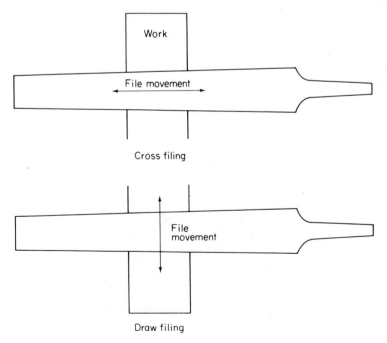

Fig. 9

light. Too light a pressure dulls the file teeth. Heavy pressure may load the teeth with chips, and these will score the workpiece. Neither files nor hacksaws should cut on the backstroke.

Draw filing (Fig. 9) is easier to do than straight filing. It removes less metal, but produces a smoother surface.

Files are made of very high-carbon steels and are therefore quite brittle. They must not be bent. The tangs of files and the edges of screwdrivers are among the commonest causes of industrial accidents. Do not file without putting a dependable handle on the file.

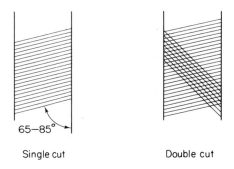

Single cut   Double cut

Fig. 10

Files have at least four patterns of teeth: single-cut, double-cut, curved, and rasp (Fig. 10). As with other cutting tools such as hacksaws, the teeth have several degrees of coarseness:

dead smooth
smooth
second cut
bastard
coarse
rough

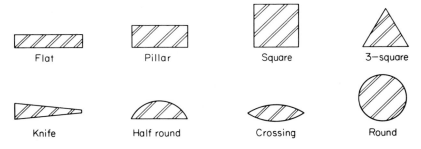

Flat   Pillar   Square   3—square

Knife   Half round   Crossing   Round

Fig. 11

The rasp and the curved tooth patterns and the coarser cuts are used on soft materials that will load finer teeth with chips.

Files are supplied in several cross-sectional shapes, chiefly those of Fig. 11. Special files are used for various functions, including die sinking and key cutting. If a corner is to be filed, a file with a safe edge (an edge without teeth) must be used. Such a file will file one side of the corner without removing metal from the other side.

The length of a file does not include the tang.

2.5 ABRASIVE AND POLISHING CLOTHS

The most commonly used sheet abrasives in machine shop operations are emery, aluminum oxide, silicon carbide, and crocus.

Emery is black in color, with rounded grains that polish rather than cut. *Aluminum oxide* and *silicon carbide* (carborundum) are harder than emery, with sharper grains and better material removal.

Crocus is a soft red material that produces an excellent polished finish. Crocus cloth must be used after rough and fine abrasive cloths have removed all scratches; crocus will not remove visible scratches.

Any workpieces that will be exposed to corrosive liquids must be polished. Corrosion proceeds more rapidly on a rough surface than on a polished surface.

COMPARATIVE TABLE OF ABRASIVE CLOTHS

Mesh	Silicon carbide or aluminum oxide	Emery	Polishing emery
600	—		4/0
500	—		2/0
400	10/0		0
320	9/0		$\frac{1}{2}$
280	8/0		
220	6/0		2
150	4/0	Fine	
120	3/0		
100	2/0	Medium	
80	0	Coarse	
60	$\frac{1}{2}$		
50	1	Extra Coarse	
40	$1\frac{1}{2}$		
36	2		
24	3		
16	4		

"Mesh" is the number of holes per inch length in a screening sieve. Thus 40 mesh has 40 holes per inch, or 1600 holes per square inch.

2.6 FASTENERS

A fastener is defined as a mechanical device for holding two or more bodies in definite positions with respect to each other. Welding, brazing, soldering, and adhesive bonding produce a permanent joint, but many types of fasteners, such as bolts, allow disassembly of the joint. The number of types of fasteners is remarkably large, and includes self-tapping screws for joining sheet metal, lock washers, lock nuts, lock bolts, wood screws, aircraft rivets for aircraft sheet, staples for sheet metal and paper products, track bolts for railroad rails, terminal strips for electric wiring, and a long list of others. Of all these types of fasteners, only those employing standard screw threads and the special types of fasteners discussed in the following sections are of special importance to the machinist.

2.7 THREAD STANDARDS

Standard threads include the Unified Thread Series, the Acme thread, the square thread, and the American Pipe Thread Series. All are helical ridges on cylindrical surfaces, but of differing cross section. Except for the Acme and square threads, all have a 60-deg included angle. A right-hand thread turns clockwise as it moves away from the observer into a nut; a left-hand thread turns counterclockwise as it moves in the same direction. Since right-hand threads are the standard type, a thread is understood to be right-hand unless expressly designated as left-hand.

Figure 12 shows the terminology applied to screw threads. The *major diameter* is the largest diameter of the thread. The *minor diameter* is the smallest diameter. The tap drill size for an internal thread should be the minor diameter, but for the protection of the tap it is almost always a larger diameter than the minor diameter. The *pitch diameter* is the average of the major and minor diameter, except for certain special thread shapes not discussed here. Pitch diameter is more properly defined as that diameter at which the length of the space between threads is equal to the length of the thread form, both measured parallel to the axis of the thread.

The *helix angle* of the thread is the angle between a plane perpendicular to the axis of the thread and the helix of the thread. The helix angle is given in thread tables, or can be calculated. Consider a bolt with a major diameter of 1 in. threaded 10 threads per inch. A nut on this thread advances 0.1 in. as it rotates one revolution about the bolt. The circumference of the bolt is 3.142 in. See Fig. 13. The helix angle is the angle whose tangent is 0.100/3.142 or 1° 40½'.

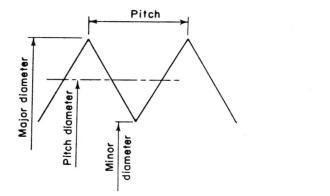

Fig. 12 Screw thread terms. **Fig. 13**

The pitch of a thread is the distance from a point on one thread to the same point on the next ridge. For 10 threads per inch (abbreviated 10 tpi) the pitch is 0.100 in. The *lead* of a thread is the distance a thread moves in one turn when in contact with its mating thread. For a single thread the pitch is the same distance as the lead. For a double thread the lead is twice the pitch.

A table of the standard Unified National Coarse (UNC) and Unified National Fine (UNF) threads is given in Sec. 5.11. These thread specifications are given thus:

$$\tfrac{1}{4}-20 \text{ UNC}$$

$$\tfrac{1}{2}-20 \text{ UNF, etc.}$$

The Unified National Screw Thread Form has a crest truncated by one-eighth and the root by one-sixth of the depth of a sharp 60-degree V-thread, giving a thread depth for an external thread from peak to valley of

$$d_o = \frac{0.6134}{N}$$

where N = number of threads per inch. For an internal thread,

$$d_i = \frac{0.5413}{N}$$

The Acme thread is a power thread for transmitting heavy thrusts. It is found on the leadscrews of lathes. Its form is given in Fig. 14. Another power thread, used with screw jacks, is the square thread of Fig. 15.

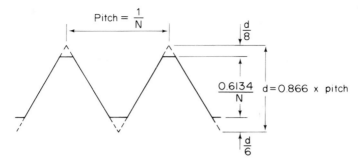

Unified national thread

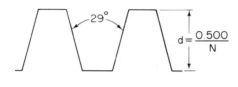

Acme thread

Fig. 14

Fig. 15

2.8 THREADED FASTENERS

Bolts are available in diameters $\frac{1}{4}$ in. and larger and are threaded in either the fine or coarse series. They are available also in a range of materials: mild steel, brass, stainless steel, or plated. Cadmium-plated steel bolts will resist the mild corrosive effects of an indoor atmosphere, but chrome-plating is necessary for outdoor use.

Machine screws are small bolts $\frac{3}{16}$ in. in diameter and smaller. These usually have a slotted head to receive a screwdriver tip, while bolts have a hexagonal head for a wrench. *Cap screws* are quality bolts machined all over to closely controlled dimensions, available in a number of shapes of heads, usually hexagon or socket head.

A clearance hole through which a bolt must pass must be drilled slightly larger than the bolt diameter. A clearance diameter $\frac{1}{64}$ in. larger makes a reasonably good fit between bolt and hole, though larger clearances are commonly used.

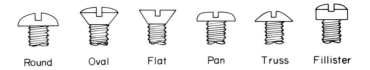

Round   Oval   Flat   Pan   Truss   Fillister

Fig. 16

Studs are threaded on both ends. *Setscrews* are short screws used in tapped holes to secure pulleys to shafts. They are not suited to large torques or high horsepower, for which purpose keys must be used.

2.9 PINS

Dowel pins are hardened unthreaded straight pins in a range of diameters and lengths. One end is radiused and the other is chamfered. The diameter of a dowel pin is ground to a very close tolerance of $+0.0002$ in. oversize. The dowel pin is inserted with a light drive fit into holes of the same diameter and is used to align very closely two parts of an assembly. The dowel hole requires reaming after drilling.

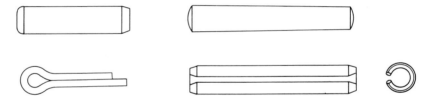

Fig. 17

Taper pins have a taper of $\frac{1}{4}$ in. per foot. These are often used to attach handles and wheels to shafts, being inserted into a drilled hole which is reamed out with a taper pin reamer.

The *cotter pin* is a familiar locking device inserted into a hole, after which its prongs are spread.

The *roll pin* or spring pin is used to pin together two components, one of which must rotate. This pin expands slightly in the holes of the components to hold them together, but with a sufficiently low force that they are not prevented from rotating with respect to one another.

2.10 KEYWAYS AND KEYS

Keyways (keyseats) are grooves of various shapes cut along the surface of a shaft or inside the bore of gears and wheels, into which steel keys are fitted to locate and drive the mating component. A keyway must therefore be cut in both mating components. The straight, round end, and Woodruff types of keys are illustrated in Fig. 18.

The rules for size of plain straight and round end keys are the following:

1. Key width should be one-quarter of shaft diameter.
2. Key thickness should be one-sixth of shaft diameter.
   (Key thickness is measured radially, key width tangentially; see Fig. 19.)
3. Minimum key length should be $1\frac{1}{2}$ shaft diameters.
4. The depth of a square keyway should be half the width of the key.

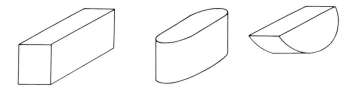

Fig. 18

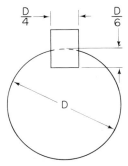

Fig. 19

Woodruff keys are semicircular. ·The circular side of the key is inserted into the shaft, the keyseat being cut by a milling cutter of the same diameter as the key. The size of a Woodruff key is given by a system of digits. The last two digits of the key number indicate key diameter in eighths of an inch, and the digits or digit preceding the last two gives the width of key in 32nds of an inch. For example, consider a 1012 size. This key has a diameter of $\frac{12}{8}$ or $1\frac{1}{2}$ in. Its width is $\frac{10}{32}$ or $\frac{5}{16}$ in.

In order to drive any key into its seat, there must be a small clearance of two to five thousandths between the keyway and the top surface of the key.

2.11 RETAINING RINGS

The use of stamped retaining rings (Fig. 20) is now common in the assembly of small and precision equipment. Some applications are shown in Fig. 21. Several will be found in record player mechanisms. The groove to hold the retaining ring is cut by a suitably ground recessing tool. The retaining ring must be inserted by special pliers.

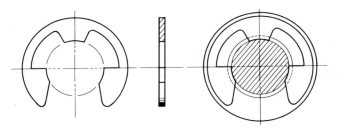

Fig. 20

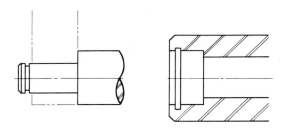

Fig. 21

2.12 O-RINGS AND O-RING GROOVES

The rubber O-ring is a familiar component for sealing of mating surfaces against the leakage of liquids and gases. These rings are usually made of nitrile rubber and are available in a wide range of sizes. The O-ring seals by compressing approximately 10 per cent of its diameter.

The O-ring is usually seated in a groove cut with a recessing tool. The machinist is not required to know how to dimension an O-ring groove, but he must know the machining requirements of such a groove. The surface finish of such a groove must be reasonably smooth so as not to abrade the O-ring. The groove must have no burrs or sharp corners that may cut the rubber of the ring. Dimensional errors in machining the groove may be serious: If the groove is cut too large, the O-ring may not seal against pressure, and if too small, the compressive force applied to the O-ring may be sufficiently high as to limit its service life.

If the O-ring is to be used as an oil seal, dip it in oil before inserting it into its groove. Do not use sharp instruments such as screwdriver tips to insert or remove an O-ring. Finally, do not insert an O-ring into its groove unless you are certain that the groove and all associated components of the fluid system are absolutely clean.

An O-ring groove may be seen in the planetary pin of Fig. 4.

QUESTIONS

1. You have to cut 16-gage (0.0598 in. thick) tubing with a hand hacksaw. Select a suitable number of teeth per inch.
2. Select a polishing cloth for the following operations:
   a. Removing a light film of rust from a piece of steel.
   b. Removing machining marks from a piece of steel.
   c. Polishing a piece of steel.
3. Explain "major diameter" and "minor diameter" of a screw thread.
4. Why is a tap drill rarely the same diameter as the minor diameter of a thread?
5. What is the pitch of the threads on the leadscrews of the lathes of your own shop?
6. Explain the difference between a cap screw and a machine screw.
7. For what kind of a joint is a roll pin used?
8. Size a rectangular key for width, thickness, and length, if the shaft size is 2 in. in diameter.
9. Why must an O-ring groove have no burrs?
10. Calculate the helix angles of the following threads:
    a. $\frac{1}{2}-13$ b. $\frac{1}{2}-20$ c. $\frac{1}{2}-28$

Chapter 3

Measurement
and Layout

The machinist's skills are only as good as his measuring skills. The machinist can measure to the ten-thousandth of an inch or better.

3.1 STEEL RULES

Accurate machining is done to thousandths of an inch and accurate grinding to "tenths" or one ten-thousandth of an inch. Machining and measuring may be done to finer accuracies even than these, even to millionths of an inch.

Rougher measurements are commonly made to 64ths of an inch, or as closely as a 64th can be estimated by rules, hand tools, and the human eye. Most steel rules, therefore, are graduated to 64ths, this being just about the smallest division on a scale that the human eye can differentiate. A 64th of an inch is 0.015625 in. or approximately 15 thousandths. A 32nd of an inch is 0.03125, or approximately 30 or 31 thousandths.

The metric system of measurements has made slow inroads into the

English system practiced in this country, and probably will replace it before the end of this century. Hospital, scientific, and some electrical equipment uses the metric system, which is also used with ball and roller bearings. The metric system is, of course, a simpler one to use than the present English system, though a change to it will be a personal inconvenience for a short time.

The basis of metric measurement is the *meter*, which is 39.37 in. The meter is divided into tenths of a meter (decimeters), hundredths (centimeters), and thousandths (millimeters). The thousandth part of a millimeter, called a *micron*, is used in both the English and metric systems. The two systems of measurement compare as follows:

$$1 \text{ meter } = 39.37 \text{ in.}$$

$$1 \text{ in. } = 25.4 \text{ millimeters (mm)}$$

$$\tfrac{1}{32} \text{ in. } = 0.794 \text{ mm}$$

$$\tfrac{1}{64} \text{ in. } = 0.397 \text{ mm}$$

$$0.001 \text{ in. } = 0.0254 \text{ mm or closely } 0.02 \text{ mm}$$

Steel rules graduated in 64ths of an inch, hundredths of an inch, or with metric measurements are available, in lengths from $\frac{1}{2}$ in. to 1 foot or longer.

The ends of a steel rule must be protected from damage, since any wear of the ends will shorten the rule. When one is measuring with a steel rule, it is better practice to take measurements from the 1-inch line or other major graduation rather than from the end.

Making a measurement with a steel rule is a very simple undertaking, but that does not mean that you will always make a correct measurement. It is surprisingly easy for any person to misread a rule. The error will usually be a large error rather than a small one. The number of 64ths may be read correctly, but the wrong number of inches, perhaps. Do not hesitate to read a measurement twice, just to be sure. If you believe that you cannot make a foolish mistake of this kind, you have much to learn about yourself.

3.2 THE "MIKE"

The micrometer, or micrometer caliper, more affectionately called the "mike," is the symbol of the machinist's skills. The mike can be read to thousandths, or, when fitted with a vernier scale, to tenths of thousandths, though it is not really an adequate instrument for reading "tenths." The range of measurement for any micrometer is 1 in. A 1-in. mike will read zero to 1 in., a 2-in. mike from 1 to 2 in., and so on for larger micrometers.

The basic element of the micrometer is an accurately ground spindle threaded 40 threads per inch. Hence one revolution of the spindle produces a movement of $\frac{1}{40}$ in. or 0.025 in. There is a mark on the micrometer sleeve for every 0.025 in. increment. The thimble over the sleeve is divided into 25 parts, each 0.001 in. When the zero graduation of the thimble is aligned with an engraved line along the sleeve, the reading is some multiple of 0.025 in., such as 0.625, 0.650, 0.675, etc. If some mark other than zero on the thimble is opposite the line on the sleeve, the number of thousandths on the thimble is added to the reading on the sleeve. Thus if the sleeve reads 0.450 (4 plus two small divisions) and if the 17 mark on the thimble aligns with the sleeve, the measurement is 0.450+0.017 or 0.467 in.

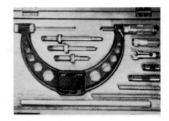

Fig. 22 A micrometer set.

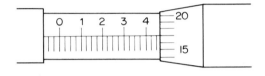

Fig. 23

The inside micrometer measures hole diameters. This is a more difficult instrument to read accurately than the outside micrometer. It must truly measure a diameter, and must be square to the hole. The operator must feel for the maximum diameter, and in any case he must make more than one reading with an inside micrometer if he is to be sure of his measurement.

Some micrometers are fitted with a ratchet stop. This limits the torque that can be applied to the mike and thus ensures consistent readings.

No micrometer is dependable unless it can be checked against some precise device such as a gage block. A reasonable check of accuracy for a

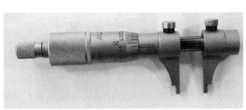

Fig. 24

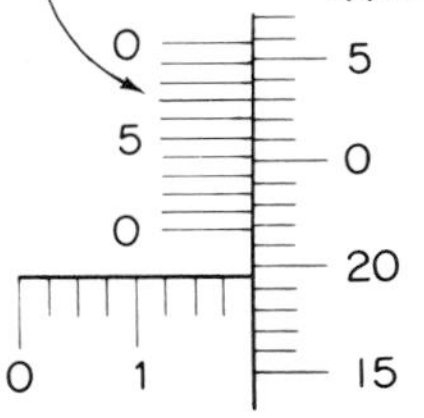

Fig. 25

1-in. micrometer is to close the spindle to a zero reading. If it does not zero, it must be adjusted in accord with manufacturer's recommendations. But 2-in. and larger mikes must be calibrated against another measuring instrument.

To read a vernier scale to tenths on a micrometer, see Fig. 25. The micrometer reads 0.175 plus almost 20 thousandths more on the thimble. The measurement is, therefore, a few tenths under 0.195. On the vernier only line 7 aligns with a line on the thimble. Therefore, the number of tenths is 7, and the final measurement is 0.1947. Hence, to read the vernier, decide which line on the vernier scale lines up best with any line on the thimble. The vernier has 11 lines in the same space as 10 on the thimble.

3.3 CALIPERS

Two types of calipers are shown in Fig. 26. In addition, the hermaphrodite caliper is illustrated in Fig. 27.

Calipers are used to transfer measurements. To obtain the outside diameter of round stock, adjust the caliper so that its own weight will cause its points to pass over the workpiece. The caliper is then held to a rule to find the actual diameter, as in Fig. 28. An inside caliper performs the same function for an inside diameter. For closer accuracy, the setting of the inside caliper may be measured with a micrometer. However, because of the flexibility of calipers, they cannot measure to accuracies better than a few thousandths of an inch. For much machining, this is not sufficient.

Fig. 26 Outside and inside bow string calipers,   inside firm joint caliper.

The *lock joint* or *transfer caliper* of Fig. 26 is used to measure recessed work, where the caliper cannot be withdrawn from the work unless one leg is moved. This caliper has a transfer arm, which is locked in position to hold the measurement. The leg of the caliper that must be moved is returned to position on this locked auxiliary arm to reproduce the measurement.

Fig. 27

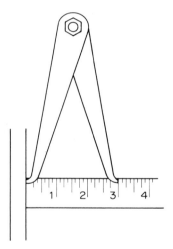

Fig. 28

3.4 VERNIER CALIPERS

Vernier calipers can provide accuracy of 0.001 in. Both inside and outside types of vernier calipers are, of course, available, though most vernier calipers are constructed to provide either inside or outside measurement. The vernier height gage of Fig. 30 and the vernier depth gage are modifications of the vernier caliper.

The vernier caliper has a fixed measuring jaw and a vernier slide assembly associated with the movable jaw. Examination of the vernier caliper shows how to lock the slide assembly before making final adjustment with the small adjusting nut. The jaws must not exert any significant force

Fig. 29

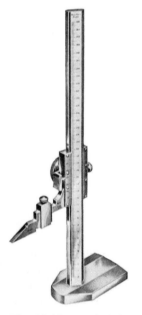

Fig. 30 Vernier height gage.

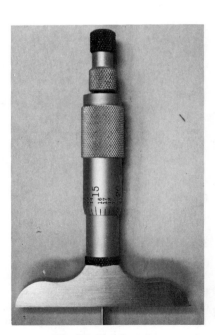

Fig. 31 Depth gage.

against the work, and like any other caliper, the accuracy of the setting is gaged by feel as the caliper is withdrawn from the work. Much usage of a caliper can lead to wear of the jaws of a thousandth of an inch or more.

Like the micrometer, the main scale of the vernier caliper is divided into fortieths of an inch or 0.025 in. The finer part of the measurement is made with a vernier. Twenty-five divisions of the vernier scale occupy the same length as 24 divisions on the beam scale. The small difference in scale is equal to 0.001 in. The vernier scale is read by finding the vernier line that best corresponds with a line on the main scale.

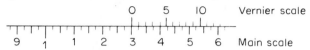

(a) Main scale in 0.025 divisions. The measurement reads 1.304

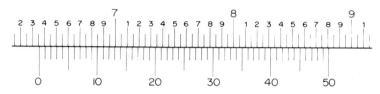

(b) Main scale in 0.050 divisions. The measurement reads 6.359

Fig. 32

Suppose that the main scale reads slightly more than 1.300 and that the 4 line on the vernier aligns accurately with a line on the main scale. The reading is 1.300+0.004, or 1.304 (Fig. 32).

3.5 THE DIAL INDICATOR

The dial indicator (Fig. 33) has a face graduated in units of 0.001, 0.0005, or 0.0001, and an indicator that moves over the dial to indicate the reading. The instrument is chiefly used to measure movement. A movable plunger drives the indicating hand through a gear train.

The dial indicator may be used to center a bar in a chuck. For this purpose the dial indicator may be mounted on the toolpost. The foot of the plunger is placed in contact with the bar in the chuck, so that the indicator gives a reading on the dial. The bar is then rotated while the dial indicator reading is watched. If in a full revolution of the bar the reading of the dial indicator does not change, then the bar is perfectly centered. If, however, in a full revolution of the bar, the dial indicator reading goes from an extreme of 0.021 to 0.033, say, then the total indicator runout is 0.012. The total indicator runout is twice the eccentricity of the bar in the chuck, so the bar must be moved 0.006 in. toward the side with the low reading.

Shafts are usually made by turning, then heat-treating, and finally grinding after heat-treating. Long, thin shafts will warp as a result of heat-

Fig. 33 Dial indicator.

treating temperature effects. Very often the specifications on the part print for the shaft will call for "TIR not to exceed 0.005 in." TIR is the usual abbreviation for "total indicator runout." To test the shaft for runout, it is mounted between a pair of centers, and the TIR is measured with a dial indicator. If the shaft is warped beyond the specification, it must be straightened on a press, though a small TIR can be removed in the final grinding operation.

A hole may have to be centered on the axis of a drilling or vertical milling machine. For this purpose the dial indicator is mounted in the spindle of the machine, and the spindle is rotated one turn. If there is no change in dial indicator reading, then of course the hole is centered on the spindle and ready for the machining operation.

The dial indicator may, therefore, have a very great range of applications. Other uses are to prove the straightness or flatness of a work-

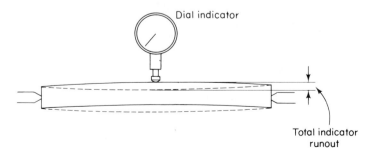

Dial indicator

Total indicator runout

Fig. 34

piece, to check alignment of bearings, to inspect a production run of parts for diameter, to determine bore sizes, to measure depths, and in materials testing to measure elongations of materials when tensioned or compressed. To serve all these varied functions the dial indicator may need a range of accessories and of mounting methods.

3.6 SURFACE PLATE MEASUREMENTS

A flat surface is the basis of all accurate measurement. Ideally, a measurement should be made from a point, but a point would wear rapidly in the course of making measurements, and accuracy would be quickly lost. For this reason the micrometer has hard flat anvils for registering on the part measured instead of two sharp points.

The surface plate is simply an accurately ground flat surface, made either of a hard metal such as cast iron, or a ceramic material such as diabase or black granite. For the sake of rigidity, surface plates are made in massive sections. The flatness of a surface plate may be as precise as ± 0.000025 in. variation, though shop plates are usually made to a lesser accuracy. Measurements are made from the flat plane of the surface plate as a reference plane by other instruments such as dial indicators, surface gages, or vernier height gages.

Fig. 35 Surface gage and surface plate. The workpiece shown is a forging die block.

Since the surface plate is the foundation for measurements, its precious surface is rigorously protected. It is not a shelf for temporary storage of parts; if so used, it ceases to be a surface plate. A surface plate must never be used unless it absolutely is required, and then only for accurate measurement. Since it can collect dirt or a film during use, it must be periodically cleaned with a surface plate cleaning compound that will not leave a film on the plate.

The surface gage, like the caliper, is a layout and measuring instrument that does not actually measure but is used to transfer measurements. The scriber of the surface gage is set to height and may scribe lines on a blued surface, often using the surface plate as a base.

The vernier height gage of Fig. 30 somewhat resembles the surface gage, but is also a direct measuring instrument, equipped with a vernier. It, too, is used in conjunction with a surface plate.

3.7 THE COMBINATION SQUARE

The complete combination square set of instruments of Fig. 36 serves for a wide range of routine layout work in the shop. The set consists of a *blade* or graduated rule, a *square head*, a *bevel protractor*, and a *center head*. The square head has both a 90-deg and a 45-deg edge for layout operations. The head is also equipped with a level bubble that may be used for rough leveling, but must not be used for precision leveling work, such as leveling the beds of machine tools.

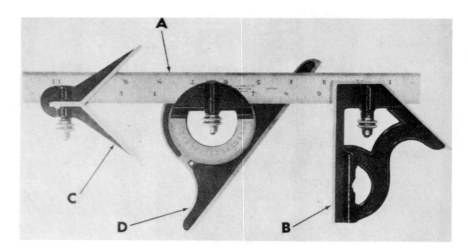

Fig. 36 Combination square set: A. Steel rule; B. Square head; C. Center head; D. Protractor.

The center head is handy for finding the center of round stock. Two intersecting lines drawn across the round stock with the centering head should intersect at the center of the stock (Fig. 37).

The bevel protractor can be locked at any angle to lay out angled lines or to measure angles.

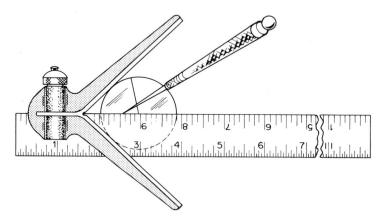

Fig. 37

3.8 BASIC LAYOUT METHODS

The hard smooth finish on a metal surface makes it difficult to read a line or mark placed on such a surface. For layout work, a dye is painted or sprayed on the surface. The dye consists of a blue pigment in volatile solvents

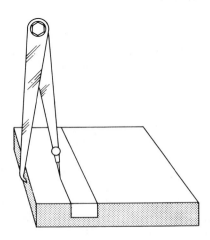

Fig. 38

that evaporate quickly for fast drying of the dye. Such dyes are called layout dye, machinist's blue, or similar names. Any lines scribed into such a dye surface are easily seen.

Scribers or dividers are used for drawing layout lines on metal surfaces. The point of a scriber is very hard, and is kept sharp by honing. When one is scribing along the edge of a rule, the scriber must be guided by the bottom of the rule, not the top, as illustrated in Fig. 39. This is done by leaning the scriber slightly away from the rule.

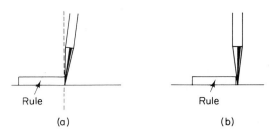

Rule   Rule

(a)   (b)

Fig. 39

A point is laid out by the intersection of two scribed lines. The actual point is permanently marked either with a center punch or a prick punch, either of which produces a small conical indentation in the surface. The prick punch has a conical point with an included angle of 60 deg, while the center punch has an included angle of 129 deg or approximately that angle. This angle is selected because it corresponds to the approximate angle at the point of a drill bit and can thus align the drill bit to the point.

3.9 A LAYOUT OPERATION

Figure 40 is a print of a part for machining. The workpiece for the part may be laid out by using a combination square. The metal stock for the part is sawed to rough size and deburred, after which layout can begin, the surface first being coated with layout dye.

If one edge of the stock is straight and true, this edge may be used for a base line for layout. If no such side is available, a scribed line must be used as a base line. A second true edge at right angles to the first layout edge, or a second scribed line at right angles, is required for layout in two dimensions. All measurements are made from the two perpendicular base lines.

All center lines for circles and arcs are next scribed. Then the circles and arcs are scribed with dividers, to be followed by the straight lines. Drill holes must be center-punched. Remember that when dimensions are given in inches and fractions, accuracy of $\frac{1}{64}$ in. is attempted.

When laying out several parallel lines, do not measure from one

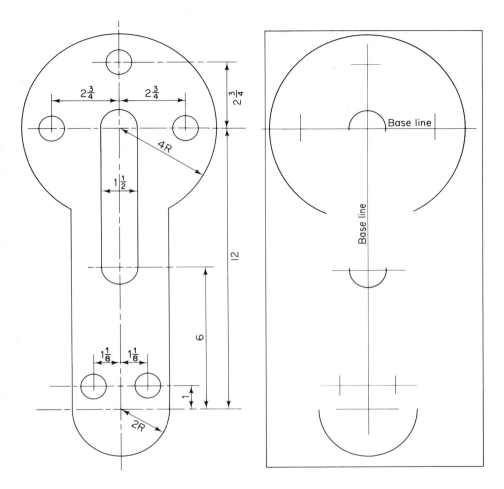

Fig. 40   **Fig. 41**

line to the next parallel line, but make all measurements from the base line. In this way errors do not accumulate from line to line.

When laying out dimensions with dividers, mark the base line intersection with a prick punch to make a small hole for one leg of the dividers.

QUESTIONS

1. Select four round bars of different diameters. For each bar, measure the outside diameter with an outside caliper, transfer the setting to an inside caliper, and finally transfer this setting to a micrometer. Then

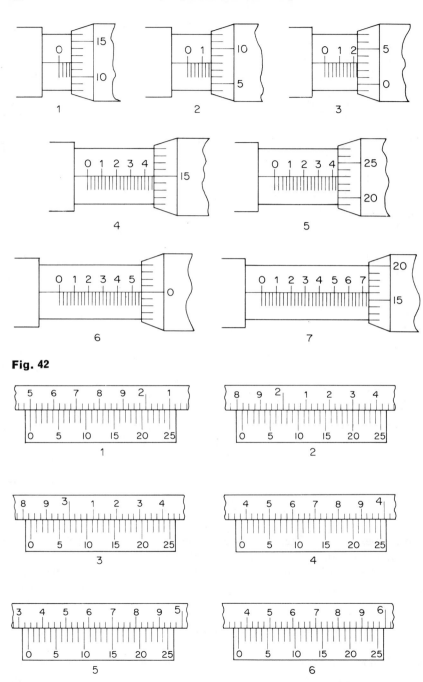

Fig. 42

Fig. 43

measure the same diameters with a micrometer. Find your error in the caliper measurements in all four cases.

2. Convert the dimensions of the planetary pin of Fig. 4 to metric.

3. Read the micrometer settings given in Fig. 42.

4. Read the vernier caliper settings given in Fig. 43.

5. Read the angle of the bevel protractor settings of Fig. 44 to the nearest 5 minutes. Sixty minutes = 1 deg.

Fig. 44

6. Does TIR measure the actual bend in a shaft? What does it measure?

7. Name the four parts of a combination square and for what each part may be used.

8. Why are the following surface plate activities not allowed?
   a. Laying a hot piece of metal on the surface plate.
   b. Setting a part that has not been deburred on a surface plate.
   c. Setting a part on the surface plate for convenience in making measurements to a 32nd of an inch with a steel rule.
   d. Using the surface plate as a table for handy placement of hammers, center punches, etc.
   e. Polishing a part with emery cloth on a surface plate.
   f. Arc welding close to a surface plate.
   g. Supporting the surface plate on an irregular surface.

9. What is the meaning of TIR?

Part II

Machine Tool Practice

Chapter 4

Power Saws

When parts are machined from a bar or tube which is passed through the headstock spindle of the lathe, usually the last machining operation is to cut the finished part off the bar with a parting tool. Sometimes, however, a sawing operation precedes the lathe work: A slug is first cut from the bar, then chucked and turned.

Hacksaws, bandsaws, and circular saws are used for power sawing. In addition, the abrasive cutoff wheel is used as a cutting machine.

4.1 THE HACKSAW

Power hacksaws use a longer and thicker blade than is used for hand hacksaw work. The weight placed on the power blade is adjustable, and should be proportional to the number of teeth in contact with the work. On better designs of machine the weight is relieved automatically on the return stroke. On completion of the cut, the saw frame drops, contacting a limit switch that cuts off the motor.

Fig. 45 Power hacksaw.

Coolant must be supplied to the blade when one is power sawing. In the absence of coolant, the blade heats and softens. Coolant, however, is not used with gray cast iron.

Most power hacksaws cut on the pull stroke, the stroke that pulls the blade back toward the motor. However, the cutting direction should be confirmed from the operating manual of the machine. When changing blades, the operator must be certain that the teeth point in the correct direction.

The principles for selection of number of teeth per inch are those for hand hacksawing. Heavy sections and softer materials require teeth with a coarse pitch. On thin material use a pitch such that at least two, and preferably three, teeth are always cutting at any time. As few as four teeth per inch are used for cutting soft steel, cast iron, and brass, and 14 teeth for thin tubing. Mild steel and softer metals are cut at about 120 to 130 strokes per minute, while stainless and tool steels should be cut at about 60 strokes per minute.

Overhanging long bars must be supported on stands; otherwise, the cut will not be square. Check that the bar is not inclined in the saw vise. The blade must be lifted from the work when the machine is turned on, and then fed gently into the work to start the cut.

4.2 HORIZONTAL AND VERTICAL BAND SAWS

The vertical band saw is chiefly used to cut die contours and similar irregular shapes, and plastic sheet. The horizontal band saw is a cutoff machine like the power hacksaw. The continuous blade of the band saw is thinner and more flexible than the blade for a hacksaw. In casual cutting, the band saw is faster than the hacksaw since it cuts continuously. On the other hand, the lighter and less expensive types of band saws may run off to one side to give an oblique cut, especially if the blade is dull.

The vertical band saw may be set up with a file blade or an abrasive polishing blade. To keep the blade in position when pressure from the work

Fig. 46 Horizontal bandsaw with band wheels exposed.

is applied to it, the blade guide is positioned to clear the top of the workpiece by half an inch.

The horizontal band saw exerts cutting pressure against the fixed jaw of the vise; the vertical band saw presses the work against the table.

4.3 SELECTION OF BAND SAW BLADES

A band saw imposes a restriction on saw blades that the hacksaw does not: The blade must flex around the band wheels without cracking. Therefore, a thick blade cannot be installed on a machine with wheels of relatively small diameter.

Saw blades are selected for the following characteristics:

1. **Width.** Saw bands are available in width ranging from $\frac{1}{16}$ to 1 in. The width is measured from the tip of the teeth to the back of the blade. The wider blades will follow a line more accurately since they are stiffer. For straight cuts, use the widest blade that the band saw can accommodate. If the radius of a contour to be cut is small, then a blade of narrow width must be used. If the contour cut contains sharp corners, drill a hole at the

corners to produce the required corner radius. A wider blade can then be used for the contour.

2. **Pitch.** This is the number of teeth per inch of blade. The usual rule is followed that at least two teeth, and preferably three, must be cutting at all times.

3. **Set.** So that the teeth will not bind in the saw kerf (cut), the teeth must be bent sideways to give a kerf slightly wider than the thickness of the blade. Three types of set are in use and are shown in Fig. 47.

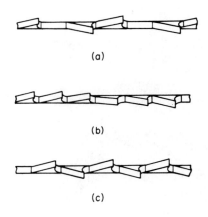

(a)

(b)

(c)

Fig. 47

Raker set has one tooth set left, the next tooth without set, and the third tooth set right. This set is suited to standard cutting such as solid stock.

Wave set has several successive teeth set to one side. This is a better set for cutting material with a varying cross section, such as tubing, angles, and channels.

Straight set is recommended for soft materials such as aluminum and wood. The set is alternately right and left.

4. **Gage.** This is the thickness of the blade.

5. **Tooth form.** The straight-face tooth form with zero rake (Fig. 48) is preferred for light feeding, and the positive rake for coarse feeding.

6. **Tooth material.** High-speed steel and alloy steel blades are the usual choice of blade material. Both materials have the same tooth hardness, but high-speed steel can sustain greater heating effects without softening. Blades are also available with tungsten carbide tooth tips and with a diamond cutting edge. Tungsten carbide teeth will resist wear much more effectively than high-speed steel. The diamond cutting edge will cut such material as quartz, glass, firebrick, and granite.

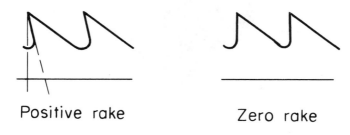

Positive rake   Zero rake

Fig. 48

Special uses of the band saw call for special blades. Such uses include friction sawing, filing, and polishing or abrasive machining.

Friction sawing uses a toothed blade at a very high speed of 6,000 to 15,000 feet per minute. Very hard metals may be cut by this method, but it is restricted to machines with large band wheels of 30 in. or larger. The material directly ahead of the cut is softened by the frictional heat resulting from the high saw velocity and heavy feeding force. The teeth are used to remove the softened material. It is possible, though not usual, to do frictional sawing without teeth on the band.

Abrasive-coated bands are available in aluminum oxide grit for hard steels or silicon carbide grit for hard ceramic materials such as glass and granite.

The spiral-edge blade of Fig. 49 will cut in any direction, so that the

Fig. 49 Spiral edge bandsaw blade.

workpiece does not need to be swung about. This blade may also be used as a filing blade. The file band converts a band saw into a filing machine, for finishing die work and other such uses.

The maximum band blade thickness that can be used on any band saw is determined by the wheel diameter. This maximum thickness is 0.001 to 0.0017 times wheel diameter in inches.

4.4 HOLE SAWS

The hole saw of Fig. 50 resembles a band saw. These saws are used for

Fig. 50 Hole saw.

cutting holes in sheet metal or plate or even curved sections such as tubing and pipe. The number of teeth is about six per inch, with a heavier set of the teeth on the inside to make removal of the sawed core easier. This tool is mounted on an arbor for use with portable tools, drill presses, or lathes. Available sizes range from $\frac{9}{16}$- to 6-in. diameter.

4.5 WELDING BAND SAW BLADES

The larger types of band saws are provided with a butt welder on the side of the machine for joining broken saw blades, for welding blades that are ordered in long coils, or for inside sawing, where the blade is passed through a hole in the workpiece and then brazed.

The correct blade length is found in the following way. Measure the distance from the center of one wheel to the center of the other wheel, multiply by 2, and add the circumference of one wheel. Before making the measurement, adjust the upper wheel to the midpoint of its vertical travel. This allows capacity to take up any stretch in the band during operation (and also allows for some error in measurement). Alternatively, a flexible tape can be passed over the wheels to measure the total length of blade.

To weld the band into a loop, first trim both ends square and make sure they are clean. Butt the ends in the jaws of the welder, being careful that they are aligned. The joint must be in the center of the jaws. Set the resistance knob for the width of band. Press and hold the WELD button until the blade ends fuse together. Let the weld cool for a few seconds and then press the ANNEAL button until the weld area becomes a dull cherry red. Hold at this temperature for about 10 seconds. The welding operation makes the area of the joint brittle, and the annealing operation restores the weld area to a tough condition.

After annealing, grind the weld area smooth and to the same thickness of the rest of the band. Grind off any roughness at the back of the blade.

When mounting the blade on the wheels, make sure that the teeth point downward. The band must also track properly on the wheels. The tension must be properly adjusted; small blades must not be tensioned as much as larger blades. Too much tension will break the band or the weld. Too low a tension will cause the band to saw off-line. Adjust the guides. These should clear the work by half an inch.

4.6 THE COLD CIRCULAR SAW

This machine uses a large circular blade. Cuts are accurate to length and square. Speeds and feeds are high. Work must be securely clamped, and speeds or feeds neither too low or too high; otherwise, the teeth are damaged.

4.7 THE ABRASIVE CUTOFF WHEEL

This type of wheel can cut hard materials, including hardened steel. The smaller, low-powered machines leave a large burr on the part and also harden the cut end of the piece. The finish is excellent and cuts are accurate.

A rubber-bonded wheel is used in this type of cutting. Speed of cutting must be high, but must not exceed the speed limit specified for the wheel because of the high centrifugal force generated. Feeds must also be sufficiently fast. Too slow a speed or feed will harden the work excessively

Fig. 51 Spark shower from a dry cutting operation on a 20HP abrasive cutoff wheel.

and greatly reduce the life of the wheel. In order to develop the required speeds and feeds for long wheel life and good cutting, very large motors are required. Most of the small abrasive cutoff machines are underpowered. At least 5 HP is required to cut 1-in. round bar and 25 HP for 2-in. bar. Even greater horsepowers are better.

As the wheel wears to a smaller diameter, the speed of rotation should, if possible, be increased to maintain the proper cutting speed. This is not possible on the smaller and lower-priced machines. The small machines require coolant for abrasive cutting.

The cutoff wheel throws a dramatic shower of sparks over a considerable distance. These sparks travel at high velocities, and the operator must wear a face mask to protect the whole face. The workpiece must be quite securely clamped, as any chatter will likely shatter the wheel. If the work cannot be cut completely through, it must not be cut by this method. Do not cut partly through and then attempt to finish the cut from the opposite side; this is a most dangerous practice.

It is not uncommon for abrasive cutoff wheels to shatter. The effect is somewhat dramatic, but not especially dangerous. The wheel is adequately protected with guards. Needless to say, all guards must be in place before cutting.

Finally, two other precautions in the operation of this wheel. Be sure of your footing. If coolant accumulates on the floor where you stand, it must be cleaned off. Do not interrupt a cut and then return the wheel into the same kerf to finish the cut.

On first acquaintance, the abrasive cutoff machine is a little frightening with its speed, sparks, and loud shriek. It is not dangerous to a careful operator.

QUESTIONS

1. Examine the power saws in your shop. Determine the direction in which each one cuts.
2. The pressure on a saw blade can be (a) too low; (b) too high. What harm is done in each case?
3. a. Is any harm done to a saw blade that is operated at too low a speed?
   b. At too high a speed?
4. What type of saw must be used to cut hardened steels?
5. Explain (a) pitch and (b) set, of a saw blade.
6. Why would you use a coarse pitch when cutting large sections of metal?
7. Why is it desirable to use the widest possible blade when sawing?
8. Cutting with an abrasive wheel is done as fast as possible. The reason for this practice is that the wheel wears away more slowly. Can you explain why?
   See Question 2(a) above. Do a saw blade and an abrasive wheel behave in the same way with respect to low cutting pressures?
9. The maximum allowable speed of circular blades such as abrasive cut-

off wheels is given in feet per minute. This is the allowable speed of a point on the periphery of the wheel in feet/minute. In one revolution, the distance travelled by a point on the periphery is, of course, $\frac{22}{7} \times$ wheel diameter. Frequently in these calculations $\frac{22}{7}$ is taken as 3 instead of $3\frac{1}{7}$. Calculate the maximum allowable spindle rpm for the following abrasive wheels:

a. twelve-inch wheel, maximum speed 6,500 fpm.
b. twenty-inch wheel, maximum speed 12,000 fpm.

Chapter 5

Drilling and Tapping

The drilling and machining of holes is a complex science which can require a remarkable range of cutting tools besides drills. Most of these special tools are needed because drill bits produce very imperfect holes.

5.1 THE HOLE AND ITS COMPLEXITIES

The drilling of a round hole in a metal part can be a surprisingly complex matter. To drill a hole of an exact diameter in a location also exact to a thousandth of an inch or two is impossible with drill bits alone and requires other tools. Some of the deficiencies of drill bits are these:

1. They are difficult to start at exactly the correct location.
2. They drill oversize holes. The larger the drill diameter, the more oversize the hole, up to perhaps 0.010 in. oversize. It is not possible to drill a hole exactly the size of the drill bit.

3. They run off line to produce a bent hole, especially if the hole is deep. Small drills especially are very flexible.

4. The drill is buried in hot metal as it drills and heats very quickly, thus softening the drill bit.

5. The drill leaves a rough surface finish in the hole.

6. Especially in thin material, the drill may not produce a perfectly round hole.

Only when these limitations of drills are understood can the novice machinist produce the kind of hole he requires. Suppose we follow the sequence of operations required to produce a hole exactly 0.625 in. in diameter at a carefully center-punched location, to receive a press-fit bushing.

It may be necessary to begin the drilling operation with a short stiff spot drill, starter drill, or perhaps a combination drill and countersink (Fig. 52) with a countersink diameter a few thousandths of an inch larger than the diameter of the drill to be used. The starter drill does not flex, but still provides no guarantee that the center punch mark will be the axis of the drilled hole.

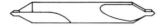

Fig. 52

The hole is next drilled with a $\frac{39}{64}$-in. drill. This size is selected because it is $\frac{1}{64}$ in. undersize. If a $\frac{5}{8}$-in. drill were used (0.625), the hole diameter would be at least 0.630 in., or even larger if the drill were sharpened offhand on a grinding wheel without a drill sharpening jig.

To produce a hole diameter of 0.625 in., the hole is brought to final size with a 0.625-in. reamer. A reamer is not a heavy metal remover, but is suited only to finishing cuts.

Thus three hole tools were required, though often the starter drill can be omitted. None of these tools guarantees that the hole will be straight or that the hole will be located exactly, or that the hole will be a uniform 0.625 in. throughout its length (if the reamer were improperly used, it could ream the hole slightly oversize at its mouth). The reamer has several flutes, thus ensuring roundness, while the drill has only two flutes, which are insufficient in number to ensure a circular hole.

Deep-hole drilling with the common two-flute drill requires a woodpecker sequence of drilling and withdrawing the tool to clear chips and cool the drill; otherwise, the drill may be softened. Inexperienced persons should drill an initial depth of about $1\frac{1}{2}$ diameters, withdraw, drill another diameter deep, withdraw, and continue until final depth is reached. Although it is possible to drill considerably more than $1\frac{1}{2}$ diameters on the first entry, drill management is best learned by experience; always be on guard against a hot drill.

A long hole may not be straight. To cut a long, straight hole, the workpiece must be revolved and the drill must be stationary. The reason for this requirement is that a drill bit will tend to follow its cutting point; the shank of the drill does not guide the drill. If the drill is rotated, once the cutting point deviates from the axis of rotation, it will continue to pursue this new direction. If the work is rotated instead of the drill, the drill point may still deviate from the axis of rotation but the workpiece, being rotated, will not allow it to follow any radial deviation. Instead, the workpiece will rotate the drill point in a circle with a radius equal to the amount of deviation. The hole will be oversize, but straight.

If a drilled hole is not exactly in its proper location, the only cure is to realign the hole with a boring tool.

5.2 HOLE TOOLS

The standard drill bit has two flutes with a helix angle of about 30 deg. Slow spiral drills with a smaller helix angle are used for drilling softer materials and for those materials which grab the drill point at the moment of breaking through the work. Straight-flute drills are used for drilling brasses and hard steels. These, too, will not grab.

Only small drills are equipped with straight shanks to fit drill chucks. The high torque requirements of large drills call for a taper shank. High torques and horsepowers can be transmitted through matching male and female tapers.

Very deep holes must be drilled with gun drills (Fig. 54), which also

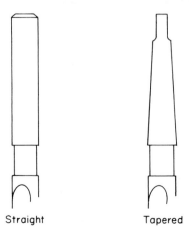

Straight   Tapered

Fig. 53

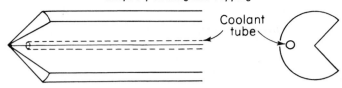

Fig. 54 Gun drill.

produce holes of great accuracy. Coolant is carried through the gun drill to the cutting point.

The core drill usually has more than two flutes. It is used to enlarge cored holes in castings or previously drilled or punched holes. The core drill cannot be used to drill into solid stock, since the edges of the flutes do the cutting. Hence this is a kind of reamer-drill. This drill may be used to correct the location of a previously drilled hole, since it does not follow its point when cutting, as the standard two-flute drill does. The hole should be bevelled before core-drilling; otherwise, the core drill may follow the hole and go off center.

The spade drill of Fig. 56 is used for drilling large shallow holes. A

Fig. 55 Core drill.

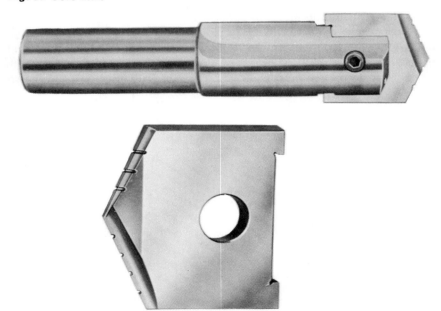

Fig. 56 Spade drill and typical blade for a spade drill.

spade drill holder is used, into which is clamped the cutting blade of the required diameter. The usual range of diameters is 1 to 5 in.

　　End-cutting operations related to drilling include counterboring, spot-facing, and countersinking (Fig. 57). The counterbore tool drills an

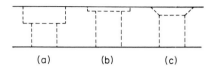

(a)　　　　　(b)　　　　　(c)

Fig. 57 (a) Counterbore. (b) Spot-face. (c) Countersink.

enlarged hole at the top of a drilled hole so that a bolt head may be recessed into the workpiece. For alignment with the drilled hole, the counterbore is fitted with a pilot that enters the drilled hole (Fig. 58). Pilots are available in sizes of 32nds of an inch. Spot-facing is the cutting of a flat seat for a bolt head that is not to be recessed below the surface of the workpiece. Countersinking produces a conical seat for flat-head bolts and machine screws.

　　A useful tool for deburring of both ends of a hole is illustrated in Fig. 59. This tool is advanced into the hole to debur the near side of the hole. A spring inside the tool shank holds the deburring blade in place against the side of the hole, spring pressure being adjusted by means of a screw. When pressure against the work exceeds the spring pressure setting, the blade

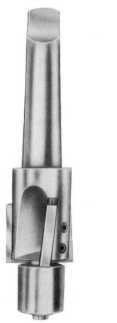

Fig. 58 Counterbore tool.　　　　　　**Fig. 59** Deburring tool.

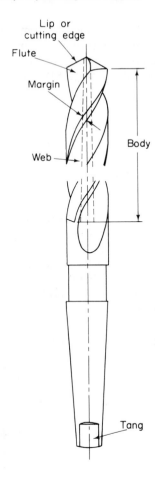

Fig. 60

retracts and the drilling machine continues to feed the retracted burring tool through the hole. As the blade emerges from the back of the hole, the spring extends it again, and the back of the hole is deburred on the return stroke. The amount of stock removal is thus determined by the spring pressure setting.

5.3 DRILL DIMENSIONS

The parts of a twist drill are named in Fig. 60. Note that the web of the drill increases in thickness from the point to the shank.

The taper shank drill has a Morse taper shank. Most drill spindles are equipped with a No. 2 or a No. 3 Morse taper. A drill with the smaller No. 2 Morse taper shank can be inserted into a No. 3 drilling machine socket with the use of a sleeve ground to a No. 2 inside taper and a No. 3 outside taper. Such sleeves are available as a standard item.

The included angle of the cutting edges (Fig. 61) should be larger for harder materials. It can be as small as 90 deg for soft materials such as wood. For mild steel, a 118-deg angle is used, and for harder steels a larger angle such as 130 deg. The reason for this variation in angle with hardness is that

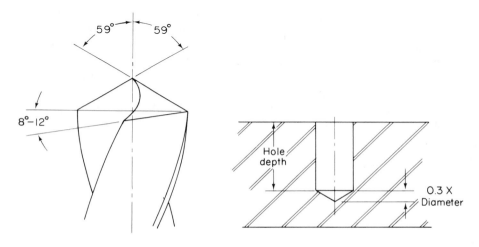

Fig. 61   **Fig. 62**

larger angles require more force to penetrate the material of the workpiece. This angle, however, is not usually a critical matter.

Drill sizes are obtainable by $\frac{1}{64}$-in. increments. In addition, there are number-size drills from #80, which is 0.0135 in. in diameter, to #1, 0.2283 in., and larger letter sizes from A (0.2340 in.) to Z (0.4130 in.).

The depth of a drilled hole is not measured to the point penetrated by the drill tip, but includes only that part of the hole drilled to full diameter, as shown in Fig. 62. When setting drill depths on a drilling machine, it is important to know that the conical point of a drill is 0.3 times the drill diameter in length (Fig. 62).

5.4 SHARPENING DRILLS

Offhand or hand-grinding of drills is not recommended except under emergency conditions. A variety of drill grinding jigs and attachments is available for the proper grinding of drills. Nevertheless, any machinist is expected to be able to do a reasonable job of offhand sharpening of a drill.

The two cutting edges of the two flutes act as two chisels. They cannot cut unless the material of the flute behind the cutting edge is relieved so that only the chisel edge touches the work. This back clearance angle should be 8 to 12 deg, and is often estimated by eye. The two cutting edges must be ground to the same angle. This is difficult in offhand grinding. If they are not the same angle, only one lip will cut and an oversize hole will be produced.

The proper hand motion for sharpening a drill point must be learned by demonstration and practice.

The web of the drill increases in thickness toward the shank. If the drill is shortened significantly, this web should be thinned by grinding. This thinning reduces the pressure required to penetrate the workpiece. It must be done equally on both sides of the web so that the web is centered.

It is preferable to complete the sharpening of the drill on a fine grinding wheel. Do not overheat the drill during the sharpening operation. A drill point gage assists in checking the success of the grinding operation, as shown in Fig. 63.

Fig. 63

Probably no cutters are abused quite so much as drills. A small drill down in its hole has no means of being cooled, and its own cross section is too small to conduct any significant amount of heat up the shank. The drill chips can pack at the bottom of the hole, producing a rapid temperature rise through friction against the walls of the hole. And, of course, much of the world's drilling is done by inexperienced operators impatient to complete the hole. As a result of this impatience, drills come out of their holes with the margins on the flutes obliterated. Repair of the drill then becomes a major problem, and the drill cannot be sharpened until the ruined end is cut off. Toward the end of its cutting operation, such a heated drill, of course, has not been cutting, but simply rubbing.

5.5 LAYOUT FOR ACCURATE HOLE LOCATION

Figure 64 illustrates the procedure for an accurate layout of a hole.

The two intersecting lines locate the position of the hole for drilling. This intersection is center-punched. Drilling may follow.

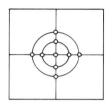 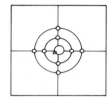 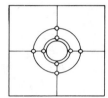 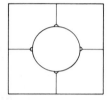

Fig. 64

If more care in location is necessary, scribe a circle the diameter of the hole to be drilled and then scribe a smaller circle inside it, as shown in the figure. The intersections of lines and circles are usually center-punched.

The drill is started, but stopped after it has slightly entered the workpiece. Suppose it is slightly off center. Cut a small groove with a center punch or small chisel to lead the drill in the proper direction, as shown in the second part of the figure. The hole is drilled another slight distance into the work and inspected again. The hole is then carried further and checked against the inner circle. If the hole approaches the outer circle concentrically, the hole can be completed. Center-punching of the four intersection points of the outer circle will help to gage by eye the accuracy of the work.

5.6 DRILLING MACHINES

The radial drill of Fig. 65 has a spindle head on an arm that can be rotated on the column. The spindle head can be ·traversed horizontally along the ways of the arm, and the arm may be driven vertically up or down the column. Radial drills commonly have a reversing spindle, power feed with depth setting, and a coolant system. The control levers may be mounted in different positions on different machines, but have the same functions on all machines. Locking clamps fix the position of the head after it is positioned. Other controls govern speed, feed, and elevation.

Smaller machines such as drill presses are used for hole sizes up to about one inch. The smaller machines are equipped with a drill chuck for

Fig. 65 Radial drill.

straight-shank drills; larger machines have a tapered spindle for taper-shank drills.

Before a drill is inserted into the machine, the taper socket, chuck, and drill shank must be clean and undamaged. The machinist's work can be no better than the control surfaces of his tools and machines permit. Drill chucks must be sufficiently tightened that the drill cannot spin in the chuck. Check that a taper shank is actually locked in the taper socket.

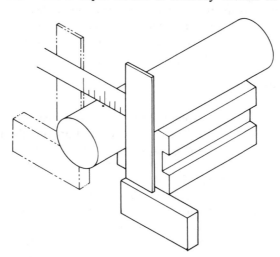

Fig. 66

Removal of a taper shank must be done with the tapered drift provided, which has rounded edges to match the hole in the machine spindle.

5.7 DRILLING METHODS

Unless the hole size is small and the workpiece reasonably large, it is a dangerous practice to hold a workpiece by hand for drilling. The flutes of a drill will grab as they break through the work, and a sudden high torque can tear the work out of the operator's hands. Drill vises or clamps must be used.

Figure 66 shows how to find the center of round stock for drilling, and Fig. 67 shows the drilling operation, both using vee-blocks.

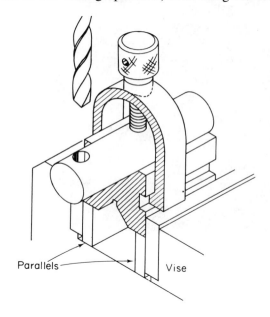

Parallels — Vise

Fig. 67

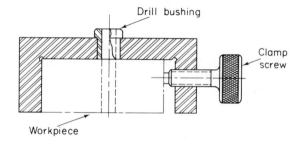

Drill bushing

Clamp screw

Workpiece

Fig. 68

If holes must be drilled in a number of identical pieces, a drill jig is used (Fig. 68). The drill jig holds and locks the piece in position. The drilling plate of the jig contains accurately located drill bushings of hardened steel to guide the drill. If relatively few pieces are to be drilled, at lesser accuracy, the drill bushings can be dispensed with, and holes to guide the drill may be made in a plate of tool steel which is hardened after it has been drilled.

For drilling more than one hole at a time, a multiple drilling head may be attached to the drill spindle. See Fig. 69. Two or more spindles may be used, and these are adjustable for position.

Fig. 69

Holes that are very deep in relation to the diameter of the drill may have to be "peck" drilled. The hole is partially completed, and then the drill is withdrawn to remove chips. Depending on circumstances, a hole depth of from 3 to 5 diameters is the maximum depth that can be penetrated in the first peck cycle; successive penetrations must be smaller than this as the hole becomes deeper and the drill bit becomes hotter. This means that a large drill might drill a few inches before being relieved, but a very small drill would have to be relieved after a few sixteenths of depth. Small drills of about $\frac{1}{32}$-in. size especially must be handled with caution. Only a minute amount of chips can pack tightly in the tiny flutes, and there is not enough metal in the drill to resist any significant torque. Chips may have to be cleared after only $\frac{1}{16}$-in. penetration.

When setting up an operation where the workpiece must be drilled through, make sure that the workpiece is raised to prevent drilling into the vise, the drill table, parallels, or other tooling used.

Difficult drilling operations can often be made easier by first drilling a pilot hole about equal to the web diameter of the final drill size. However, a pilot hole must be accurately located, because the larger drill will center on the pilot hole.

5.8 CALCULATION OF RPM FOR A DRILL

The suggested cutting speed for a drilling operation must be known or found from a handbook. Suppose a cutting speed of 80 fpm (feet per minute) is recommended for a low carbon steel. This handbook figure is the recommended maximum speed for a point on the periphery of the drill bit to be travelling, and is often termed sfpm (surface feet per minute).

Now suppose a 1-in. hole must be drilled into this material. The circumference of a 1-in. hole measures $\frac{22}{7}$ in., but since there is little value in accurate calculations when one is determining cutting speeds, $\frac{22}{7}$ is taken as 3. Therefore in one revolution a point on the margin of the drill travels 3 in. or $\frac{1}{4}$ ft. The recommended speed is 80 sfpm.

$$80 \text{ sfpm} = \tfrac{1}{4} \text{ ft} \times \text{rpm}$$

and

$$\text{rpm} = 320$$

A $\frac{1}{2}$-in. bit would be rotated twice as fast.

$$\text{By formula, rpm} = \frac{4 \times (\text{sfpm})}{\text{drill diameter}}$$

(The drill diameter must be in inches.)

Frequently, the drilling machine does not have a speed setting that corresponds to the rpm desired. Use the nearest lower speed.

5.9 TOOLHOLDERS FOR TAPPING AND REAMING

Quite commonly when one is reaming or tapping a hole, the hole and the tool are slightly misaligned. A reamer must float freely into the hole; otherwise, the hole will be bell-mouthed or out-of-round, or the surface finish may be defective. Therefore floating holders are used for such conditions. These allow the tool to "float" or move slightly sideways to adjust for misalignments.

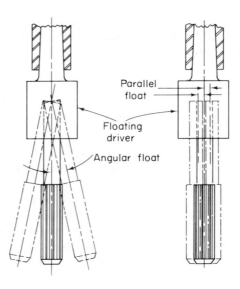

Fig. 70

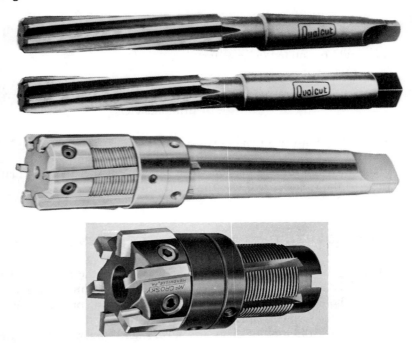

Fig. 71 Types of reamers: machine, hand, expansion, and shell reamers.

Additional problems arise when one is machine tapping. Suppose that a small $\frac{1}{4}$-20 tap is being driven by a 2-HP drilling machine, and that the tap must thread through a hard spot in the steel. The drilling machine has adequate power to drive the tap through the hard spot, but the small tap cannot absorb 2 HP and will snap off. Toolholders for machine tapping must, therefore, have a means of presetting the torque.

Still another problem arises in machine tapping. The operator sets up a certain rpm on the drilling or tapping machine and a certain rate of feed. Suppose that the tap is $\frac{5}{16}$-18. In each revolution the feed must advance the tap 0.05555 in. to produce 18 threads per inch. But the feed will be set at a certain number of inches per minute and cannot be set exactly. Suppose the feed is actually 0.0530 as set up on the drilling or tapping machine. Then in 10 threads the tap must either find 0.0255 in. of slack in its holder or must jam in its threads and break. Therefore, machine taps must use either a tension or a compression tap driver. In a tension-type tap holder, the spindle feed lags behind the thread advance, and the tap pulls forward in its toolholder. In the compression-type toolholder, the spindle feed over-runs the thread advance, and the tap retracts into the holder as the thread is cut.

The tapping machine must reverse the tap at the bottom of the hole and retract the tap at the same speed with which the tap advanced.

Leadscrew tapping machines use a leadscrew of the same pitch as the desired thread to control the movement of the tap in and out of the hole. When a different thread is to be produced, the leadscrew must be changed in the machine.

5.10 REAMERS

Reamers are used to bring a drilled hole to accurate size and circularity and to improve the surface finish of the hole. About $\frac{1}{64}$ in. of material is left in the hole for the reamer to remove, though a smaller reamer allowance must be used with small reamers and hand reamers. Machine reaming operations must be carried out at somewhat lower speeds than are used for drilling.

Reamers are made in many types:

> hand reamers
>
> machine reamers
>
> shell reamers
>
> expansion reamers
>
> taper reamers

The taper reamer is used to ream a tapered hole. Shell reamers require mounting on an arbor. The expansion reamers can be adjusted in diameter over a limited range.

5.11 TAP DRILLS

Before tapping can be performed, there must be a hole for the tap to enter. The diameter of this hole must not be so large as to leave insufficient metal for threading. If, however, the hole size is too small, the tap will be broken by the heavy torque requirement of tapping into too much metal.

Tap diameters of $\frac{3}{16}$ to $\frac{1}{4}$ in. seem to be most susceptible to breakage. Smaller taps remove very little metal when threading, and though the tap may be small, it can sustain the required torque as the tap is twisted into the metal. Large taps have a husky cross section and are unlikely to be snapped off in the tapping operation.

The tap drill size provided for the tap is not made the diameter of the root of the threads (minor diameter). If this size of hole were adopted, most taps would be broken during the tapping operation. The tap drill size, then, must be slightly oversize. The usual choice for most materials and operations is a tap drill size that provides only 75 per cent of the full depth of thread after tapping. This choice of drill size does not affect the fit of the threads and has a minor effect on the strength of the threaded joint. The machinist does not usually calculate the tap drill size, but consults a table of sizes. There is a formula for tap drill size for 75 per cent of full thread, however:

$$\text{Tap drill size} = \text{tap diameter} - \frac{1}{\text{tpi}}$$

where tpi = threads per inch.

For certain materials and operations, even 75 per cent of full thread is too risky a tap drill size. The 300 series stainless steels, for example, work-harden when machined or tapped, and require a slightly larger tap drill size in some operations. Again, in automatic lathe or numerically controlled operations, serious production costs and delays result if a tap breaks. In such cases, the tap drill size is larger, giving only 70, 65, or even as little as 60 per cent of full thread depth after tapping.

Figure 72 shows a combination tap and tap drill. This tool is a time-saver if a large number of holes must be tapped.

Fig. 72 Combination tap and tap drill.

TAP DRILL SIZES

Unified National Coarse and Fine Threads, 75 per cent full depth of thread.

Dia.	TPI UNC	Tap drill UNC	TPI UNF	Tap drill UNF
$\frac{1}{4}$	20	#7 (0.201)	28	#3 (0.215)
$\frac{5}{16}$	18	#F (0.258)	24	#I (0.272)
$\frac{3}{8}$	16	$\frac{5}{16}$ (0.314)	24	#Q (0.334)
$\frac{1}{2}$	13	$\frac{27}{64}$ (0.425)	20	$\frac{29}{64}$ (0.541)
$\frac{5}{8}$	11	$\frac{17}{32}$ (0.536)	18	$\frac{37}{64}$ (0.571)
$\frac{3}{4}$	10	$\frac{21}{32}$ (0.653)	16	$\frac{11}{16}$ (0.689)
$\frac{7}{8}$	9	$\frac{49}{64}$ (0.767)	14	$\frac{13}{16}$ (0.805)
1	8	$\frac{7}{8}$ (0.878)	12	$\frac{59}{64}$ (0.919)
$1\frac{1}{2}$	6	$1\frac{11}{32}$ (1.338)	12	$1\frac{27}{64}$ (1.419)

Machine Screw Sizes

Size	TPI	Tap drill
4–40	40	#43
6–32	32	#46
8–32	32	#29
10–24	24	#25
10–32	32	#21

5.12 TAPPING

The usual tap has four straight flutes. For threads $\frac{3}{8}$ in. in diameter or less, the sizes most subject to breakage, a two-flute tap is stronger. Ground taps are superior to cut taps and less subject to breakage because of their better accuracy of shape. The difficult threading sizes, around $\frac{1}{4}$ in. in diameter, are sometimes produced by using a roughing tap followed by a finishing tap, the roughing tap removing about two-thirds of the metal.

Most taps are taper taps, with a leading chamfer angle of about 4 deg removing the tops of the first eight to ten threads of the tap. Full thread form, therefore, is not produced until the ninth to eleventh thread begins to cut. Such a tap cannot thread to the bottom of a blind hole. For blind hole tapping, plug and bottoming taps are used, with chamfer angles of about 9 deg and 30 deg respectively, giving about four threads and two threads ground off. Spiral-fluted taps are also recommended for blind hole tapping. This type is also useful for tapping aluminum and copper.

The fluteless tap of Fig. 73 will produce threads in ductile materials. No chips are generated, the threads being formed by the displacement of metal. The fluteless tap will not perform in a brittle material such as gray cast iron.

Fig. 73 Kinds of taps: plug tap and bottoming tap, both spiral-fluted; fluteless tap; and pipe tap.

When tapping by hand, drill the tap drill hole, and chamfer the top of the hole with a countersink. Either an 82-deg or a 90-deg countersink is suitable. Countersink to the major diameter of the thread. Without chamfering, the tap will raise a burr around the hole.

With the tap in the tap wrench, align the tap axis carefully with the hole. Turn the tap into the hole with pressure enough to enable the tap to bite. After every three or four revolutions, reverse the tap to break the chips. The fluteless type of tap does not produce chips and therefore does not require to be backed off.

If a through hole is being tapped, make sure the first chamfered threads of the tap pass out of the hole. If a blind hole is being tapped, the taper tap must be followed by a plug tap and a bottoming tap to shape the last threads cut.

5.13 THE UNIVERSAL BORING AND FACING HEAD

Germany has always specialized in machine tools, and produces types of machine tools that other countries do not generally manufacture, especially for the railroad industry. In discussing the universal boring and facing head, the Wohlhaupter head will be mentioned in this section, since, whether true or not, this German head enjoys the reputation around the world of being the best. Of course, other countries, including the United States, manufacture excellent boring and facing heads.

The Wohlhaupter head, shown in Fig. 74, has the same general appearance as other heads of this type. The tool has a taper shank for inserting into spindles of drilling machines, lathes, or other machine tools. Such a tool has a very wide range of uses: facing, turning either inside or outside diameters, precision boring, recessing, and turning inside or outside tapers.

The boring head has a toolholder which slides on dovetail ways. This toolholder slide is drilled with several holes to receive boring and turning bars. The toolholder can be slid out and in on its ways to make accurate

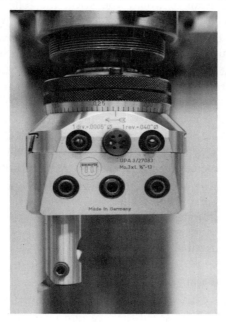

Fig. 74 Wohlhaupter drilling and boring tool.

adjustments for the size of circle to be cut. Such adjustments are made with a collar graduated to 0.00025 in. For cutting a taper, or for facing operations, the toolholder slide can be made to feed outward at a controlled rate.

A universal boring and facing head, when mounted in the spindle of a drilling machine, in effect converts the drilling machine into a vertical spindle lathe.

QUESTIONS

1. Should drill horsepower be proportional to drill diameter or drill cross-sectional area? Why?
2. Drill the following holes in a piece of $\frac{3}{8}$-in. plate: $\frac{1}{2}$, $\frac{3}{4}$, 1 in. Mike the drills close to the drill point. Measure the hole diameters. What are the

differences between drill and hole diameters, in thousandths and as a percentage of diameter?

3. Name the five possible defects of a hole that are possible when using standard spiral-flute drills.

4. What is the purpose of a starter drill?

5. What is the purpose of peck drilling (woodpecker drilling)?

6. Under what circumstances would you select the following drills: (a) spade, (b) core, (c) gun drill?

7. A tool steel is to be drilled at 60 sfpm. Determine the theoretical rpm for a drilling machine to drill (a) $\frac{5}{8}$-in., (b) $\frac{3}{4}$-in. diameters in this material.

8. If in a certain material a hole length equal to four diameters is the limit before the drill is retracted to clear the flutes, what length of hole does this represent for the following drills: (a) $\frac{3}{4}$ in., (b) $\frac{1}{32}$ in.?

9. When a tap breaks, it usually does so at the edge of the hole and with a 45-deg break, making it virtually impossible to remove. Find out how such a tap can be removed with a spark erosion machine.

10. What is the difference between a taper, a plug, and a bottoming tap?

11. State for the following cases when you would bore out and when you would ream an undersize hole:
   a. The hole is not straight.
   b. The hole has a poor surface finish.
   c. The hole is off location.

12. State the reasons why the following must float in the holder: (a) a machine reamer; (b) a machine tap.

13. What is the difference between a tension and a compression tap holder?

14. The recommended drilling speed for a certain material is 100 fpm.
   a. What is the recommended rpm for drilling a $\frac{5}{16}$-in. hole in this material?
   b. What should be the rpm for a $\frac{5}{8}$-in. hole?

Chapter 6

The Lathe

The lathe is the general-purpose machine tool that is best adapted to the machining of shapes circular in section. It is used principally for turning, facing, screw-cutting, boring, drilling, and reaming, though a range of special operations is possible with suitable accessories, including spring-winding, grinding, and milling. The workpiece is rotated against the cutting tool, which is usually capable of powered longitudinal and cross feed. Longitudinal feed is parallel to the lathe bed, and crossfeed is perpendicular to the axis of the lathe.

The size of a lathe is usually specified by swing and length of bed. The swing is the largest possible diameter of workpiece that can be rotated over the ways. The length of the bed is the full length of the slideways. The maximum length of workpiece that can be turned in the lathe will be shorter than the bed length, because both headstock and tailstock must also be accommodated within the length of the ways. Thus a 72-in. bed may be able to accept a maximum workpiece length of perhaps only 49 in.

The weight of chips that the lathe can remove in a certain period of

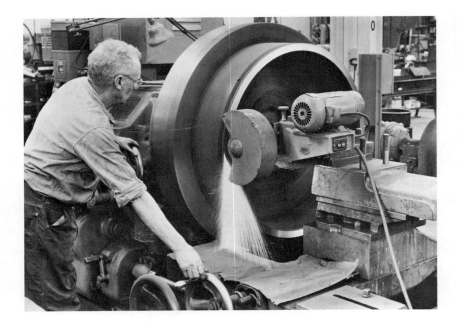

Fig. 75 A faceplate operation on a lathe. The workpiece is being ground with a a 3HP Dumore toolpost grinding attachment as it is rotated by a faceplate on the machine spindle.

time is determined by the horsepower of the lathe. Roughly one cubic inch of steel chips can be removed per one horsepower of the driving motor. The volume of chips is understood to be measured in the workpiece before being divided into chips.

6.1 THE PARTS OF THE LATHE

The bed is the base and frame of the lathe. The *ways* are formed on the upper surface of the bed and run the full length of the bed. The ways maintain the alignment of the headstock, tailstock, and tool carriage. The ways provide the basis of the accuracy of a lathe, and they must be protected from any damage, from abrasive grit, and from rust. Note in Fig. 75 the paper protecting the ways from grinding dust.

The *headstock* is always found at the left-hand side of the bed, and carries the headstock spindle and the mechanism for driving it. The *spindle* is hollow so that long bars may be fed through it, and it has an internal Morse taper to receive a live center.

The geared-head lathe has a transmission similar to an automotive gear transmission, except that there are more gear-shift combinations and

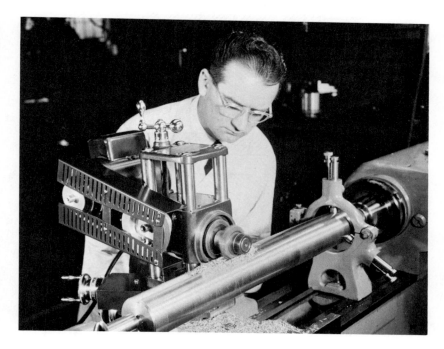

Fig. 76 Milling a $\frac{3}{4}$-in. by $\frac{3}{8}$-in. keyway in a steel shaft with a Dumore Versa-Mil machining unit mounted in a conventional engine lathe.

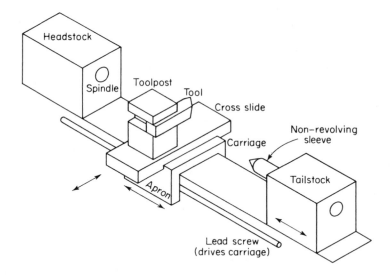

Fig. 77 Parts of a lathe.

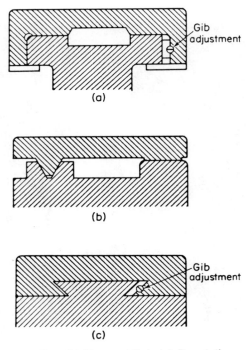

Fig. 78 Types of ways: (a) Flat. (b) Vee and flat. (c) Dovetail.

therefore a greater variety of speed changes. A speed index plate attached to the headstock indicates the lever positions for obtaining the different speeds. The lathe must be stopped before gears are shifted, to prevent damage to gear teeth, which are not synchronized.

The operating controls for lathes differ from one machine to another, and these therefore cannot be discussed here. The starting of a lathe must be learned from the operator of it, or from the operating manual for the lathe. General remarks on this subject are not useful.

The *tailstock* holds the dead center that supports the back end of the workpiece carried between centers. The tailstock spindle will also hold taper-shank drills, reamers, and drill chucks, if the taper corresponds to the spindle taper. The tailstock spindle has the same internal taper as the headstock spindle, often a no. 3 Morse taper.

When inserting a chuck, drill, or center into a lathe spindle, first clean the tapered shank of the tool and wipe out the tapered hole of the spindle. If you are learning the operation of a lathe, do this as a routine and begin to look like a professional.

The several parts of the tailstock are shown in Fig. 79. Handwheel 9 cranks the tailstock spindle forward or back. A drill may be inserted into the spindle, and the drill may be fed forward by this handwheel. Handle 10

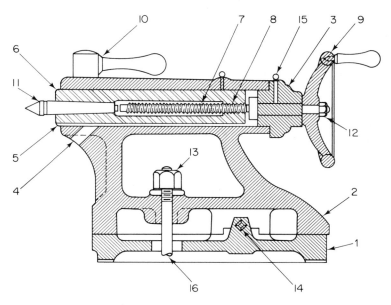

1. Tailstock base	9. Handwheel
2. Tailstock top	10. Spindle binding clamp
3. Tailstock nut	11. Dead center
4. Key	12. End of tailstock screw
5. Keyway (in spindle)	13. Tailstock clamp nut
6. Spindle	14. Tailstock set-over
7. Tailstock screw	15. For oiling
8. Internal threads in spindle	16. Tailstock clamp bolt

Fig. 79

clamps the spindle when there must be no movement of the spindle. The tailstock assembly has a base 1 and a top 2.

The axis of the tailstock spindle must be exactly the axis of the headstock spindle. If the two axes are misaligned, a straight cut on a bar will produce a slight taper from headstock to tailstock. If one axis is higher than the other, either tailstock or headstock must be shimmed. This, however, does not usually occur. More commonly, the two axes are out of alignment horizontally, the tailstock spindle axis being in front of, or behind, the headstock spindle axis. To ensure alignment, the witness lines on the back of the tailstock base and top should be lined up by eye (Fig. 80), the adjusting screws provided for that purpose being used. However, this alignment of axes cannot be made by eye to sufficient accuracy. To check alignment, turn a bar of metal at its two ends and mike the two turned diameters. If the two diameters do not correspond, the tailstock must be set over to remove this taper. If the tailstock end of the bar has a slightly smaller diameter than the

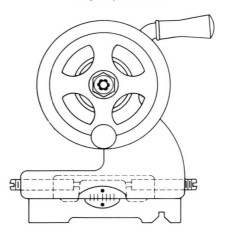

Fig. 80

headstock end, then the tailstock must be shifted slightly away from the operator.

The tailstock, of course, may be placed out of alignment in order to cut slight tapers in a bar. After such a taper is cut, the tailstock alignment must be restored, since it is possible to forget that the tailstock is misaligned for the next job.

The *carriage* of the lathe contains various control handles for operation, and supports the compound rest. The toolpost is mounted on the compound rest. The carriage is supported on the ways by an H-shaped saddle contoured to fit the ways. A carriage clamp screw is used to lock the carriage in position when motion along the ways is not desired, as when making a face cut, a plunge cut, or when cutting off work. The clamp screw must be loose if the carriage is to move along the ways.

The front of the carriage is called the *apron*. This contains the mechanisms for controlling carriage movement along the ways and for lateral movement of the cross slide. No one should operate an unfamiliar lathe until the operation of the apron controls is explained. These controls vary from lathe to lathe. They cannot usefully be discussed here, but require personal instruction.

A pair of half-nuts will be found under the apron. These engage the long leadscrew when turning and cutting threads. When one is moving the carriage along the ways by hand, the half-nuts must be disengaged from the leadscrew. For hand control of the carriage, a hand wheel rotates a pinion, which engages a rack on the bed of the lathe.

The leadscrew is a very accurately cut Acme power thread driven by the spindle through a gear train. The rotation of the leadscrew bears a direct relation to the rotation of the spindle, this ratio being adjustable by gearing changes. When the carriage is driven by the leadscrew, in one rotation of

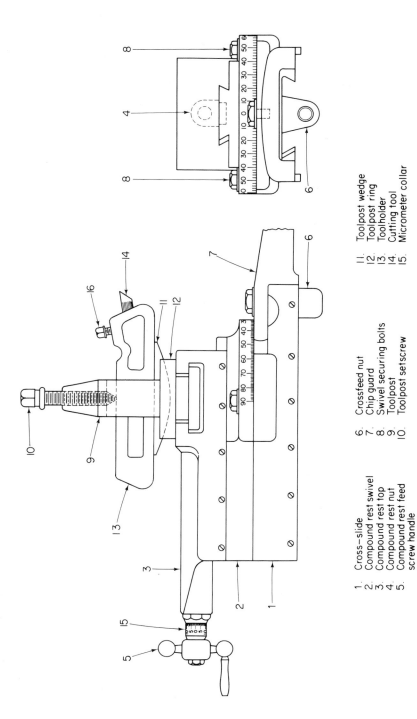

1. Cross-slide
2. Compound rest swivel
3. Compound rest top
4. Compound rest nut
5. Compound rest feed screw handle

6. Crossfeed nut
7. Chip guard
8. Swivel securing bolts
9. Toolpost
10. Toolpost setscrew

11. Toolpost wedge
12. Toolpost ring
13. Toolholder
14. Cutting tool
15. Micrometer collar

Fig. 81

89

the leadscrew the carriage moves a distance equal to the lead of the Acme threads. The lead is the distance between corresponding points on adjacent threads. Because of the geared connection between leadscrew and spindle, for each revolution of the spindle the carriage moves a fixed distance.

A plunge cut, in which the tool is fed toward the center of the bar being cut, may be made with the crossfeed, manually, or automatically by engaging the crossfeed handle.

The compound rest may be swung around to any angle and clamped in position. It is graduated over 90 deg of angle on both sides of center position. Short and steep tapers may be produced by swivelling the compound rest and feeding the tool by means of the compound rest handle.

The cross slide may be too tight or too slack. The gibs (Fig. 78) must be adjusted in either case, by using a screwdriver in the gib adjustment screws.

6.2 LEADSCREW GEAR TRAINS

Suppose that the leadscrew is operated by a gear mounted on the leadscrew and driven by a gear on the spindle. See Fig. 82. (Because the leadscrew and spindle are a considerable distance apart, actually a drive of several gears must be used so that no gear is overly large.) As each tooth on spindle gear A

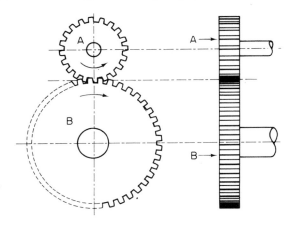

Fig. 82

passes by, a tooth on the leadscrew gear must also be driven past the same point. Then if 60 teeth of gear A go by in one minute, 60 teeth on the leadscrew gear also are driven. If both gears have the same number of teeth, then both shafts turn through the same number of revolutions in a minute. But if gear A has 20 teeth and gear B (leadscrew) has 40, gear B rotates half as fast as A. In 20 teeth, gear A meshes a full revolution but gear B only half a revolution.

$$\frac{\text{rpm of B}}{\text{rpm of A}} = \frac{\text{number of teeth on A}}{\text{number of teeth on B}}$$

Hence, the speed of the leadscrew relative to that of the spindle can be changed by changing gears to obtain the ratio desired. A speed ratio of 1:2 can be given by any combination of teeth giving a 1:2 ratio, such as

$$\frac{20 \text{ teeth}}{40 \text{ teeth}}, \frac{16}{32}, \frac{34}{68}, \text{ etc.}$$

Since the spindle and leadscrew are separated by a considerable distance for gears to bridge, idler gears must be used between the main gears. A little thought will establish that any number of idlers may be interposed between the driving and driven gear without the original gear ratio's being changed.

Suppose the machinist wishes to cut eight threads per inch with a leadscrew having six threads per inch. Then the leadscrew must transport the carriage one inch along the ways while the spindle and workpiece rotate eight revolutions. The leadscrew must revolve six times to move the carriage 1 in. The lathe must be geared to give six revolutions of the leadscrew while the spindle rotates eight revolutions. The leadscrew must rotate $\frac{6}{8}$ as fast as the spindle. Tooth ratios of $\frac{60}{80}$, $\frac{45}{60}$, etc., must be used.

Hence, the thread to be cut must have the same ratio to the leadscrew thread as the two gears have to each other. If the spindle gear is smaller than the leadscrew gear, the thread cut will be finer than the leadscrew thread, and vice versa.

$$\frac{\text{number of teeth on spindle gear}}{\text{number of teeth on leadscrew gear}} = \frac{\text{threads per inch, leadscrew}}{\text{threads per inch to be cut}}$$

As a further example, suppose that 8 tpi must be cut on a lathe with a leadscrew threaded 4 tpi. The gear ratio must be

$$\frac{\text{tpi leadscrew}}{\text{tpi to be cut}} = \frac{4}{8} = \frac{33}{66}, \text{ etc.}$$

A more complex example is a fractional thread. Some pipe sizes are threaded $11\frac{1}{2}$ tpi. Again suppose that the leadscrew has 4 tpi.

$$\frac{\text{tpi leadscrew}}{\text{tpi to be cut}} = \frac{4}{11\frac{1}{2}} = \frac{8}{23} = \frac{24}{69}, \text{ etc.}$$

QUESTIONS

If you have access to a change gear type of lathe, determine for that lathe the gear trains to cut the following common types of thread:

a. $\frac{1}{2}$—20 UNF
b. $\frac{1}{2}$—13 UNC
c. $\frac{5}{16}$—18 UNC
d. 14 tpi (pipe thread)

Figure 83 shows the gear train of a change gear lathe. The spindle gear drives the stud gear at a fixed ratio, which may be 1:1. The stud gear drives the screw gear, mounted on the leadscrew, through the idler gear. Both stud gear and screw gear are removable, and to change the gear ratio between spindle and leadscrew in order to cut different threads, gears with the required number of teeth are placed on the stud shaft and leadscrew shaft.

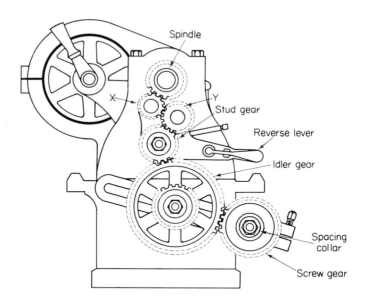

Fig. 83

The rule followed in determining what stud and screw gear to use is the following. Multiply the number of threads per inch to be cut and the number of threads per inch on the leadscrew by the same number. If the resulting two numbers correspond to the number of teeth in any available pair of gears, use these gears. If not, try some other multiplier.

For example, 16 tpi are to be cut; the leadscrew to be used has 5 threads per inch. Using 5 for a multiplier, we obtain

$$5 \times 16 = 80$$
$$5 \times 5 = 25$$

Suppose, however, that one or both of these teeth numbers are not available in the gear set. Try 6:

$$6 \times 16 = 96$$
$$6 \times 5 = 30$$

If 96 and 30 are available, use 30 teeth on the stud shaft and 96 teeth on the leadscrew.

The changing of gears is an inconvenience and a considerable loss of time in the setting up of jobs. Only a few types of small lathes, therefore, are equipped with change gears, most lathes having quick-change gear boxes.

6.3 TOOLHOLDERS

Three common types of toolholders are in use on lathes: the standard, castle, and quick-change or turret types.

The standard type of Fig. 81 is mounted in the T-slot of the compound rest. The tool or toolholder is inserted into the slot in the toolpost and clamped by the setscrew in the top of the toolpost. A rocker or wedge is

Fig. 84 Castle toolpost with boring bar.

inserted under the toolholder. The rocker can be rotated to adjust the cutting edge of the tool to the required height.

This standard type of toolholder is suitable only for light work. Vertical cutting pressure on the tool can cause the rocker to skid or rotate, thus lowering the height of the cutter from its initial position. Side pressure on the tool can also rotate the toolholder. Because of this lack of rigidity or fixity, there is a tendency to use heavy clamping pressure between the tool-post setscrew and the toolholder, causing the toolholder to crush or mush-room.

The castle type of Fig. 84 is useful for boring tools. This toolpost has much improved rigidity and resistance to displacement of tool position.

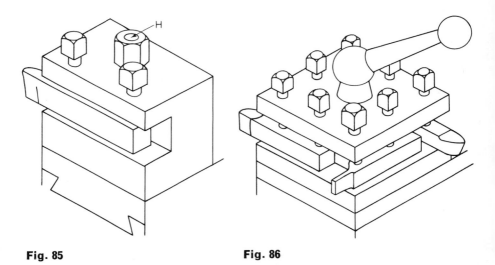

Fig. 85   **Fig. 86**

The quick-change or turret toolpost can carry several tools. Each tool can be quickly rotated into position as needed. Such toolholders are always designed with adequate rigidity against cutting forces.

6.4 WORK-HOLDING DEVICES

Chucks

The Lathe Chuck. Chucks are mounted on the nose of the spindle. The work is held between chuck jaws which are moved in radial slots by means of a chuck wrench. On production lathes, pneumatic chucks may be used.

The most useful of the various styles of chuck is the *four-jaw inde-pendent chuck*. This has four jaws, which can be reversed in the chuck slots, each jaw being independently adjusted. Such a chuck will hold square,

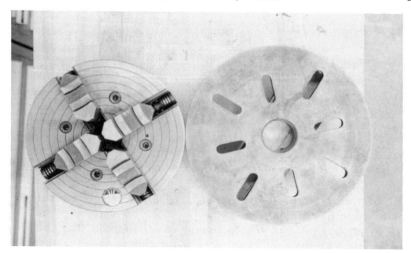

Fig. 87 Four-jaw chuck and faceplate.

round, and irregular shapes, or will even hold stock in an eccentric position if required.

The *three-jaw chuck* will hold round or hexagonal bar. All three jaws converge on the workpiece together as the chuck wrench is turned. The jaws are not reversible, so that this style of chuck requires a set of jaws for external chucking and a second set for internal chucking. The three-jaw chuck is faster to set up, but loses accuracy with use. It does not center workpieces exactly; a worn chuck may show a runout of 0.020 in. or more.

To mount jaws in a three-jaw chuck, first make sure that all mating surfaces are clean, since chips will interfere with movement, damage the chuck, and contribute to misalignment. A spiral scroll can be seen inside the chuck. With the chuck key, turn the scroll until the first thread of the spiral does not quite show in jaw slot 1. Slide jaw 1 into its slot as far as it will go and turn the scroll until it engages the teeth on the jaw. Do the same for jaws 2 and 3. The slots and the jaws are both numbered. The numbered jaws should not be placed in slots of the wrong number.

Soft jaws are obtainable for chucks. Such jaws can be machined to fit unusual shapes.

Large lathes carry the chuck on a taper-nose spindle. On small lathes the chuck is usually screwed onto the spindle. The threaded nose and the chuck thread must be clean before the chuck is mounted. Do not run the chuck on by engaging the spindle motor. To remove a chuck, first place a wood board across the bed ways. It is easy to drop the heavy chuck on the ways.

The *collet chuck* (Fig. 88) is a split cylinder that is closed over the bar to be machined, thus holding it all around its periphery. The collet centers the bar with high accuracy. The size of the hole in the collet deter-

Fig. 88 Spring collets for holding (a) round and (b) hex bars that pass through
the lathe spindle.

mines the diameter of bar that it can accommodate. Collet sets are made
with hole sizes in $\frac{1}{64}$-in. steps. The individual collets will not hold bars
securely if the bars are several thousandths of an inch undersize.

Step chucks are used to hold short workpieces of larger diameter.
They function like a collet.

When using collets or step chucks, it is important that no chips or
dirt interfere with the contact surfaces of the collet.

The *drill chuck* is usually equipped with a taper shank to match the
taper of the tailstock spindle. This chuck is used to hold center drills,
straight-shank drills, reamers, taps, small rods, etc., for work involving light
cutting forces. The jaw pressure of a drill chuck is not capable of resisting

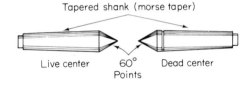

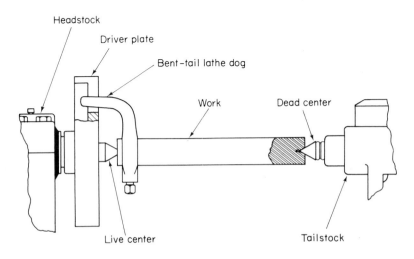

Fig. 89

high torque or horsepower. Larger drills must be taper-shank for insertion directly into the tailstock spindle.

Faceplates

The *faceplate* holds work of irregular shape or large dimensions. The workpiece is clamped to the faceplate by means of the holes or other openings in the faceplate.

A *driving plate* is a small faceplate used for driving work held between centers. A radial slot in the plate receives the bent tail of a lathe dog, which is clamped to the bar workpiece. The workpiece is carried on a *live center* inserted into the headstock spindle and a *dead center* inserted into the tailstock spindle. The centers have 60-deg ground points. The dead center is a hardened center, since it must withstand the heating effect of the workpiece turning against it. The live center is often soft, and, if so, it cannot be interchanged with the dead center. The dead center usually has a groove machined around it to indicate that it can be used as a dead center.

Special Devices

For machining hollow cylinders such as pipe and tubing, a pipe center is used (Fig. 90). The conical disk of this center revolves on the collared end of the center. Several sizes of disks are available to suit the range of pipe sizes.

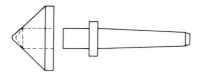

Fig. 90

The *center rest* is shown in Fig. 76. This may be used to support the end of a long bar that must be drilled or bored from the tailstock. The work is also supported by a headstock chuck. The three jaws of the center rest must be carefully adjusted both to align the workpiece and to allow it to turn freely.

The *follower rest* of Fig. 91 is bolted at its base to the saddle of the lathe and therefore follows the cutting tool as it travels along the work. The follower rest provides back-up pressure to prevent the work from springing away from the tool, as is necessary with long thin bars. The adjustable jaws bear on the finished diameter of the work opposite and above the cutter. Both center rest and follower rest must be lubricated with white lead and oil, and must not run too hot.

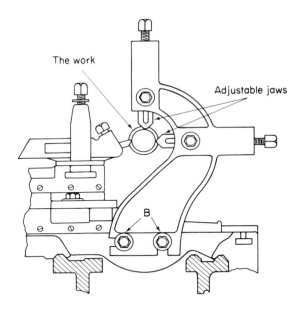

Fig. 91

Fig. 92 Taper attachment, showing the dovetailed guide bar and shoe underneath the cross-slide.

The *taper attachment* of Fig. 92 is used for the turning or boring of tapers. It is bolted to the rear of the lathe saddle. It is connected to the cross slide such that it moves the cross slide laterally as the carriage moves horizontally, thus producing a tool movement at an angle to the axis of the lathe. The angle of the taper is set on the guide bar of the taper attachment. The guide bar support is clamped to the lathe bed. The cross slide is connected to a shoe that slides on the guide bar. Thus the tool follows a line parallel to the angle guide bar.

It is sometimes necessary to machine the outside diameter of a part accurately concentric with a previously bored hole. To produce an accurate outside diameter, it is usual to use the hole for a reference by mounting the work on a *mandrel*, the mandrel being supported between centers. The mandrel is a hardened and ground steel bar with a slight taper of a few thousandths of an inch per foot. The workpiece must be pressed onto the work with an arbor press, and is then mounted between centers and turned with a lathe dog.

QUESTIONS

1. Define swing and length of bed.
2. Why can a live center not be used for a dead center?
3. What is the purpose of the half-nuts in the apron?
4. a. Find the number of threads per inch for the leadscrews of all the lathes in your shop.
   b. Find the number of threads per inch for the milling machines of your shop.
5. What is a mandrel?
6. Clamp a round bar in a three-jaw chuck. Measure the runout of the bar with a dial indicator.

Chapter 7

Elementary Lathe Operations

The basic lathe operations are discussed in this chapter. The cutting of threads and tapers on a lathe is discussed in Chapter 9.

7.1 SETTING UP

Observe all safety precautions when setting up and operating a lathe or any other machine tool. Loose clothing, long sleeves, and watches may become caught when one is operating a machine. Provide a chip guard if the lathe will be throwing hot chips at you, as can happen when tool steels are machined. A face shield is more comfortable and better protection than goggles. Make sure that the floor area is clear of obstructions. Accumulations of chips or oil spots on the floor can cause you to lose your footing.

Do not make the most splendid of all beginner's mistakes: leaving the chuck key in the chuck while you turn on the spindle motor. This makes a projectile of the chuck key.

Be sure that the lathe has been lubricated. Provide a tool pan for your hand tools.

Become acquainted with the lathe and its operational controls. Shift the speed change levers into various combinations—when the spindle is stopped, of course. Try the action of the power feed and hand feed.

7.2 RIGIDITY

A lack of rigidity in your setup of workpiece and tool marks you as a beginner. See Fig. 1 for what not to do. Check the following points:

1. The workpiece should be set as far back in the chuck as it can go.
2. The tailstock spindle should be run out as short a distance as possible.
3. Drills must be set well back in drill chucks.
4. The compound rest must not overhang its support.
5. Expose as little as possible of the tool bit from the toolholder.
6. Use the largest possible cutter size. Small cutters overheat and lack rigidity.
7. Use the huskiest toolpost available for the job.
8. Do not machine a part that projects several inches from the chuck unless it is also supported by a dead center or other means.
9. Use the shortest length of boring bar that will reach the bottom of the hole to be bored.

Lack of rigidity is one of the causes of chatter during turning. The heavier the cut, the more important rigidity becomes. Rigidity of setup is especially important if accurate machining is to be done, or if aerospace metals or 300 stainless steels are to be cut. You cannot see the deflections, but light toolposts and small cutters can deflect several thousandths of an inch.

To repeat, think rigidity at all times. When setting up for rigidity, you can assume that the vertical force on the tool is twice the side force during cutting. This is not strictly true for all cuts—it cannot be true for knurling and cutting off, for example—but it is a useful rule of thumb.

7.3 PREPARING THE CENTERS

The dead and live centers and the tapered spindle sockets must be undamaged and quite clean. The centers must be accurately finished to an angle of 60 deg.

Dead centers especially become worn out of shape. If the live center needs truing, and is soft, it is trued in the lathe by taking a cut with the compound rest set over at 30 deg. The dead center is hard, and must be ground in the lathe with a toolpost grinding attachment.

7.3 ALIGNMENT OF HEADSTOCK AND TAILSTOCK SPINDLES

The use of the two witness lines on the back of the tailstock for aligning the tailstock spindle with the headstock spindle has been mentioned. These two witness lines can be lined up by eye, but this does not remove the last several thousandths of an inch of misalignment. Subject to the same lack of accuracy, the points of the live and dead centers may be brought together and their alignment may be checked by eye.

The only method of ensuring accuracy of alignment is to support a bar of material at least a foot long between centers, and to take a light cut at the headstock and the tailstock end of the bar, both cuts to be made without disturbing the tool setting. The two cut diameters are compared with a micrometer. A caliper may be used to compare these diameters, but a micrometer gives actual dimensions. If, for example, the cut diameter at the tailstock end is the smaller diameter, then the tailstock axis is displaced toward the operator, and must be moved toward the back of the lathe by a fractional turn of the tailstock adjusting screw. After adjustment, the test is repeated until a satisfactory alignment is obtained, preferably equal diameters on both cuts.

In this adjustment, the tailstock must be clamped to the ways and there must be no end play in the bar between centers. The student must be shown the proper pressure between the bar and the dead center. The dead center must be lubricated with an extreme pressure, heat-resistant lubricant. Grease is not suitable. Absence of a suitable lubricant will burn the dead center very rapidly. If heavy cuts are made over a period of time, the bar will expand and put excessive pressure on the dead center. If so, the center will be burned. Soon after cutting has begun, stop the lathe and check the dead center for high temperature.

7.5 SETTING UP THE CUTTING TOOL

The cutter setup must be rigid. This statement applies to the tool bit, the holder, the toolpost, and the cross slide. Any looseness in the slides will give trouble, and may cause the tool to hog suddenly into the work.

The height of the cutter edge should be the center of the workpiece. The edge can be adjusted to this height by lining up with the point of the dead center. Generally, no harm results if the tool is slightly higher than this, unless the front of the tool rubs on the work. The tool should not be low, however, because then it is prone to sudden hogging into the work, and because chip friction is higher and will dull the tool more quickly.

7.6 HOLDING WORK BETWEEN CENTERS

To mount work between live and dead centers, the end faces of the workpiece must first be drilled to receive the centers. The center of each face of the bar is drilled with a combination drill and countersink (Fig. 93). This type of drill is available in several sizes; choose a size that will give adequate bearing

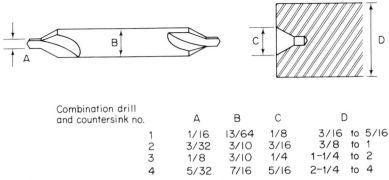

Combination drill and countersink no.	A	B	C	D
1	1/16	13/64	1/8	3/16 to 5/16
2	3/32	3/10	3/16	3/8 to 1
3	1/8	3/10	1/4	1-1/4 to 2
4	5/32	7/16	5/16	2-1/4 to 4

Fig. 93

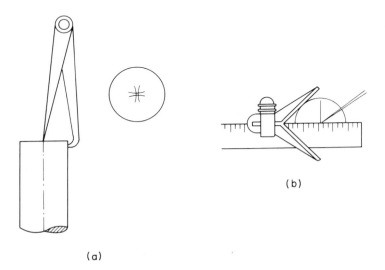

(b)

(a)

Fig. 94

area between work and center and countersink to sufficient depth. The figure supplies information for this operation. The hole must not be drilled to a depth exceeding the countersink portion of the drill, as then the hole will no longer be 60 deg. conical.

If the bar is not too long, it can be held in a chuck on the headstock, and the center hole can be drilled from the tailstock. As the length of the bar increases, this method drills the center hole considerably off center, unless the center of the bar is first laid out and center-punched.

The center of the bar can be found by scribing with hermaphrodite calipers or with a centering head (Fig. 94), or with vee block and surface gage, or a variety of other methods. Both the scribing and the center drilling operations are more difficult if the end of the bar has a rough surface or is not square, and it may be best to take a surface cut across the face of the bar to true it. When the center location is found, it is center-punched. If the center punch mark is slightly off, the punch is angled slightly and repunched to move the mark in the proper direction, then punched vertically.

7.7 CENTERING WORK IN CHUCKS

When centering a bar in a four-jaw independent chuck, the bar can be approximately centered by eye by lining up the four jaws with the ring marks on the face of the chuck. With a piece of chalk mounted in the toolpost, the high spot on the bar can be marked. The bar is centered by adjusting a pair of opposite jaws and then the other pair of opposite jaws.

A dial indicator in a toolpost mounting is better for centering, since it gives a measurement of runout. If the dial indicator shows a variation of, say, 0.014 all around the bar, an adjustment of half this amount, or 0.007, from the high point will center the bar.

Centering a bar accurately in a three-jaw chuck is more difficult, since the jaws are not independent, nor are they in opposite pairs. This chuck is, of course, preferred if a small degree of runout can be tolerated. In the case of the three-jaw chuck, a runout in the range of 0.006 can be corrected with a shim of paper under a jaw. Centering is relatively easy if only one jaw requires a shim, but more difficult if two jaws must be shimmed. Accurate centering in a very old and worn three-jaw chuck can sometimes be a hopeless undertaking.

When a number of duplicate parts must be chucked, use a four-jaw chuck. Release two adjacent (not opposite) jaws and insert the next piece. Two adjacent jaws are left undisturbed.

A word of warning. When preoccupied with the problem of centering work in a chuck, the student machinist is most prone to leave the chuck key in the chuck while switching on the motor.

7.8 MACHINING OPERATIONS

Turning is the machining of the outside surface of a cylinder.

Boring is the machining of the inside surface of a cylinder.

Facing is the machining of the flat ends of workpieces by a tool movement across the ways.

Cutting off is the separation of the finished workpiece from the material by a plunge cut to the center of the bar, a special cutoff tool being used.

A plunge cut is a cut toward the axis of the workpiece, as when one is making a groove in a bar.

Recessing is the production of an internal groove in a bored workpiece.

Ordinary mild steel bars 1 ⌀ (1 in. round) can be rough-turned at speeds up to about 450 rpm if high-speed steel bits are used. Metals may be machined at almost any speed, but the life of the cutting edge falls drastically with relatively small increases of cutting speed. The cutting speed adopted is a fast enough one that does not require too many stops for resharpening or replacing of cutters.

Finish turning can usually be done at slightly higher speeds than rough turning. With the smaller cut used in finish turning, there is less frictional heat generated between chip and tool. Boring, thread-cutting, and grooving must be done at slower speeds than turning.

If a finished surface must be held in a lathe dog, protect this surface from damage by the dog setscrew with a sleeve of some material.

When making heavy cuts, machine toward the headstock. If it is necessary to machine toward the tailstock, very heavy cuts should be avoided, because additional pressure is being placed on the dead center.

Heavy roughing cuts must not be made with small, sharp-pointed tools. More heat is generated in heavy cuts, and a bigger tool with more mass is needed to absorb heat and to conduct heat away from the tool point. A nose radius is always used for rough or finish turning.

If the bar being machined is hot-rolled, it has a surface of mill scale.

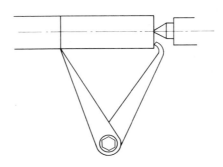

Fig. 95

The first cut must get underneath this scale, which otherwise can destroy the tool point.

Heavy cuts will make the bar material hot, so that it expands. This expansion can be as much as 0.003 in., sufficient to soften the dead center by excessive pressure. Check the dead center for excessive force against the work and for high temperature.

When one is facing large surfaces, the carriage should be clamped against longitudinal movement. It is usual to face from center to outside of the bar. If best accuracy in obtaining a given length of part is required, set the compound rest over at 30 deg. In this position, a 0.001-in. movement of the compound rest will move the tool exactly half a thousandth of an inch parallel to the lathe axis.

In turning to a shoulder, the shoulder may be marked out by hermaphrodite calipers, as in Fig. 95. Sometimes a parting tool is used to groove the shoulder to depth before the bar is turned down to size. If an angular shoulder is to be machined, cut from the small to the large diameter.

7.9 PARTING

Parting-off is a little more difficult for beginners, especially if this operation is to be learned on a small lathe with loose motion in the slides.

The parting tool must be kept sharp. If it is not, it tends to take up the loose motion of the lathe and hog in. The cutter must be set up exactly 90 deg to the workpiece, with the cutting edge exactly at center height of the work, or perhaps very slightly higher for work over 1 in. in diameter. The parting tool should have zero back rake.

On a lightly built lathe the parting speed may have to be reduced below turning speed. The tool must be fed continuously so that there is no interruption in cutting action. If the feed is too heavy, or if the tool barely cuts, the tool will tend to pull into the work and jam.

On a heavy and rigid machine parting is not difficult. Tool pressure is high in this operation, so the cut must be made close to the chuck.

7.10 KNURLING

Knurling notches or embosses the surface of the work to provide a surface that the fingers or hand can grip. This lathe operation is not machining in the sense of removing metal as chips, but instead causes the metal of the workpiece to cold-flow into the impressions in the knurling tool.

The forces required to cause the metal to flow into the knurling pattern are very large. Therefore, the section of the workpiece to be knurled must be close to the chuck jaws or live center. If a long and slender piece is

Fig. 96 (a) Knurling tool. (b) Parting tool.

knurled, a steady rest or follower rest will be needed. A slow turning speed must be used, and small lathes may have to be back-geared. A rather rapid feed is required, and this should be toward the headstock.

The knurl rolls must be at right angles to the work and rigidly clamped in the toolpost. Both rolls must bear against the workpiece with equal force. Sometimes one roll will double-cut; that is, one wheel makes twice as many ridges as the other. This condition indicates that the other roll does not exert sufficient force against the work.

The lathe must not be stopped while the knurls are against the work. This condition can produce a permanent bend in the workpiece.

7.11 CHATTER

The student machinist who is unaware of the meaning of the word "chatter" need not trouble himself to find out. Sooner rather than later, chatter is a condition that will come to annoy him, perhaps on a parting cut.

Chatter is a heavy and noisy vibration set up between the cutter and the workpiece. The condition produces a rough finish on the workpiece, distinguished by a characteristic pattern of grooves as the cutter moves to and away from the work. The chatter problem is often serious on small lathes with lighter construction and lightweight toolposts, but can appear even on robust lathes, especially if a wide chip is being produced.

Sometimes the solution to the problem of chatter is not easy to find.

Look for any lack of rigidity, such as slack in the crossfeed, loose gibs, or overhanging cutter. Try a narrower chip. Rotate the cutter into a slightly different position. When everything else fails, reducing the spindle speed may solve the problem.

QUESTIONS

1. What will be the result of—
   a. A dead center not tight enough in the countersunk hole in the end of the bar?
   b. A dead center too tight against the bar?
2. What is a "plunge cut"?
3. Why should heavy cuts not be made toward the tailstock?
4. Why will a cutter with a large nose radius outlast a more pointed cutter?

Chapter 8

Cutting Tool and Workpiece Materials

In earlier decades of this century the machinist used high speed steel cutters to shape soft steel, brass, and gray cast iron. Nowadays much machining is done with carbide cutters, and the range of workpiece materials is quite astonishing, including hundreds of steels, stainless steels, brasses and bronzes, aluminums, and plastics. More knowledge is now required, both of cutter materials and of workpiece materials.

8.1 HARDNESS

The hardness of materials must often be known, since hardness is an indication of service and processing characteristics. A steel bar may be too hard for turning on a lathe and may have to be ground instead. Abrasion resistance in such materials as excavator teeth and vehicle tires is roughly proportional to hardness. Finally, hardness tests are used to check the success or failure of a heat treatment.

There are a considerable number of hardness tests in use, chiefly because a single hardness method cannot span the whole range of hardnesses from the soft plastics to the hard ceramics such as carbide cutters. However, almost all these hardness methods measure indentation resistance to an indentor. The indentor is pressed into the specimen; a small indentation indicates a high hardness, whereas a large indentation indicates a low hardness.

Through experience everyone acquires the notion that hardness is related to strength in tension and compression. Metals are both hard and strong; the plastics usually are both soft and of low strength. Harder metals are stronger metals.

8.2 THE BRINELL HARDNESS TEST

A Brinell hardness tester is shown in Fig. 97. A hardened steel ball 10 mm in diameter is forced into the test part at a load of 3000 kilograms for steels or 500 kg for nonferrous metals such as brass and aluminum. The Brinell test should not be made on very hard quenched steels, since these may deform the penetrating ball. Neither should this test be made on any thin material, such as plate less than $\frac{1}{4}$ in. thick, such that the underside of the plate shows bulging due to penetration on the opposite side.

Fig. 97 Brinell hardness tester.

The Brinell hardness number BHN is found from the diameter of the impression. This diameter is read in millimeters on a special Brinell low-power microscope. The BHN is found from a table of millimeter values and BHN numbers. The BHN is actually related to the diameter of the impression by the formula

$$\text{BHN} = \frac{P}{\frac{\pi D}{2}[D - \sqrt{D^2 - d^2}]}$$

where P = load in kilograms.

D = diameter of indentor ball.

d = diameter of impression in the specimen.

The denominator is the surface area of the impression, so that the BHN is actually the indenting force per square inch.

The ultimate tensile strength of a steel can be closely approximated by multiplying the BHN by 500.

8.3 THE ROCKWELL HARDNESS TEST

The Brinell test is neither as quick nor as convenient to perform as the Rockwell test. It leaves a rather large impression which is usually damaging

Fig. 98 Rockwell hardness tester.

to the part tested. The Rockwell impression is small enough that sometimes such an impression may not harm the part tested.

The Rockwell tester uses a hardness dial graduated in two scales, Rockwell B and Rockwell C, abbreviated R_b and R_c. Rockwell B tests are performed on soft and annealed steels, whereas the Rockwell C test must be used with hardened steels. An R_b test uses a $\frac{1}{16}$-in. diameter hardened ball with a 100-kilogram load. A 10-kg load is first applied by the tester, and then the operator turns the dial to the SET mark and applies the major load of 100 kg. The major load is then removed, and the hardness is read on the R_b scale. The R_c test uses a conical diamond indentor, called a Brale, with a major load of 150 kg. The procedure is the same as for an R_b test. The Rockwell tester actually measures the further indentation of the major load beyond the indentation of the minor load, but the scale is graduated in Rockwell numbers instead of depth of penetration.

Any movement of the specimen under test will give a false reading. Very often the first Rockwell reading on a specimen is untrustworthy and and can be discarded.

Some significant hardness numbers:

1. Mild steels have an R_b of 60 to 80. These hardnesses are less than R_c zero.
2. Wear-resistant steels must have a minimum R_c of 55.
3. The maximum hardness obtainable in any steels is R_c of 65 to 67.
4. Steels with R_c greater than about 35 cannot be machined with high-speed steel cutters and drills.

8.4 HARDNESS AND MACHINABILITY

Machinability may be roughly equated to the speed with which a material may be cut. Generally it is true that softer materials are easier to machine than harder materials, but this relationship between hardness and machinability is not entirely true. Free-machining bars of mild steel which include lead have the same hardness as ordinary mild steel, while those free-machining bars that are cold-drawn or include sulfur are made slightly harder to improve machinability. The harder bars have an improved chip performance, because the machinability of a metal is influenced by chip performance as well as hardness. Gray cast iron is not highly machinable, because it does not produce a continuous chip. This material would be easier to machine if its chips were longer, because a long chip can extract more heat from the machining operation. The heat not carried away by the chip must be withdrawn into the tool or the workpiece.

The cutting tool breaks down from the wear and high temperature that result when chips are removed. Tool life too is related to hardness,

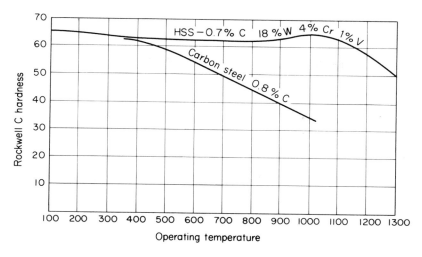

Fig. 99

but in this case it is the hardness of the cutter material at the cutting temperatures, which will be in the range of 1000° to 1500°F.

Most cutters and drills are made of high-speed steels. At room temperature, high-speed steels are actually slightly softer than carbon tool steels. At the elevated temperatures developed during machining operations, the difference in hardness between high-speed steels and plain carbon tool steels is considerable, as indicated in Fig. 99. At 1000°F a high-speed steel may have a R_c of 60, while a carbon steel may be softened to a R_c of 20 at this temperature, a hardness too soft for cutting. Carbon steel cutters and drills, therefore, are suited only to the machining of wood, plastics, and the softer alloys of aluminum and copper, where little heat is generated. The high-speed steels are used where cutting speeds are not too high, 100 fpm or somewhat more for mild steels, and where cutting temperatures, therefore, are not excessive. They are tough materials, and must be used for interrupted cuts where impact of the part against the tool would chip such materials as sintered carbide cutters. For more severe duty, additional cobalt is added to the high-speed steel alloy composition.

The cast Stellite cutters allow higher machining speeds to be used than are usually possible with high-speed steel cutters. The Stellites are high carbon alloys of tungsten, chromium, and cobalt.

The sintered carbides are harder than other tool materials both at room temperature and at cutting temperatures. They can be used at cutting speeds as much as four times the speeds possible with high-speed steel cutters if the horsepower and rigidity of the machine tool permit. But carbides are not tough and can easily be chipped in such operations as interrupted cuts or on machines that lack rigidity.

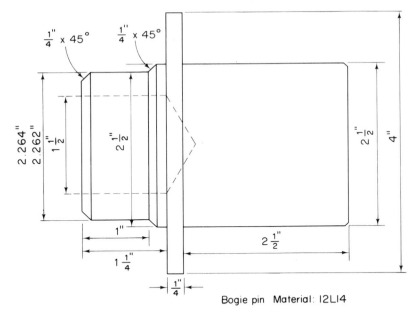

Bogie pin Material: 12L14

Fig. 100

Figure 100 shows a bogie axle machined from solid 4-in. free-machining mild steel bar with carbides. The depth of cut is $\frac{3}{4}$ in., feed is 0.015 ipr, and spindle speed is 600 rpm. This performance is possible only with carbides. What the figure does not show is that an 80-HP motor is required to make such a performance possible.

The ability of a cutter to withstand the abrasion and heat of machining is provided generally by microscopic carbide particles in the cutter material. Similarly, a workpiece heavily loaded with carbide particles will be more difficult to machine. Consider the high-speed steel number T-1, which analyzes 0.7 per cent carbon and 18 per cent tungsten, 4 per cent chromium, and 1 per cent vanadium. The tungsten, chromium, and vanadium alloy content are included in this cutter material for the reason that all of them combine with carbon to make carbides. (Some alloy additions in steels, such as nickel, have little or no tendency to combine with carbon, and are not, therefore, used in cutter materials.) For T-1 steel, therefore, there will be approximately 23.7 per cent of carbides, and the balance of the cutter material will be iron. This assumes that no iron combines with carbon, an assumption that is not true.

An improved cutter material would require a higher carbide content. Sintered carbide cutters contain 75 to 95 per cent of carbide particles, or almost four times as much carbide as high-speed steels, and allow machining speeds to be increased by as much as four times. Carbide content, therefore, controls the maximum machining speeds that are obtainable for any workpiece material, though other factors also have an influence. These other factors may include the cobalt content of the cutter material, lack of rigidity in the machine tool, or simply insufficient motor horsepower to drive the workpiece against the cutter. Hence, there is little reason to use carbide cutters on a light 12-in. engine lathe with a $1\frac{1}{2}$-HP motor; the lathe and its components are simply not husky enough to exploit the possibilities of a carbide cutter. Generally a minimum of 5 HP on a solidly built lathe is required for carbides. Indeed, carbides may not perform as well as high-speed steel on lightweight machines. A lightly built machine tool may be rather flexible, causing small tool and workpiece movements with chatter. A high-speed steel cutter will not be harmed by such flexibility, but a carbide cutter may chip.

Carbide cutters are made of small particles of metal carbides sintered together with cobalt as a binder. While the performance of a high-speed steel is given by its carbide and cobalt content, the selection of a suitable carbide cutter is somewhat more involved. The characteristics of carbides are outlined in the following two sections.

8.5 STRAIGHT TUNGSTEN CARBIDE GRADES

We consider first the simpler case of straight tungsten carbide grades of cutter bits. These may be used to cut any material except steels, but including gray cast iron. These grades consist of tungsten carbide particles bonded with cobalt. Only two characteristics of these grades may be varied: the size of the particles and the percentage of cobalt.

The carbide particles in such cutters are offered in a size range from about 1 micron to 8 microns. A micron is 0.001 millimeter, or 1/25,000 in. The 8-micron size particles would measure about 3 tenths of a thousandth. Cobalt content ranges from about 5 to 25 per cent.

The less the cobalt content, the more brittle and susceptible to chipping the cutter becomes. With 5 per cent cobalt, you would not, for example, take a roughing cut on a hexagonal bar in a turning operation, since the corners of the bar would chip the cutter. But the less the cobalt, the higher the hardness and wear resistance of the carbide. More cobalt must be used with roughing cutters; less cobalt is possible in finishing cutters. Hardness also is increased by smaller grain size. Therefore, the hardest carbide cutter has the least cobalt and the smallest carbide grains, though this may be a risky carbide to machine with.

8.6 CARBIDES FOR CUTTING STEEL

The tungsten carbides cannot be used for machining steel. As the steel chip slides across the top surface of a tungsten carbide cutter, it tends to weld to the cutter, pulling out particles of carbide. The cutting edge, lacking support, then breaks away. This effect is called *crate, 'ng*.

The problem of cratering does not occur when one is machining steel if mixed carbides are used. The cutter material for steels is tungsten carbide plus titanium carbide. Roughing cutters contain about 10 per cent titanium carbide, while high-speed finishing cutters contain about 30 per cent titanium carbide. That is, for higher lathe speeds, the titanium carbide content must be increased.

The abrasive wear of the cutting carbide is increased by titanium carbide, which provides only cratering resistance. Since titanium carbide provides only cratering resistance, with a loss of both strength and wear resistance, it is not usual to use mixed carbides for cutting nonferrous metals. For nonferrous metals, straight tungsten carbide grades are entirely satisfactory.

8.7 CEMENTED OXIDE CUTTERS

A limited amount of lathe work is done with cemented aluminum oxide cutters. This material maintains its hot hardness to temperatures of about 2000°F, and therefore is capable of remarkable machining speeds, actually beyond the capacity of most lathes, which lack both rigidity and sufficient power for oxide applications.

Aluminum oxide is also used in grinding wheels.

8.8 SPEED, FEED, AND DEPTH OF CUT

The speed of machining does not mean revolutions per minute, but refers to the circumferential speed or surface speed of cutting in feet per minute, usually abbreviated sfpm. The speed of cutting in a turning operation is equal to the length of cut or length of chip removed in one minute. For example, the leaded free-machining mild steel 12L14 can be machined at a speed of 180 sfpm with a high-speed steel cutter. At this cutting speed a chip 180 ft long, if continuous, would be developed every minute.

$$\text{Cutting speed} = \text{circumference of work in feet} \times \text{rpm}$$

$$= \frac{\pi D}{12} \times \text{rpm}$$

if D (diameter of bar) is in inches.

But since π is closely equal to 3 and accurate computation serves no useful purpose here,

$$\text{Cutting speed} = \frac{3D}{12} \times \text{rpm} = \frac{D}{4} \times N$$

Example. If 12L14 is to be turned at 180 sfpm, select an approximate rpm for a 1 ϕ bar.

$$180 = \frac{N}{4} \quad \text{and} \quad N = 720$$

If this speed is not available in the range of speeds of the machine tool, always select the next *lower* available speed.

Other types of mild steel must be machined at lower speeds. Ordinary mild steel 1-in. round bars can be turned at about 450 rpm with HSS lathe tools in roughing cuts. These cutting speeds are for straight turning only and do not apply to drilling, tapping, cutting off, or milling. Machinable grades of yellow brass and of aluminum can usually be turned at the maximum speed of the lathe that gives no chatter or other difficulties.

The feed is the number of inches that the leadscrew advances the cutting tool along the bar in one revolution. A coarse feed, 0.015 in. or more, will be used for roughing cuts, and a fine feed, 0.005 in. or more, for finishing cuts that must have a smooth surface. If the maximum amount of metal is to be removed, consistent with a reasonable tool life, use a heavy feed with a slower speed, rather than a shallow cut with a high speed. For better finish, substitute a deep cut for heavy feed. A heavier chip resulting from a deep cut or a heavy feed carries away a greater amount of the heat of machining.

To improve surface finish, use a tool with a large nose radius. Where possible, avoid filing the work for final finish, since filing has a number of disadvantages:

1. A file wears out before any significant amount of metal is removed.
2. Filing is time-consuming.
3. It is possible to file the part out-of-round.
4. If particles load the file, these particles will score the work.

However, a file is useful for cleaning off burrs and for light chamfering of corners.

The depth of cut in rough turning is determined by the amount of metal to be removed, the size of the cutter, the size of the lathe and the motor horsepower, and perhaps by the type of material being turned. Quite substantial depths are possible in mild steel even on small lathes.

8.9 CHIP FORMATION

Machining chips are either continuous or discontinuous. Brittle materials such as gray cast iron produce discontinuous chips, while ductile materials such as mild steel produce continuous chips. A continuous chip is undesirable and unsafe, since it tangles around tool, toolpost, and workpiece, and is then difficult to remove. Various types of chipbreakers are shaped into tools to break up a continuous chip into segments.

When one is machining with carbide cutters, a chipbreaker becomes a serious necessity. A continuous chip, hot, razor-sharp, and of large cross section, coming off the workpiece at 600 or more feet per minute, which is seven miles per hour, would be a hazard indeed to the machinist.

The high pressure between chip and cutter may produce either cratering or a built-up edge. Cratering results when the chip wears or gouges a crater behind the tool point. A crater may either cause the tool point to chip off from loss of supporting material, or may contribute to a built-up edge.

The high pressure and high temperature at the chip-to-cutter interface may weld part of the chip to the tool, producing a built-up edge. This may happen when one is cutting ductile materials such as mild steel. When the

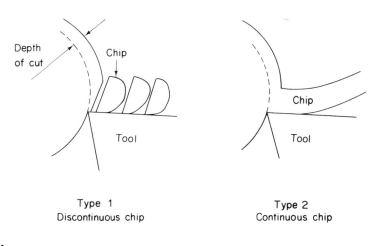

Type 1
Discontinuous chip

Type 2
Continuous chip

Fig. 101

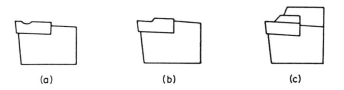

(a)   (b)   (c)

Fig. 102

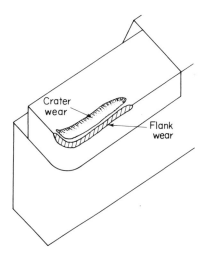

Fig. 103

built-up edge becomes sufficiently large, it breaks off, sometimes removing part of the cutter material.

8.10 COOLANTS

Coolants serve two purposes: removing the heat of machining and reducing friction between chip and cutter. Some coolants also serve to improve the surface finish. Coolants are especially important in thread cutting.

Many brand-name coolants are remarkably effective in their influence on machining, but are more often used in production machining with automatic and turret lathes. For more casual machining, even a standard lubricating oil has a favorable effect.

Cast iron should be machined dry. Kerosene or turpentine is used on nonferrous metals. Special sulfurized oils are required for cutting the stainless steels.

When coolants are used with carbide cutters, the flow of coolant over the carbide must not be interrupted, and the coolant should commence flowing before cutting begins. These cutters are sensitive to thermal shock, and a sudden loss of coolant could cause the tool to crack.

8.11 CUTTING TOOL SHAPES (High-speed Steel)

Most cutter bits are ground to cut only in one direction. A right-hand cutting tool cuts from right to left (toward the headstock); a left-hand tool cuts from left to right. See Fig. 104.

Off-hand grinding is the sharpening of cutter bits and drills manually on a hand grinder. This is not the best practice, and is not allowed in production machining, but gives passable results for more casual kinds of machining work.

The various tool angles for a lathe cutter of high-speed steel are shown in Fig. 105. The angles used for carbide cutters will not necessarily be the same. These several tool angles are required to prevent interference or rubbing between workpiece and cutter, to reduce cutting force, to reduce chip friction, and at the same time to preserve the maximum amount of tool material to

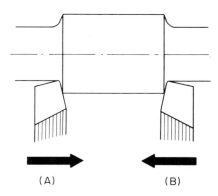

(A)   (B)

Fig. 104

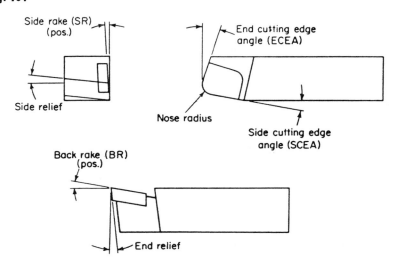

Fig. 105 Cutting tool angles.

absorb the heating effects of metal cutting. The following angles are recommended:

	Mild steel (deg)	Aluminum (deg)	Gray cast iron (deg)
Back rake	8–12	25–50	6–8
Side rake	15	10–20	10–12
Clearance	8–10	7–10	6–9

Tool life is increased with a side cutting edge angle (SCEA). By means of this angle in the cutter, the cutting force and heat of cutting are distributed over a greater length of cutting edge. In the case of an interrupted cut, such as the machining of a square bar to round, the first contact of the work with the cutting tool is back from the point of the tool when such a side cutting edge angle is employed. As the SCEA is increased, the force against the workpiece increases, and there is an increasing tendency to push the workpiece away from the tool. Chatter and close control over dimension may become more serious with large SCEA.

The end cutting edge angle is a relief angle to prevent friction between workpiece and the portion of the tool surface that is not cutting. Only a few degrees are necessary for this purpose.

The back rake angle may be negative on carbide cutter bits, but is

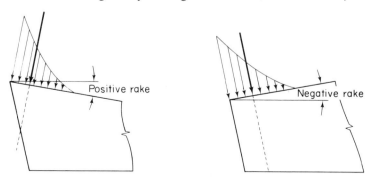

Fig. 106

usually positive for high-speed steel cutter bits. A positive angle is such that the cutter material is ground out behind the point; a negative angle means that the point is ground back. See Fig. 106. A positive rake must be ground to suit the material of the workpiece. A pronounced rake may be required for such materials as aluminum and hard rubber and for those metals which work-harden. If the rake angle is sharp, there is less force and friction between cutter and chip. But a sharp rake angle weakens the cutter by removing supporting material in the cutter. Tool pressure is increased with negative rake, since the tool becomes more of a scraper and less of a knife. Negative rake is used for brass, since a positive rake tends to pull the tool into the brass material, or "hog." However, the scraper action of negative rake tends to harden those work-hardening materials such as the 300 series stainless steels. Because of the poor impact resistance of carbide cutters, negative rake may be used for increased strength of the cutter.

A nose radius reduces cutting pressure against the tool and improves the surface finish.

The side rake angle is often made large, because a large angle produces less chip deformation and thus less heat. Brass and copper can be machined with zero side rake, to prevent hogging of the cutter into the work.

8.12 CARBIDE CUTTERS

Carbide cutters are either brazed to a high-carbon or low-alloy steel tool shank or supported mechanically in a toolholder.

Carbides must be sharpened on diamond-impregnated or silicon carbide grinding wheels, though disposable carbides have become popular. Disposable carbide tips are discarded when worn, though some production shops have reground disposable carbides. After grinding, the carbide should be honed manually with a small silicon carbide honing stick. Carbide tips require more care in grinding than high-speed steel cutter bits. They are readily cracked by overheating or rapid cooling. Very often such cracks are too small to be visible. The use of a hard or unsuitable grinding wheel may generate excessive heat and result in cracking.

The grinding difficulties and delays in changing cutters are removed by the use of disposable carbides, also called throwaway carbides. The small carbide tip is held by a small clamp in a pocket in the toolholder (Fig. 107). When the cutting edge becomes dull, another edge of the same tip is indexed into position. When all cutting edges of the tip are worn, the tip is discarded. In a throwaway operation, the carbide tip is designed for as many cutting edges as possible. A triangular tip has a maximum of six cutting edges, a square eight, and a pentagon tip 10. The use of all possible cutting edges requires negative rake angles.

Toolholders for disposable inserts are so designed that a replacement insert is held almost exactly in the position of the tip it replaced; the new tip may be out of position by as little as 0.003 in. in the case of precision inserts. This makes for convenience when one is resetting a new tip for depth of cut. Lower-quality utility inserts will not give such accuracy.

Some of the types of throwaway tips are illustrated in Fig. 108. The round insert offers cutting edges all around two circles. This type has the obvious applications for fillets, contouring, and radiused grooves and gives

Fig. 107 Toolholder for disposable carbide tips.

a good finish. The round shape without corners makes a strong insert. But the large radius means that a wide and thin chip is generated, together with a high force against the tool. Such conditions are exactly those which can lead to chatter when one is machining ductile materials.

The square insert offers corner strength for heavy cutting, since 90 deg is a reasonably generous angle. A triangular insert has only a 60-deg rounded corner. The latter can machine into a 90-deg shoulder, whereas the square insert cannot—it must be canted to provide a small end-cutting edge angle. The triangular insert must, of course, be used for 60-deg vee threads.

The pentagonal insert is more restricted in its applications, but makes a good finishing or chamfering tool.

The diamond-shaped insert is useful for numerically controlled and tracer-controlled lathes, where a single cutter must shape a complex contour that may include shoulders, tapers, straight turning, and facing. For such work a very large end-cutting edge angle is required to prevent gouging the workpiece on contours. The most popular angle is 55 deg. A four-sided diamond can twist in its pocket, but the elongated or six-sided diamond is more resistant to twisting. Obviously, a disposable carbide insert can be only as good as its pocket. This pocket must be accurately made, quite flat, and of hard steel. It must, of course, be kept scrupulously clean.

The whole toolholder includes, besides its shank, a seat or pad under the carbide tip, the tip, and a clamp. The clamp commonly is shaped to act as a chipbreaker. Sometimes the carbide tip is made with a ridge or groove to act as a chipbreaker. With very heavy cuts, often no chipbreaker is used, because the chip can be made to break as a result of its large cross section. Very heavy chips are highly destructive to chipbreakers.

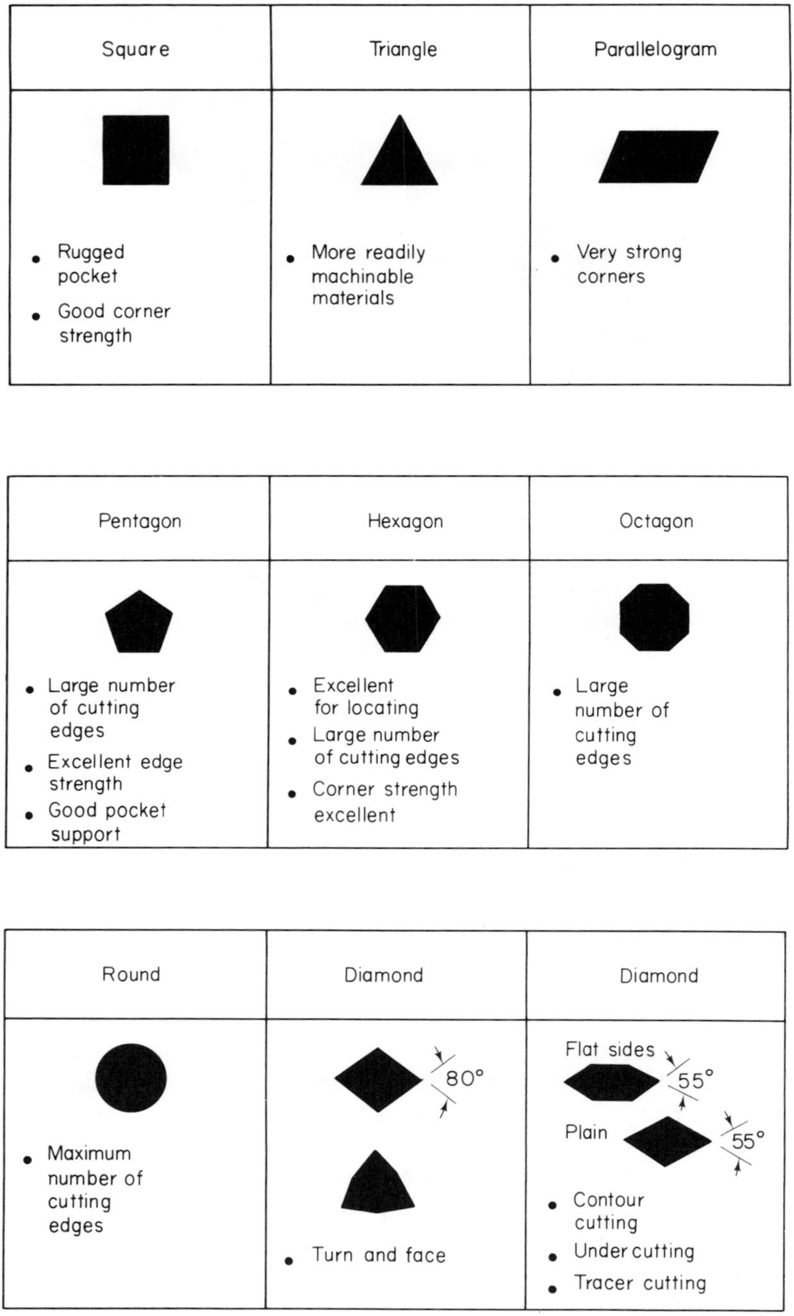

Square	Triangle	Parallelogram
• Rugged pocket • Good corner strength	• More readily machinable materials	• Very strong corners

Pentagon	Hexagon	Octagon
• Large number of cutting edges • Excellent edge strength • Good pocket support	• Excellent for locating • Large number of cutting edges • Corner strength excellent	• Large number of cutting edges

Round	Diamond	Diamond
• Maximum number of cutting edges	80° • Turn and face	Flat sides 55° Plain 55° • Contour cutting • Under cutting • Tracer cutting

Fig. 108

8.13 THEORY OF TOOL LIFE

The life of perishable tools and cutters is drastically reduced by an increase in cutting speed. By tool life is meant the time of cutting until the tool becomes too worn to do its work effectively and it must be sharpened or replaced.

Although it cannot be applied to every machining operation, nevertheless most cutting operations on most materials appear to follow the relationship

$$VT^n = C$$

where V is the cutting speed in surface feet per minute.

T is the tool life in cutting minutes.

C is a constant that is subject to the variables of work material, cutting tool material, type of tool, tool angles, and other factors.

With such a machining formula, the production planner can work out the lowest cost of machining. Obviously, the fastest possible machining

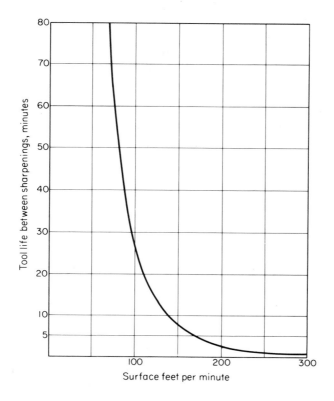

Fig. 109

speed will give the lowest cost per cubic inch of chips. The fastest machining speed, however, will not give the lowest machining cost, because it will entail frequent tool changes and tool sharpenings. In the time required to change a cutter perhaps 25 cubic inches of chip making may be lost. At the other extreme, if a very slow machining speed is adopted, there will be continuous chip-machining with almost no time lost for dull tools, but excessive time will be required to produce each piece. The production planner must, therefore, select some compromise speed. He must balance the cost of tool change and tool sharpening against the speed of machining to reach a minimum over-all cost.

Note, however, that this problem of finding a minimum machining cost applies only to repetitive or production machining. A job shop operation may require 45 minutes of setup and preparation time and only 10 minutes of chip-making; under such circumstances it is not a critical matter that the machining speed is slightly too high or too low.

The relationship $VT^n = C$ is not a scientific law. It was discovered by practical experience, and only practical experience will make it work in a shop. It is possible to find approximate values for C to use in this formula, but generally such handbook values are unsafe to use. The machine shop must find the actual value of C for a *specific cutter and cutter material* by trial and error. This can be done in the following way.

Select the cutter for which you want to determine the tool life. This must be a cutter with a specific set of tool angles and made of a specific material, perhaps T-15 high-speed steel. The tool life figures will apply only to that specific cutter and cutter material. With this cutter, make a series of trial cuts until you find that cutting speed which wears out the tool in one minute. Then $T = 1$ minute, and you have determined V. Suppose $V = 225$ sfpm.

$$\text{Then } 225 \times 1^n = C \quad \text{and} \quad C = 225$$

For this cutter, $VT^n = 225$. You do not yet know the value of the exponent n.

To find n, you must operate the cutter over a range of selected speeds less than 225 sfpm, finding values of tool life T for various machining speeds V. To find n, you must manipulate some logarithms, a type of mathematics to which most technical personnel are not attracted.

If the values of V and T obtained by investigation are plotted on a sheet of log-log graph paper (the vertical and horizontal divisions on such paper are proportional to logarithms of numbers instead of proportional to the numbers), the points obtained can be approximated by a straight line. (There are some exceptions. The data for machining operations on certain difficult aerospace metals do not give a straight line.) An example is given in Fig. 110.

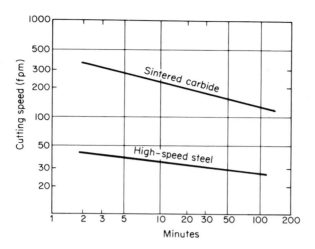

Fig. 110 Typical curves, showing the effect of cutting speed on tool life between sharpenings.

The equation for such a line is

$$\log V + n \log T = \log C$$

Pick any two points on the high-speed steel line, such as $T = 50$, $V = 30$, and $T = 1$, $V = 50$. Substitute in the above equation to obtain two equations:

$$\log 30 + n \log 50 = \log C$$

$$\log 50 + n \log \; 1 = \log C$$

Obtain values for log 30, log 50, and log 1 (log 1 $= 0$) and solve simultaneously for n and C. Do not pretend to any serious accuracy. Then $n = 0.132$ and $C = 50$, so that for this machining operation

$$VT^{0.132} = 50$$

For the turning of mild steel,

$n =$ about 0.125 and $C =$ about 220 when HSS bits are used

$n =$ about 0.25 and $C =$ about 3000 when sintered carbides are used

The cutting speed in surface feet per minute V_m that gives the minimum cost per piece when one is balancing cutting speeds against tool-changing cost is best determined from the following formula taken from the *Machining Data Handbook* of Metcut Research Associates, Inc., of Cincinnati, Ohio. This book is a vast compendium of machining and grinding information.

$$V_m = \frac{C}{\left\{\left[\frac{1}{n}-1\right]\left[\frac{k_2}{k_1}+TCT\right]\right\}^n}$$

where

    C = value of V in sfpm for a tool life of 1 minute.

       = 220 for high-speed bits turning mild steel.

       = 3000 for sintered carbides turning mild steel.

    n = slope of the tool life curve, or the value of n in $VT^n = C$.

    k_1 = machine labor and overhead rate for machining in dollars per minute.

    k_2 = tool cost per cutting edge, including any sharpening cost, in dollars.

TCT = tool changing time in minutes.

The denominator in this equation includes the sum of two time values to the nth power:

1. $(1/n-1)k_2/k_1$, which is the tool life for minimum cost.
2. $(1/n-1)TCT$, which is the tool life for maximum production.

For turning mild steel, the values of n are very closely

$$n = 0.125 \text{ for high-speed steel cutters}$$

$$n = 0.25 \text{ for sintered carbide cutters}$$

If these constants are substituted in the Metcut equation, then for high-speed steel bits turning mild steel

$$V_m = \frac{220}{\left[7\left(\frac{k_2}{k_1}+TCT\right)\right]^{1/8}}$$

and for carbide cutters machining mild steel

$$V_m = \frac{3000}{\left[3\left(\dfrac{k_2}{k_1}+TCT\right)\right]^{1/4}}$$

Example. For turning mild steel with high-speed steel cutters, $k_2 = 0.78$, $k_1 = 0.13$, and tool changing time = 4 minutes. Find the most economical cutting speed.

$$V_m = \frac{220}{[7(6+4)]^{1/8}} = \frac{220}{1.71} = 130 \text{ sfpm}$$

If the bar is 2 in. in diameter, what spindle rpm would be selected?

A 2-in. bar has a circumference of 6 in., or $\frac{1}{2}$ ft. The rpm selected would be 260, if such is available in the lathe gearing. (The exact circumference of the bar is 6.28 in., but there is no virtue in working such calculations to any high degree of accuracy.) What is the tool life for a cutting speed of 130 sfpm?

$$VT^n = 220$$
$$T^{1/8} = \tfrac{220}{130} = 1.7$$
$$T^{1/4} = 1.7^2$$
$$T^{1/2} = 1.7^4$$
$$T = 1.7^8 = 72 \text{ minutes}$$

8.14 PIPE AND TUBE

Tubing is a commonly used material for machining operations, though the machinist usually is less concerned with pipe. Pipe is designed to transmit liquids, and has an outside diameter suited to the special series of pipe threads. The machines that cut pipe threads are not operated by machinists. Tubing is basically designed neither to convey liquids nor for threading, even though it is employed for these as well as many other purposes. The outside diameter, inside diameter, and wall thickness of pipe are not standard or easily remembered measurements, while tubing uses inch and fractional inch sizes, with wall thickness in sheet metal gage or fractional sizes. The machinist should consider pipe to be a conduit for liquids, and tube to be hollow bar.

Tubing is ordered to specified outside diameter and wall thickness. Outside diameters are available in all inch and fractional sizes: $\frac{1}{2}$, $\frac{9}{16}$, $\frac{5}{8}$, etc. to large diameters. Wall thicknesses are available in the gage sizes shown in the table of sheet metal gages, and in fractions of an inch up to 1 inch.

DIMENSIONS OF STANDARD (SCHEDULE 40) PIPE

For heavier and lighter wall pipe, consult any piping handbook.

Nominal pipe size	O.D.	I.D.	TPI	Weight/foot (lb)
$\frac{1}{8}$	0.405	0.269	27	0.25
$\frac{1}{4}$	0.540	0.364	18	0.424
$\frac{3}{8}$	0.675	0.493	18	0.57
$\frac{1}{2}$	0.840	0.622	14	0.85
$\frac{3}{4}$	1.050	0.824	14	1.13
1	1.315	1.049	$11\frac{1}{2}$	1.68
$1\frac{1}{4}$	1.660	1.380	$11\frac{1}{2}$	2.27
$1\frac{1}{2}$	1.900	1.610	$11\frac{1}{2}$	2.72
2	2.375	2.067	$11\frac{1}{2}$	3.65
3	3.500	3.068	8	7.5
4	4.500	4.026	8	10.75
6	6.625	6.065	8	19

8.15 SHEET METAL GAGES

The following table shows the thickness of sheet and the diameter of wire of the even-numbered gages. Odd-numbered gage sizes are available, but are less commonly used. U.S.S. means United States Standard Gage; B & S means Brown & Sharpe Gage.

1. To find thickness of steel sheet: Use U.S.S. column.
2. To find thickness of nonferrous sheet (aluminum, brass, etc.): Use B & S column.
3. To find diameter of steel wire: Use U.S.S. Wire Gage.
4. To find diameter of nonferrous wire: Use B & S column.

Gage size	U.S.S.	B & S	U.S.S. wire
10	0.1345	0.102	0.135
11	0.1195	0.091	0.120
12	0.1046	0.081	0.105
14	0.0747	0.064	0.080
16	0.0598	0.051	0.062
18	0.0478	0.040	0.047
20	0.0359	0.032	0.35
22	0.0299	0.025	
24	0.0239	0.020	
26	0.0179	0.016	

The following are aids to memory. Eleven-gage is virtually $\frac{1}{8}$ in. thick for steel sheet; 16-gage steel is $\frac{1}{16}$ in., and 14-gage is $\frac{1}{14}$ in. thick. The most convenient way to recall weights of steel sheet or plate is to remember that a square foot of $\frac{1}{4}$-in. steel plate weighs 10.2 lb, or approximately 10 lb.

8.16 BAR STOCK FOR MACHINING

The following are the weights per foot of common sizes of round bar. Other sizes can be determined mentally by proportion, if it is recalled that the weight is proportional to the cross-sectional area: a 2-in. bar is four times as heavy as a 1-in. bar.

Diameter of bar	Weight of bar per foot (lb)
$\frac{1}{2}$	$\frac{2}{3}$
$\frac{3}{4}$	$1\frac{1}{2}$
1	$2\frac{2}{3}$
$1\frac{1}{2}$	6
2	$10\frac{2}{3}$

Bars for machining are usually 12 ft. long, since this length is convenient for the bar feeders of turret and automatic lathes. Cold-rolled bar (C.R. bar) has a clean surface; hot-rolled bar (H.R. bar) is covered with black mill scale. This mill scale is extremely hard, and the cutter must go underneath it to remove it. Hot-rolled bars are not suited to grinding operations, since the particles of scale attach to the grinding wheel and harm both it and the part being ground. Bars of mild steel that are cold-drawn are somewhat easier to machine. Cold-drawing increases hardness, giving the benefits of better surface finish and a chip that breaks up more readily.

QUESTIONS

1. Name the tool angles indicated in Fig. 111.
2. Sketch a right-hand lathe cutter bit.
3. What is the maximum Rockwell C hardness obtainable in any steel?
4. Plain carbon steels can be heat-treated slightly harder than high-speed steels at room temperature. Why, then, are carbon steels not used for lathe and milling cutters?
5. What is meant by tool cratering?
6. Why is an SCEA used on lathe cutters?
7. Why is negative rake used with a carbide cutter but rarely with a high-speed steel cutter?

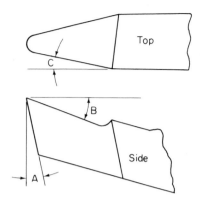

Fig. 111

8. Very soft materials should be machined with a generous back rake. Can you think of a reason why this is advisable?
9. What are the two materials blended into a carbide cutter?
10. Why are straight tungsten carbides not recommended for turning steels?
11. For an interrupted cut, would you select a carbide with little or much cobalt?
12. Why is titanium carbide included in carbide cutters for steel?
13. If a machining speed of 600 sfpm is selected, at what rpm would you turn a 3-in. bar?
14. If a machining speed of 1000 sfpm is selected, at what rpm would you turn a 4-in. bar?
15. The depth of cut on a lathe is $\frac{3}{4}$ in., and the feed is 0.015 ipr (inches per revolution) at a cutting speed of 600 sfpm. How many cubic inches of chips are removed per minute? Bar diameter is 4.0 in.
16. What is the approximate weight of 1 square foot of 1 in. thick steel plate?
17. If aluminum weighs one-third as much as steel, what is the weight of 16 square feet of $\frac{1}{8}$ in. thick aluminum plate?
18. Determine the cutting speed for minimum cost, given the following data:
    a. High-speed steel turning mild steel, with a labor and overhead rate of $0.25 per minute, a tool-changing time of 1.5 minutes, and a cost per cutting edge of $2.00.
    b. Carbide bit turning mild steel, labor and overhead rate $0.25 per minute, tool-changing time 0.5 minute, and cost per cutting edge $1.00.
    c. Carbide bit turning leaded mild steel 12L14, labor and overhead rate $0.15 per minute, tool-changing time 0.5 min, and cost per cutting edge $1.00.

Chapter 9

Advanced Lathe Operations

9.1 BORING

Boring is an internal machining operation for the purpose of enlarging a hole or for producing an internal taper.

The boring cutter may be set exactly at the center height of the hole or slightly below. If a taper is being bored, the cutter must be exactly on center to ensure an accurate taper. (When one is turning an outside taper, the tool should be set on center also.) Tool angles for boring are the same as for turning, though additional front clearance is needed in small holes to prevent the bottom of the tool bit from rubbing on the work.

The size of boring bar that may be used is, of course, limited by the size bar that may be inserted into the hole to be bored. If the hole is small, the boring bar must be of small diameter. Such a bar has insufficient rigidity: it will deflect under tool pressure and may chatter. Use the largest possible boring bar. To improve rigidity of setup, the boring bar should extend out of the holder only far enough to reach the depth of bore. Because of the flexibility of boring bars, light cuts are necessary. Springiness also makes the depth of cut uncertain; if the tool is fed a few thousandths on the cross slide, this feed may be entirely taken up by spring, leaving no depth of cut. For this reason it is difficult to bore a small hole to exact size. Small holes, therefore, are more easily brought to accurate diameter by leaving a few thousandths of an inch on diameter to be taken out in a final cut with a reamer.

Large workpieces that are difficult to hold on a faceplate may be clamped to the top of the carriage for boring from the headstock. The boring bar is supported between centers and driven by a lathe dog, the workpiece being fed into the cutter by the leadscrew.

9.2 TAPERS

Taper is the uniform increase or decrease in diameter of a machine part. All tapers, therefore, are cones. Taper shanks and their matching sockets are used in machine tools for a number of reasons:

1. Excellent alignment.
2. Ease of insertion.
3. Great holding power.

Taper shanks are used on such cutters as drill bits because the wedging action between matching tapers develops very high friction effects. This large friction force can transmit high torque and horsepower into the tool to drive it.

Taper is measured either in taper per foot or per inch, or in degrees, minutes, and seconds. Taper is always a measurement of diameter, not radius (see Fig. 112). The taper, therefore, is double the slope per foot.

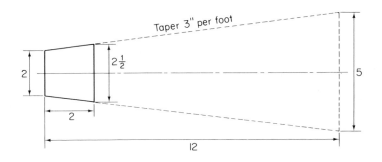

Fig. 112

Example. A turned workpiece includes a taper of 0.050 in. per inch, and the small end of the taper measures 0.369 in. What is the taper per foot and the diameter at the large end if the taper length is $3\frac{1}{8}$ in.? Finally, determine the angle of the taper.

The taper per foot is 0.600 in.

The diameter of the large end is 0.369 in. plus the increase in diameter in $3\frac{1}{8}$ in.

The increase in diameter = 3.125/12 × 0.600 = 0.15625.

The diameter of the large end = 0.369 + 0.1563 = 0.5253 in.

To determine the angle of the taper, see Fig. 113. The increase in radius of the taper in a 1-in. length is $\frac{1}{2}$ × 0.050, or 0.025 in. Therefore, the tangent of the taper angle is 0.025/1. This corresponds to an angle of 1 deg 26 min.

The taper is double the angle that the surface of the taper makes with the centerline of the taper. The angle with the centerline is, of course, the

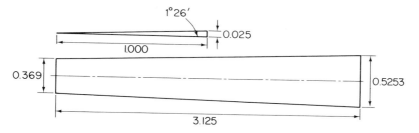

Fig. 113

slope of the taper. Consider that in turning, the diameter of the workpiece is reduced by twice the depth of cut. Expressing the taper as a slope is less convenient for machining purposes than as an increase in diameter.

There are a number of tapers in common use for machine tools. Milling machine spindles use a standard taper of $3\frac{1}{2}$ in. per foot. Pipe threads have a taper of $\frac{3}{4}$ in. per foot. The taper holes in lathe and drill spindles, and the matching tapers on live and dead centers and drill bits are Morse tapers, which are about $\frac{5}{8}$ in. per foot. The Morse tapers are tabulated in Fig. 114. The Brown & Sharpe tapers, used in milling machine spindle shanks, are tapered $\frac{1}{2}$ in. per foot.

9.3 TURNING TAPERS

A taper may be turned by either of two methods. The workpiece may be mounted at an angle to the axis of the lathe, or the cutter may move at an angle to the lathe axis. Four machining possibilities are available:

1. Setting over the tailstock. This moves the dead center off the axis of the lathe.
2. Setting the compound rest at the required angle, causing the cutter to feed at this angle.

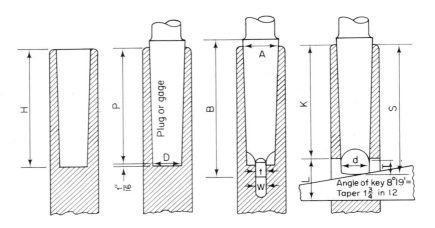

Detail dimensions

Number of taper	0	1	2	3	4	5	6	7
Diameter of plug at small end. D	0.252	0.369	0.572	0.778	1.020	1.475	2.116	2.750
Diameter at end of socket .... A	0.3561	0.475	0.700	0.938	1.231	1.748	2.494	3.270
Shank:								
Whole length of shank ..... B	$2\frac{11}{32}$	$2\frac{9}{16}$	$3\frac{1}{8}$	$3\frac{7}{8}$	$4\frac{7}{8}$	$6\frac{1}{8}$	$8\frac{9}{16}$	$11\frac{5}{8}$
Shank depth .... S	$2\frac{7}{32}$	$2\frac{7}{16}$	$2\frac{15}{16}$	$3\frac{11}{16}$	$4\frac{5}{8}$	$5\frac{7}{8}$	$8\frac{1}{4}$	$11\frac{1}{4}$
Depth of hole. .... H	$2\frac{1}{32}$	$2\frac{3}{16}$	$2\frac{5}{8}$	$3\frac{1}{4}$	$4\frac{1}{8}$	$5\frac{1}{4}$	$7\frac{3}{8}$	$10\frac{1}{8}$
Standard plug depth .... P	2	$2\frac{1}{8}$	$2\frac{9}{16}$	$3\frac{3}{16}$	$4\frac{1}{16}$	$5\frac{3}{16}$	$7\frac{1}{4}$	10
Tongue:								
Thickness of tongue ...... t	$\frac{5}{32}$	$\frac{13}{64}$	$\frac{1}{4}$	$\frac{5}{16}$	$\frac{15}{32}$	$\frac{5}{8}$	$\frac{3}{4}$	$1\frac{1}{8}$
Lenght of tongue .... T	$\frac{1}{4}$	$\frac{3}{8}$	$\frac{7}{16}$	$\frac{9}{16}$	$\frac{5}{8}$	$\frac{3}{4}$	$1\frac{1}{8}$	$1\frac{3}{8}$
Diameter of tongue .... d	0.235	0.343	$\frac{17}{32}$	$\frac{23}{32}$	$\frac{31}{32}$	$1\frac{13}{32}$	2	$2\frac{5}{8}$
Keyway:								
Width of keyway .... W	0.160	0.213	0.260	0.322	0.478	0.635	0.760	1.135
Length of keyway L	$\frac{9}{16}$	$\frac{3}{4}$	$\frac{7}{8}$	$1\frac{3}{16}$	$1\frac{1}{4}$	$1\frac{1}{2}$	$1\frac{3}{4}$	$2\frac{5}{8}$
End of socket to keyway. .... K	$1\frac{15}{16}$	$2\frac{1}{16}$	$2\frac{1}{2}$	$3\frac{1}{16}$	$3\frac{7}{8}$	$4\frac{15}{16}$	7	$9\frac{1}{2}$
Taper per foot	0.625	0.600	0.602	0.602	0.623	0.630	0.626	0.625
Taper per inch.	0.05208	0.05	0.05016	0.05016	0.05191	0.0525	0.05216	0.05208
Number of key.	0	1	2	3	4	5	6	7

Fig. 114

3. Using the taper attachment, which also causes the cutting tool to move at the required angle.
4. Programming a sloping cut on a numerically controlled lathe. This method is not discussed.

9.4 TAPER TURNING BY OFFSET TAILSTOCK

This method is suited only to external tapers. After the taper is turned, the tailstock must be reset to the axis of the headstock.

There are a number of methods of measuring the setover required of the tailstock.

If the bar to be tapered is circular and of uniform diameter, as would be the case with a cold-drawn bar or a previously turned bar, then measurements for taper may safely be made from the bar. The bar can be set up between centers, with the tailstock spindle in its usual position in alignment with the headstock spindle. Mount a dial gage in the toolpost.

Feed in the dial gage to make contact with the bar near the headstock, and adjust the dial gage to zero. Move the gage down the bar a distance of, say, 12 in. toward the tailstock. The tailstock can then be set over until the dial gage indicates the required deflection. Make the measurement a second time against the possibility of error. The tailstock is then locked in position.

Recall that when turning a bar, the bar is reduced in diameter by twice the depth of cut. Consider that offsetting the tailstock by a certain amount produces the same effect as feeding the tool by the same amount. That is, if the tailstock is offset 0.500 in., then the taper will be twice this amount or 1.000 in., in the taper length. By formula

$$2 \times \text{tailstock offset} = \text{length of taper in inches} \times \text{taper per inch}$$

$$2 \times \text{offset} = L \times \text{taper/inch}$$

Or, if the taper per foot is known,

$$\text{Offset} = \frac{L \times \text{TPF}}{24}$$

Sometimes on a drawing the taper is not given, but diameters are given instead, as in Fig. 115, which shows a bar with a straight and a tapered section. The total bar length is 12 in., with a 6-in. long taper. The large taper diameter is 1.125 in. and the small diameter 0.875 in.

In this case the whole length of bar must be carried on the offset tailstock, even though only a part of the bar is to be tapered. Call the large taper diameter D and the small diameter d. The amount of taper in 6 in. is

Fig. 115

$(D-d)$, or 0.250 in. Then the amount of taper in the full bar length is, by proportion,

$$\tfrac{12}{6} \times 0.250 = 0.500 \text{ in.}$$

The tailstock must be set over half of this amount, or 0.250 in.

Such calculations are more safely made by common sense considerations, but for those who prefer to work by formula (less reliable!):

$$\text{Tailstock offset} = \frac{L \times (D-d)}{2L'}$$

where L = total length of bar.

L' = taper length.

In the case of a taper to be made to closely controlled dimensions, you should find that the tailstock setover that was calculated does not give exactly the taper expected. If so, the explanation is probably the condition of misalignment at the tailstock center shown in Fig. 116. Therefore, do not

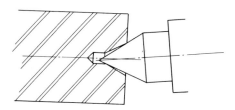

Fig. 116

depend uncritically upon calculations, but be prepared to make an additional adjustment of the tailstock after trial cuts. Since the taper on the dead center does not conform to the center-drilled bar when the tailstock is offset, offsetting should be avoided as a lathe operation unless no alternative method is available.

Note that if the cutting edge of the tool is not exactly at the height of the live center, then this condition will also produce an error in the taper.

Offsetting of the tailstock may also be done by the following method, which uses the micrometer graduations on the cross slide handle. In this method, any backlash in the cross slide must be accounted for.

Set up a round-nose tool in the toolpost. The bar is again carried between centers, and the tailstock is not yet offset. A piece of hard paper, such as white bond paper, is introduced between the cutter and the bar, and the cross slide is adjusted so that the cutter just nips the paper. The cutter is then moved down the bar a convenient distance, such as 12 in. or the length of the taper. Move the cutter in or out the required number of thousandths of an inch for the taper. Offset the tailstock to close the paper against the cutter again. Rough-cut the taper, check it, and make any final corrections to the tailstock offset.

9.5 TAPER TURNING WITH THE COMPOUND REST

With the compound rest, either internal or external tapers may be cut. The setting-up is easily executed. However, the taper length is limited to the maximum movement of the compound rest.

Because the base of the compound rest is graduated in degrees, the taper must be converted to degrees. Set the compound rest over to the required

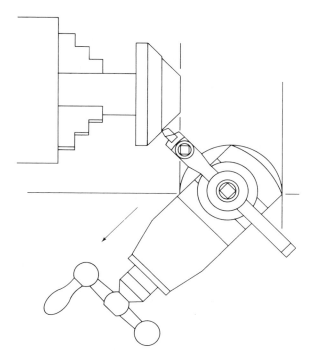

Fig. 117

angle as closely as can be read, and cut the taper from the small to the large diameter. If the angle is in degrees and minutes, a rough cut of the angle must be checked for final corrections. The height of the cutting tool must be exactly the height of the dead center, as in all taper cutting. Be sure the carriage is locked in position. If the taper is internal, it is preferable to make the finishing cut with a taper reamer.

9.6 TAPER TURNING WITH THE TAPER ATTACHMENT

The taper attachment was discussed in Sec. 6.4. The guide bar of the taper attachment is set at the angle to the lathe axis required to produce the taper. The guide bar is graduated in degrees at one end and in inches per foot of taper at the other end. A shoe slides on the guide bar as the carriage moves longitudinally. This shoe produces the lateral movement of the cross slide that gives the taper. Thus the cutter moves along a line that is parallel to the guide bar.

When turning a taper by this method, run the carriage to the approximate position of the work to be tapered. Check that the taper attachment is in such a position that the cutter can travel the full length of the taper. The tool point must be exactly at center height. Set up the guide bar and clamp the attachment. Final adjustment of the cutter must be made by means of the compound rest feed screw, since the crossfeed screw is inoperative.

When making a blind tapered hole, drill the hole to depth with a drill of the size of the small diameter of the taper (recall that a drill will drill a few thousandths of an inch oversize). Material then does not need to be removed at the very end of the bore, a difficult operation, especially if the hole is small and deep.

To test a taper for accuracy when it is almost finished, make a chalk mark along the length of the turned taper or the mating taper. Place the test piece in the taper hole and turn it carefully by hand. Remove the test piece and examine the chalk mark. A perfect taper will smear the whole length of the chalk mark. If the taper is not quite right, the chalk smear will indicate the required correction.

9.7 THREAD CUTTING

The cutting tool must be sharpened to the same form as the thread to be cut. No side rake or back rake is used for vee threads. A center gage (Fig. 118) is used to check the form of the cutter for vee threads and for setting the cutter in position.

It is preferable to cut first a groove at the end of the threaded part of the bar. This groove provides a gap for terminating the threading cut and

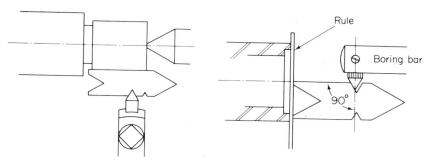

Fig. 118

ensures that the thread is cut to full depth and form for its whole length.

The gearing of the lathe is set up to produce the required number of threads per inch. The compound rest is swivelled 29 deg to the right for a vee thread. This is half of the 60-deg thread form less 1 deg. This angle is used so that the tool cuts only on one side, with a slight shaving action to smooth the opposite side. The cutter must be exactly on center elevation of the bar and exactly at right angles to the bar, as checked by the center gage (Fig. 118).

Usually a thread cannot be cut to full depth in a single pass of the tool. After the first pass, the tool must be withdrawn and a second cut made. This second cut must find the path of the first cut and follow it, and not start a new thread. So that all following cuts will find the original thread helix, a *thread dial* is fitted to the carriage of the lathe. The thread dial is rotated by the leadscrew when half-nuts are not engaged and indicates when to engage the leadscrew to catch the original thread pass. On the rotating face of the thread dial there are several graduations (Fig. 119) and an index mark. When a graduation aligns with the index mark, the half-nuts are quickly engaged, in accord with the following rules.

1. Even-numbered threads per inch, such as $\frac{1}{2}$–20, $\frac{3}{4}$–10: Close the half-nuts at any graduation on the dial.
2. Odd-numbered threads, such as $\frac{1}{2}$–13, $\frac{7}{8}$–9: Close the half-nuts at any numbered line on the dial.

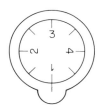

Fig. 119

3. Threads with a half-thread per inch, such as $11\frac{1}{2}$: Close the half-nuts at any odd-numbered line on the dial.
4. Threads with fractional threads per inch: Insert the tool into the cut, wind the tool back to the start of the cut, and make the next cut.

A relatively slow turning speed is used for thread-cutting. When the thread dial gives the proper indication, engage the half-nuts for the first cut, which should be a light marking cut. Check the number of threads per inch with a screw pitch gage or by any other suitable means. Then advance the cutter with the compound rest feed screw—only the compound rest must be used for feeding. All cuts are relatively light. The last cut should be only a few thousandths in order to produce a good finish. A suitable cutting fluid should be used if threading a stringy metal such as mild steel.

The best way to check the finished thread is to test it with a mating part such as a nut. Or a thread micrometer may be used. This instrument gives the pitch diameter.

Left-hand threads are cut by the same method as right-hand threads. However, the compound rest is rotated 29 deg to the left, and the leadscrew is reversed so that the cutter moves toward the tailstock. Acme threads are cut by rotating the compound rest to 14 deg.

Internal threads must be cut with a boring bar and threading cutter. The hole must first be drilled and bored to the required minor diameter. Recess the bore at the termination of the thread with a recessing tool. The recess depth must be at least as large as the major diameter. The compound rest is rotated 29 deg to the left, and of course the cutter is fed out toward the operator on successive cuts. The half-nuts must be disengaged before the boring bar bottoms in the hole.

If a tapered thread must be cut by using the taper attachment, the thread cutter must be set up exactly at right angles to the axis of the lathe, not at right angles to the tapered surface.

9.8 TOOLPOST GRINDING

With the use of a grinder mounted on the lathe carriage (Figs. 120 and 75) such grinding operations as sharpening of reamers, truing of lathe centers, and finish-grinding of shafts are possible.

Although shafts are preferably ground on a cylindrical grinding machine, casual grinding on a lathe is sometimes necessary. Frequently shafts must be machined, hardened, and ground. The hardening operation warps the shaft, and the warp or runout is removed by the final grinding operation, which also supplies the required smooth surface finish and final accurate size. Any heat-treating scale should be removed before grinding,

Fig. 120 Dumore toolpost grinder.

since scale can load the grinding wheel and score the shaft being ground. A grinding allowance of 0.010 to 0.015 in. is suitable.

The abrasive and metal particles produced by the grinding operation are extremely small and therefore are difficult to remove from the areas of the lathe where they deposit. They can be the cause of excessive wear to the components of the lathe. To protect the lathe from such grinding dust, cover the bed of the lathe with a cloth. Paper is not as suitable as cloth, since it is stiffer and can spill accumulations of the particles. Note the protection of the ways from grinding dust in Fig. 75.

The grinding wheel must be trued or dressed before the grinding operation is begun. Dressing of the wheel should also be performed before the last passes over the workpiece. The dresser is a small industrial diamond mounted in a steel shank. The grinding wheel is traversed across the diamond with about 0.001 in. removed from the wheel with each pass. Only the minimum amount of material is removed from the wheel to true it, in order to preserve the life of both diamond and wheel.

Dressing may also be necessary if the wheel "loads" with metal particles and thus scratches the work.

The workpiece is ground at about 80 to 100 rpm. The wheel should remove only a few thousandths per pass. The wheel is rotated to throw abrasive particles downward toward the lathe bed, with the workpiece rotating in the opposite direction.

When one is internally grinding a hole, the quill on which the wheel is mounted will be of small diameter and will flex under grinding pressure. This flexing will produce a large diameter at the opening of the hole. To reduce this tendency to "bell-mouth," the cuts in internal grinding must be extremely light.

Finally, when finishing off a grinding operation, allow the wheel to spark out. This is done by making the last cuts without changing the depth of cut—the last passes, therefore, produce no sparks.

9.9 TRACER ATTACHMENTS

Tracer attachments are mounted on lathes when several identical pieces with complex contours must be machined. A template of the shape to be cut is fabricated of heavy-gage steel and attached to the bed of the lathe. The tool slide is driven by a hydraulic circuit, and as a stylus moves over the surface of the template, the movements of the stylus are duplicated by the tool slide. Accuracy of a couple of thousandths of an inch is possible in a properly adjusted tracer mechanism.

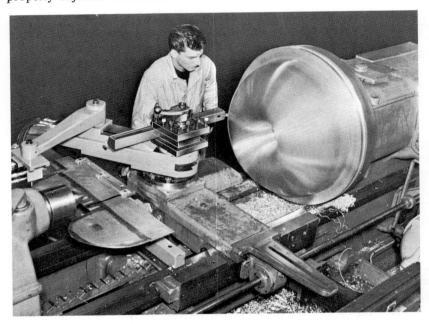

Fig. 121 A hydraulic tracer attachment for a lathe spinning operation.

A round-nose cutter bit or a button carbide insert is best suited to the variety of tool movements involved in tracer operation.

Profiling by means of a hydraulic tracer attachment is also carried out on shapers, planers, and mills.

In Fig. 121 a template is mounted across the lathe bed at the left of the photograph. The template controls a spinning operation on sheet metal.

QUESTION

Determine the slope angle to the axis and the taper per foot of Morse tapers nos. 1, 2, and 3 of Fig. 114.

Chapter 10

The Shaper, Planer, and Broach

The shaper and planer are similar machines in that a single-point tool is reciprocated across a workpiece clamped to the machine table. In the case of the planer, the tool is fixed and the work moves; the reverse is the case for the shaper. Both machines are suited primarily to the production of flat surfaces and grooves, though not limited to flat surfaces.

A machining operation on a shaper usually occupies considerable time. Therefore, this machine is normally restricted to tool room and some job shop operations. The milling machine and broaching machine are considerably more productive in producing flat work, especially if tooled with a large diameter inserted-carbide cutter.

10.1 THE SHAPER

The shaper may be hydraulically operated. Most shapers, however, are driven with a crank mechanism that provides a faster speed on the idle return stroke than on the cutting stroke. The shaper size is the maximum length of workpiece that can be cut by the stroke of the machine. Thus a 16-in. shaper can machine across a workpiece 16 in. long. In order for it to do so, the stroke will be longer than this distance, perhaps 17 in.

The table of the shaper is made of cast iron, with slots on top, sides, and front. The table may be elevated either by hand or power feed. In some

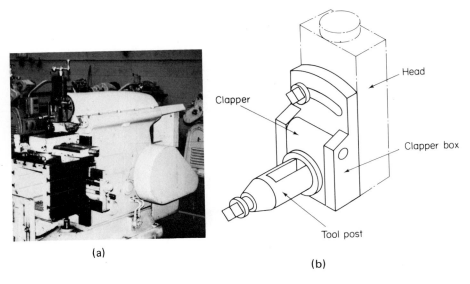

(a)

(b)

Fig. 122

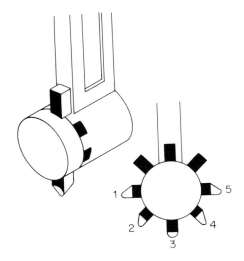

Fig. 123

machines the table can tilt in either direction for the machining of angular work.

The ram moves to and fro' across the work on a dovetailed slide machined in the top of the column, with the toolhead and tool supported at the front of the ram. The cutter is clamped in a toolpost of the type used with lathes, the toolpost being carried on a clapper and clapper box as shown in Fig. 122. In addition to a lathe-type toolholder, the universal toolholder of Fig. 123 is also used.

The work is held in a vise or clamps, tee-bolts in the tee slots of the worktable being used. If the workpiece or a vise must be accurately square with the stroke of the ram, a dial indicator may be used to check the alignment. Figure 124 shows the use of a dial indicator and a machinist's square for checking alignment. The workpiece is frequently levelled by resting in the vise or in clamps on steel parallels. These are precision-ground hardened steel bars.

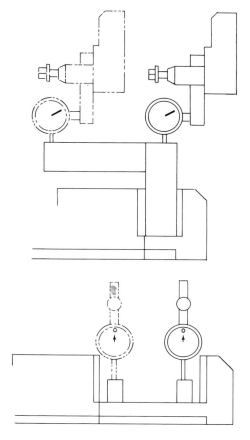

Fig. 124

One side of the work may be square and even, and the other side rough or uneven. In these circumstances the square side should lie against the fixed jaw of the vise. A soft metal rod (mild steel, aluminum, or brass is suitable) may be used between the rough side of the work and the movable jaw (Fig. 125). The soft bar conforms to irregularities in the rough surface of the workpiece. Also, if the movable jaw tends to lift the workpiece when tightened, the soft bar will tend to roll the workpiece down into the bottom of the vise.

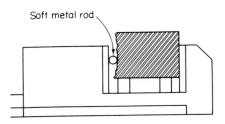

Soft metal rod

Fig. 125

In all cases, the longer dimension of the workpiece should lie in the direction of the ram stroke to reduce the number of strokes required to shaper the surface.

The stroke must be adjusted both for length and for starting position. Procedures for ram positioning and stroke setting may be found in the operating manual for the machine or from an operator with experience with the machine. The stroke should extend $\frac{1}{4}$ in. past the end of the workpiece (Fig. 126) for chip separation and clearance, and at least $\frac{1}{2}$ in. at the start of the stroke to allow the clapper box to drop back to cutting position.

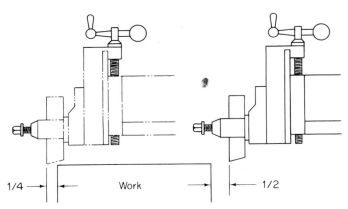

1/4   Work   1/2

Fig. 126

10.2 SHAPERING OPERATIONS

Shaper operations must be governed by a paramount safety consideration: The machine must not be operated until it is quite certain that the ram and the tool will not cause a collision.

A frequently occurring operation on the shaper is the squaring of the four sides of a rough block. The operation sequence of Fig. 127 is used. The first surface to be shapered is placed against the fixed jaw of the vise, with a soft copper, brass, or steel rod against the movable jaw. The soft rod

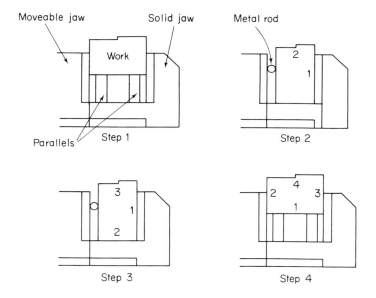

Fig. 127

conforms to irregularities in the workpiece to hold it more securely against cutting forces. The second surface to be shapered is then located on the bottom, perhaps on parallels, with the first surface once again placed against the fixed jaw. The remaining two sides are shapered. Always hammer the part down on the parallels with a soft hammer that does not bounce.

When one is shapering a horizontal surface, the toolholder should be as close to vertical as possible. If it is at an angle to the vertical, tool forces may cause it to rotate and thus alter the depth of cut. Machine the surface from right to left, with the solid jaw of the vise on the left so that tool pressure is against this jaw.

When a vertical surface is to be machined, it is convenient to shaper on the right-hand side. A vertical cut may be made by hand-feeding the tool downward, or by the table elevating control if such a control is available.

Be on guard against elevating the workpiece into the ram. The clapper box must be swivelled away from the work so that the cutter will not drag on the work when returning.

The shapering of angular work is illustrated in Fig. 128. The toolhead is swivelled to the angle of the cut, and the clapper box is also swivelled to a suitable angle. The cutter is hand-fed into the cut. Feed the tool toward the work during the return stroke.

Contours such as the one of Fig. 129 can be successfully cut by hand control of the changing depth of cut. The required shape is scribed on the

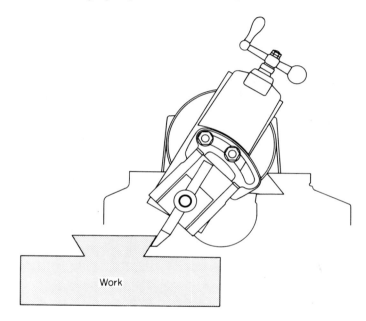

Fig. 128

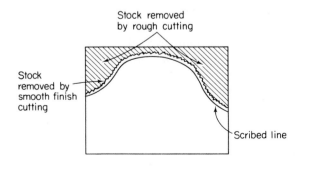

Fig. 129

end face of the work. It is preferable to rough out the shape first and then to produce the final contour at a conveniently slow speed.

10.3 KEYWAYS

Keyways in shafts can be cut with shapers, even though either or both ends of the keyway terminate within the length of the part. Since the shaft must be carefully aligned for the cutting of the keyway, scribe a center line along the length of the shaft and across one end of the shaft. Use these lines for setting up the shaft for cutting. Scribe also the two lines that define the two edges of the keyway.

At the end of the keyway, drill a hole with a diameter equal to the width of the keyway and slightly deeper than the keyway. Two holes will be needed at the start of the cut, to allow enough length to drop the tool into cutting position.

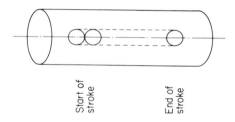

Start of stroke

End of stroke

Fig 130.

The center line scribed on the end of the shaft must be exactly vertical as checked by a machinist's square or other means. The length of the shaft must be parallel to the ram. If the keyway is "blind" at both ends, adjust the stroke and position of the ram so that the cutter does not impact at either end of the stroke. The tool is fed down to the depth required, as indicated by the micrometer collar on the feed. The cutting edge should be the widest part of the tool, so that the sides of the cutter do not rub in the keyway.

When one is shapering a gear rack, two tools are necessary. The roughing tool is a square tool that is narrower than the tooth space. All teeth are first roughed out; then the finishing tool is used. This is ground to the required tooth profile. The depth of feed is manually controlled by using the graduated collar; exactly the same distance for each tooth is fed.

10.4 THE PLANER

A planer is more heavily and rigidly constructed than a shaper and hence is especially suited to the machining of heavy work and large surface areas requiring long cuts. The weakness of the shaper is its reciprocating ram. As the ram extends, it loses rigidity, and, as so often remarked in this book, the paramount consideration in machining is rigidity. When the unsupported length of the ram doubles, its deflection increases eight times (deflections are proportional to the cube of the overhang). The planer has a better construction, since the stationary toolhead is supported on a heavy cross rail and the reciprocated workpiece is always supported by the bed of the machine.

The worktable or platen is a heavy and rigid iron casting. It is reciprocated back and forth by a gear and rack or by a hydraulic cylinder. The work is clamped to the table with the use of tee slots running the full length of the table. Between the tee slots is a row of holes to accept stop pins, which are used to prevent movement of the work under the thrust of heavy cuts. The cutting tool is fed at right angles to the platen motion as in the case of the shaper. Cutting is done on the forward stroke, the tool being fed across the work during the return stroke of the machine.

The planer size is designated by the largest workpiece that can be machined; thus a 24-in. by 24-in. by 4-ft planer can accommodate a workpiece of these dimensions.

The housings or uprights are the vertical members of the planer. The front of the upright has a set of ways machined into it, these ways carrying the cross rail. The cross rail is the heavy horizontal member with ways for the toolhead or toolheads. If two toolheads are mounted, one head can be moved to the end of the cross rail to allow the other head to make a cut across the full width of the workpiece.

The double housing planer has an upright on each side of the table. The open side planer of Fig. 131 has a single column to support the cross rail.

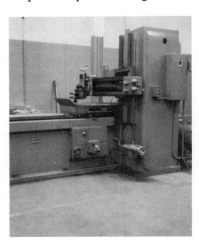 

Fig. 131 Open-side planer and a view of the toolhead on the cross rail.

The open side type has the advantage that work can be reciprocated that is too wide to pass between the uprights of a double housing machine.

The toolheads are carried on the cross rail by saddles. The heads can swivel on the saddles or be moved up or down on them. On small planers, the toolhead, toolpost, and tools are usually of the same general types as used in shaper operations.

Vertical screws in the columns provide a means of making vertical adjustments to the cross rail to ensure parallelism with the table. Parallelism is checked by mounting a dial indicator in the toolpost and reading across the worktable with it.

The specific details of the operating controls of a planer, as for any other machine tool, must be obtained from the operating manual or an experienced operator. As with the shaper, cranks or handwheels are provided for positioning the toolhead along the cross rail or for feed adjustment. The cross rail may be raised or lowered, either manually or by power feed. All setup positions must be finally clamped before the planer is operated.

10.5 PLANER OPERATIONS

A variety of tooling components is used to position and clamp workpieces to the platen. These include step blocks (Fig. 132), clamps of various types

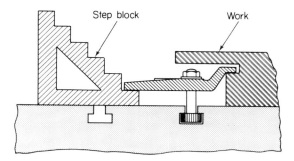

Fig. 132

(Fig. 133), small planer screw jacks, stops to prevent movement of the part along the table under tool force, and others. Security of the workpiece is more critical on a planer than it is on the lighter shaper. Correct and incorrect clamping methods are shown in Fig. 134. The work must be set up in such a way that the surfaces to be machined are free of obstructing clamps. Note that strap clamps must be set up so as to apply the maximum leverage to the work, not to the heel block.

Sometimes a part with a very large surface area, too large for the shop's surface grinder, must be ground by using a planer. This is possible by mounting

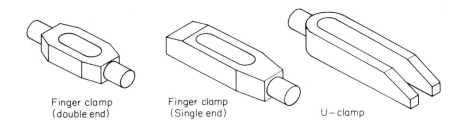

Finger clamp
(double end)

Finger clamp
(Single end)

U – clamp

Plain slotted
clamp

Gooseneck clamp

Fig. 133

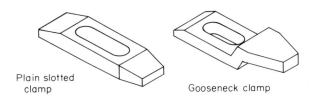

Block   Block

Work   Work

Correct   Incorrect

Block   Block

Work   Work

Correct   Incorrect

Fig. 134

a toolpost grinder on the toolhead, grinding speeds being used for the traversing of the work. To use a somewhat Irish phrase, the machinist should only do this if he realizes that it shouldn't be done. Or, in English, the machinist is creating fine grinding dust that can enter the hydraulic oil or harm the ways and other parts. Certainly the surface grinding machine is driven by a hydraulic system, but the grinder is designed for operations with grinding dust; the planer is not. To grind on a planer, every precaution must be taken to collect grinding dust and to protect the machine from it. When the grinding job is finished, the planer must be thoroughly cleaned inside and out, and the hydraulic oil filtered or changed. Obtain proper advice on filtering procedures for this condition, since easy hit-and-miss methods may be quite useless. The grinding dust remaining in the machine will cause continuous damage to hydraulic valves and to the mechanical parts of the machine. A planer is an expensive machine to ruin by careless practice.

10.6 BROACHING

A broaching machine is another type of reciprocating machine, either horizontal or vertical. The cutting tool (Fig. 136) is a long bar with many cutting teeth, each of which removes a couple of thousandths of an inch of

Fig. 135 Horizontal broaching operation. (Courtesy of the LaPointe Machine Tool Co.)

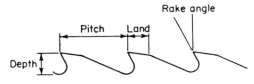

Fig. 136 Teeth of a broaching cutter.

material. The cumulative cut of all the teeth on the broach produces the final depth of the cut and the final contour, which may perhaps be a keyway in a gear or sprocket. The cross section of the finishing teeth must, therefore, produce the required cross section of the hole or recess that is broached. Broaches, therefore, can cut square holes, internal splines, round holes, keyways, or even flat surfaces. The broach is either pushed or pulled through the part, the part being stationary except on automatic broaching machines.

The broaching operation is normally completed in a single pass of the broaching tool. If too many teeth are required to produce the final contour, so that the broach will be too long for the broaching machine, two broaches may be used to complete the contour. The broach teeth must be designed for the material to be cut, as is the case for any cutting tool. The front rake or hook angle varies from 6 deg for gray cast iron or hard steel to 20 deg for soft steel. The cutting speed is rather slow, and the cutting force on the broach quite large.

It is always more difficult for the machinist to produce an internal contour than an external contour. The broach overcomes the difficulties of these internal shapes, with no loss of accuracy. In addition, the broach is often the cheapest method of machining. Because of the low cost of production broaching operations, even the external flat surfaces of engine connecting rods and of the adjustable jaws of crescent wrenches may be broached.

10.7 THE SLOTTER

The slotter is a vertical type of shaper, with the ram moving vertically up and down. Such a machine is employed for such purposes as cutting keyways

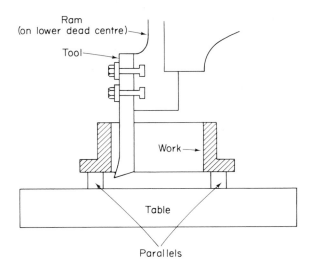

Fig. 137

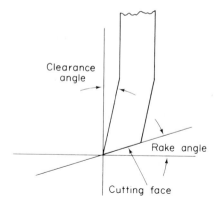

Fig. 138

and slots on internal and external surfaces. The table of the slotter can move transversely or longitudinally, or it can be rotated.

If the slotter stroke must cut to the bottom of the workpiece, the part must be supported on parallels or other means of elevation from the table to give the tool clearance to complete the stroke. Stops should be set up to prevent movement of the workpiece due to side pressure from the tool.

Since the cutting stroke is vertical, the cutter shaves off material with its front face (Fig. 138).

10.8 SHAPERING AND PLANING CAST IRON AND FLAME-CUT STEEL

Gray cast iron is weak in tension. At the end of the shaper or planer stroke the tool will chip the surface of the casting as a result of this weakness. If a clean and sharp corner must be produced on the casting, the edge at the end of the cut should be bevelled to the depth of cut or very nearly this depth. Nonferrous cast materials may present the same problem when one is shapering, planing, or broaching.

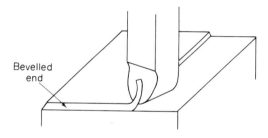

Fig. 139

Cast iron also may have a hard skin or may contain sand in the skin. A hard skin will destroy the tool point, and it is important that a sufficient depth of cut be used to get underneath this hard or sandy surface. The same remarks apply to the hard mill scale on steel plate.

A similar hard surface is produced at an edge that has been cut with an oxyacetylene flame. It is usually preferable to remove such an edge with a deep cut on a planer rather than using a shaper.

QUESTIONS

1. What advantage does the open-side planer offer over the double housing type? What is the advantage of the double housing type?
2. The block used to level a strap clamp must not be placed too close to the tee bolt. Why?
3. Describe or sketch the sequence of shaping the four sides of a rough rectangular block.
4. How is a vise jaw protected from damage by a rough casting?
5. A workpiece is hammered down into a vise with some type of hammer that does not rebound, preferably a lead hammer. Why?
6. An 18-in. shaper has a stroke longer than 18 in. Why?
7. Why would you bevel the end edge of an iron casting that is to be shapered?

Chapter 11

Elementary Milling Operations

The term "milling" as used in machine shop work and metal manufacturing is understood to be any process which removes metal by means of a rotating circular multi-edged cutter, with the exception of hole-making processes such as drilling. However, the difference between milling and drilling is perhaps a little vague, since two-lipped end mills, also called slot mills, are used for both drilling holes and milling slots. One type of mill that does not usually mill is the "vertical boring mill," which is actually a large vertical lathe. However the milling machine may be defined, it is the most versatile of all the machine tool family. It can produce gears, worms, fluted cutters, helical shapes, flat surfaces, grooves and splines, drilled and bored holes, and contoured shapes such as cams, helicopter blades, tooling, and dies.

11.1 MILLING MACHINES

Milling machines may be of either the horizontal spindle (Fig. 140), vertical

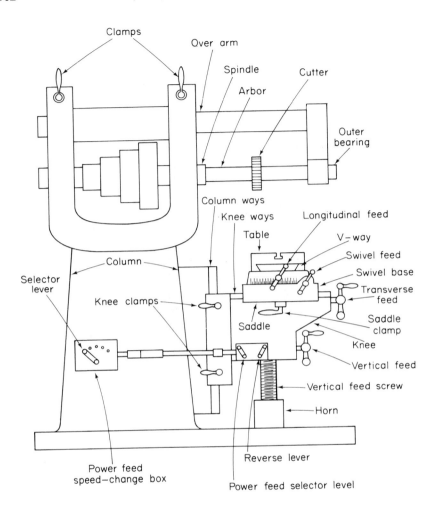

Fig. 140

spindle (Fig. 141), or multiple spindle types. The horizontal spindle machine is perhaps the best for general-purpose job shop work; the vertical spindle type is required for much profiling and tool and die work, in which work the Bridgeport machine of Fig. 141 has made its reputation. Vertical spindle attachments are available for converting horizontal mills to vertical work. Figure 142 shows a vertical spindle attachment above the horizontal spindle of the mill.

Although a drilling machine is a vertical spindle machine, it differs from a vertical spindle mill in that its spindle must resist only end thrusts; the spindle of the vertical or horizontal mill must also resist side thrusts.

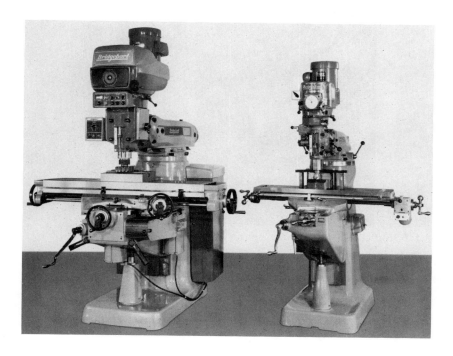

Fig. 141 Standard Bridgeport vertical-spindle mills.

The fixed bed type of milling machine is often used in production operations, but is less flexible than the *knee and column* type of milling machine found in most machine shops. The plain knee and column machine is distinguished by a massive vertical structure at the rear of the machine, called the *column*, and a bracket or *knee* that is mounted on the column and moves vertically on it. A *saddle* is mounted at the top of the knee and is traversed in and out across the knee. The *worktable* moves longitudinally across the top of the saddle. These three motions of knee (vertical), saddle (cross), and table (longitudinal) enable the operator to position the workpiece in three-dimensional space. Both manual and power feeds are available for these motions.

The *universal milling machine* has a fourth movement. The worktable also swivels about a vertical axis. This facility may be needed in machining tapers and helical grooves.

Near the top of the column of a horizontal milling machine is the spindle, and above the spindle a single or double overarm to carry the outboard end of the arbor. The overarm with two arbor supports, and the milling cutter on the arbor may be seen in Fig. 141. The overarm or overarms may be retracted into the column or extended to suit any length of arbor. If the

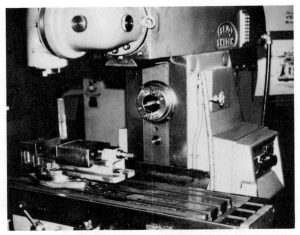

Fig. 142 Vertical-spindle attachment on a horizontal mill.

Fig. 143 Overarm and cutter arbor of a mill.

overarm may deflect under the force of heavy cuts, overarm supports are provided to fix it in position.

The spindle nose has a standardized internal taper of $3\frac{1}{2}$ in. per foot (other tapers are also in use). Driving lugs are machined on the face of the spindle nose to drive the arbor or the short adapters on which certain types of milling cutters are mounted, such as end mills.

The milling machine arbor supports the cutter at the desired position along the length of the arbor, and also drives the cutter by means of a key in the arbor. To prevent the cutter's moving along the arbor, the remainder of the arbor length is packed with spacing collars of various widths, as may be seen in Fig. 143. These collars are hardened and accurately ground, with square ends, and have an internal keyway. Small shim collars less than $\frac{1}{8}$ in. thick are not hardened or ground. The assembly of spacing collars and cutter or cutters are clamped together by a threaded nut on the end of the arbor.

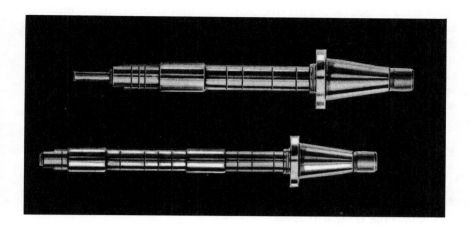

Fig. 144

Milling machine arbors are made in various lengths and in standard diameters of $\frac{7}{8}$, 1, $1\frac{1}{4}$, and $1\frac{1}{2}$ in. The shank of the arbor has an American Standard Milling Machine Taper corresponding to the taper in the spindle of the milling machine, usually no. 30, 40, or 50, with large diameter of $1\frac{1}{4}$, $1\frac{3}{4}$, and $2\frac{3}{4}$ in. respectively. The arbor is held in the spindle by a draw-in bar that goes through the spindle and screws into the arbor (Fig. 145).

There are two types of arbors: style A and style B, shown in Fig. 144. Style A has a small diameter at its end; style B has a large end. The end on the style A is made small so that the surface of the work or of the milling

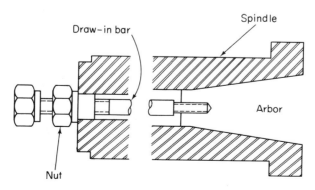

Fig 145.

vise can be brought closer to the arbor than is possible with the huskier style B. This may be necessary with cutters of small diameter. The style B arbor must be used for heavier work. Different sizes of arbor support bushings are used to accommodate these different arbors.

The accuracy of the milling machine is dependent on the cutter mounting devices. These must be handled with care and kept clean. Make sure that all mating surfaces are clean before mounting any tooling, including spacing collars. Use wrenches of the correct size, preferably avoiding crescent wrenches, because they do not fit as closely as wrenches of fixed size.

To remove an arbor, use the following procedure:

1. Loosen the nut on the draw-in bar a few turns.
2. Tap the draw-in bar with a soft hammer to loosen the arbor from the spindle.
3. Support the arbor while the draw-in bar is unscrewed.
4. Remove the arbor with care.
5. Clean the arbor.
6. Store it vertically in a safe position.

11.2 MILLING CUTTERS

All milling cutters fall within two general types (Fig. 146):

1. *Face milling.* The surface being milled is parallel with the end face of the cutter.
2. *Peripheral milling.* The surface being milled is parallel to the side or periphery of the cutter.

Cutters are made either of high-speed steel or inserted carbide teeth

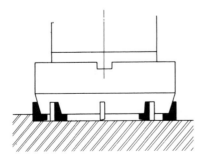 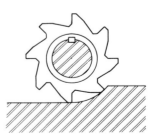

Fig. 146

clamped in place in an alloy steel body. Cemented carbide tips are preferred for long tool life, hard materials, abrasive scale, or for very high rates of metal removal. Three mounting styles are in use:

1. Arbor-mounted cutters. These are equipped with a hole and keyway for mounting on the milling arbor.
2. Shank-mounted cutters. These have either a straight or taper shank for holding in special sleeves or adapters inserted into the spindle. End mills are shank-mounted.

Fig. 147 Milling cutters: plain helical mill, convex mill, and staggered tooth cutter; face mill, end mill, and shell end mill; slitting saw.

3. Facing cutters, which may be mounted directly on the spindle nose or a stub arbor.

Examples of these mounting styles may be found in the illustrations.

Most milling cutters are named for their use, such as gear cutters, tee-slot cutters, convex cutters, etc. Besides the standard cutter types, there are many special cutters; we shall discuss only the more familiar types.

11.3 THE PLAIN MILLING CUTTER

This cutter, illustrated in Fig. 147, is probably one of the most widely used of all the milling cutters. This is a peripheral mill for flat surfaces, with teeth on the periphery of the cutter only. It is available in a range of widths, diameters, and number of teeth. The teeth may be straight, that is, parallel to the axis of the cutter, or spiral (helical). The spiral-tooth cutter is used if the cutter width is greater than $\frac{3}{4}$ in. The straight-tooth cutter produces a significant impact when each tooth strikes or leaves the workpiece, this condition causing chatter and growing worse with increased cutter width. The helical tooth makes a continued contact with the workpiece, with a greatly diminished shock effect and less tendency to chatter.

The smallest possible cutter diameter suited to the job is selected, for the reason that the axis of a cutter of larger diameter must begin the cut farther back from the workpiece and must finish farther past the workpiece. The total length of cutter travel to produce the cut and the time of the cut are, therefore, longer for cutters of larger diameter.

The number of teeth is selected to suit the material to be machined. Softer materials do not exert severe force against the cutter teeth, and since heavier cuts may be made in these materials, more chip space is required between adjacent teeth. For these reasons fewer teeth are used in cutters for aluminum, magnesium, and plastics.

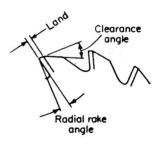

Fig. 148 Basic cutter angles.

The basic cutter angles are indicated in Fig. 148. A positive rake, as shown in the figure, is employed with high-speed steel cutters. Higher positive rake angles are used for soft materials and for the austenitic stainless steels (these steels harden when they are worked, and the cutting action has less work-hardening effect if the rake angle is larger). Rake angles range from about 2 to 10 deg. Cutters with inserted carbide teeth are usually ground with a negative rake to protect the more fragile carbide cutting edges.

The *land* is the narrow peripheral surface of the tooth. This must not be ground too wide, or the tooth will rub against the work and generate destructive heating effects. Clearance is ground into the tooth behind the land.

11.4 ARBOR-MOUNTED MILLS

1. *Side milling cutters* are narrow, with teeth either on one side or both sides in addition to peripheral teeth. When used in pairs on an arbor with a spacer between them of appropriate length, these cutters can straddle-mill the two opposite sides of a workpiece.

2. *Staggered-tooth cutters* (Fig. 147) are made for deep cuts in steel. These have alternating left-hand and right-hand helical teeth to reduce chatter, with generous chip clearance space. Such a cutter is suited to deep slotting. The side teeth are not ground for cutting but for chip clearance, and have a land of $\frac{1}{64}$ to $\frac{1}{32}$ in. This land tends to maintain an accurate width of cut. The side-milling cutter, on the other hand, is not the best choice for accurate slot milling, because its side teeth produce a slot wider than the cutter.

3. *Angle-milling cutters* have a single or a double vee angle for such milling operations as dovetails.

4. *Slitting saws* are thin plain milling cutters. The thickness of this cutter is reduced toward the center to provide clearance in deep slots or in cutting-off operations. The hub of the cutter, however, is the same thickness as the cutting edge.

5. *Contour cutters.* Standard forms in contoured cutters include the concave, convex, sprocket and gear tooth cutters, and for keyway and slot work the tee-slot, Woodruff keyseat, and dovetail cutter.

11.5 END MILLS

1. *Face mills and shell mills.* These are large-diameter end mills with teeth on both the periphery and the cutting face. For heavy metal removal

rates, replaceable carbide inserts are used. When the cutter is less than 6 in. in diameter, it is usually referred to as a shell end mill, while larger diameters are called face mills. Such mills are mounted to the face of the spindle instead of to the arbor.

2. *End mills.* These have a relatively long length-to-diameter ratio, and therefore resemble drills. The two-lipped end mill is often called a slot drill and is used to drill into the work to start a slot milling operation. The four-lipped end mill cannot cut at its center, but can enlarge a previously drilled hole.

The depth of cut of the end mill must not exceed twice the mill diameter as a maximum. Even this is not possible in many cases. A small $\frac{3}{32}$ in. end mill, for example, cannot mill a slot $\frac{3}{32}$ in. deep in steel, since this is a very fragile cutter.

End mills have an integral shank for sleeving into an adapter. They are stocked in many sizes from $\frac{1}{16}$ in. to large diameters. Both flat end and ball end types are available.

As shown in Fig. 149, the flutes of an end mill may have either a right-hand or a left-hand cut. The cut refers to the side of the flute on which the tooth cuts, as viewed from the cutting end of the mill. The right-hand cut is used with counterclockwise spindle rotation. Again, the helix of the mill may be right-hand or left-hand. As shown in Fig. 147, the hand refers to the direction toward which the helix trends. Usually a right-hand cut is given a right-hand helix.

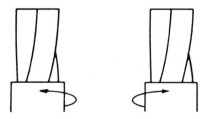

Fig. 149 Helix and hand span end mill. Both the cutters shown have a right-hand helix. The first cutter has a right-hand cut, and the second has a left-hand cut.

3. *The fly cutter.* This is an improvised single-point cutter, usually resembling a cutter mounted in a boring bar, carried either in the spindle or on the arbor. Such cutters are made up when a suitable manufactured mill is not available. The fly cutter may be ground to any contour. Since there is only a single cutting edge per revolution. this is an inefficient cutter. operating best at fine feeds and high speed.

The use of various types of milling cutters is illustrated in the milling operations used to produce the part of Fig. 150.

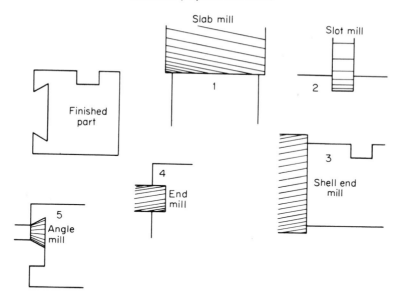

Fig. 150 Milling operations with different types of mills.

11.6 SPEEDS AND FEEDS

Speed refers to surface feet per minute and feed to inches per revolution or inches per tooth.

All machining tools—mills, drills, and turning tools—display the same behavior for tool life. An increased speed significantly reduces tool life. High speeds (surface feet per minute) will complete the cut very quickly, but will call for frequent tool grinding or replacement. Very slow speeds will give excellent tool life, but a lengthy production time. A desirable speed is, therefore, a compromise speed.

Though the influence of cutting speed on tool life is the dominant consideration, a number of other aspects complicate the problem of determining a suitable speed and feed. The life of the cutter will be longer for sufficiently deep cuts but will be reduced by shallow cuts, which generate more heat and also work-harden the surface of the metal. The fragility of small end mills must be kept in mind; the machinist will not attempt to find the best tool life at the risk of breaking the cutter. He will simply run the cutter at a sufficiently slow rate. Again, if an improvised fly cutter must complete only one part, the machinist does little harm in wearing out the cutter in the only cut to be made.

For milling cutters of any substantial diameter, the speed and feed must be determined in the light of the following conditions:

1. The machining characteristics of the material.

2. The power of the spindle motor.
3. The rigidity of the machine.
4. The quality and condition of the cutter.
5. The required surface finish.
6. The required accuracy.

Some degree of experience is required to safely drive a milling cutter to its reasonable limits, and it is not possible to state a "correct" cutting speed or feed. Except for special conditions, such as fragile cutters, it is usual to adopt as coarse a feed as possible, such as 0.030 to 0.050 ipr (inches per revolution) for rough milling with high-speed steel cutters. A smaller feed provides a better finish.

The following is an example of the calculations for speed and feed. Suppose a handbook suggests 180 sfpm and a feed of 0.006 in. per tooth for a two-lipped end mill $\frac{1}{2}$ in. in diameter.

Determine first the required rpm. The cutter is $\frac{1}{2}$ in. in diameter; therefore, its circumference is $1\frac{1}{2}$ in. (multiplying by 3 instead of $\frac{22}{7}$). This circumference is $\frac{1}{8}$ ft. To obtain 180 sfpm, the rpm should be $180 \times 8 = 1440$ rpm. However, it is unlikely that the range of speeds for the milling machine includes this particular speed. We select the nearest lower available speed, which might be, say, 1410 rpm.

For the feed, we have adopted 0.006 ipt (inches per tooth), which for a two-lipped mill is 0.012 ipr. If we assume a speed of 1410 rpm, the feed in inches per minute is

$$0.012 \times 1400 \ (1410 \text{ rounded off}) = 16.8 \text{ ipm}$$

An excellent reference for machining speeds and feeds is *Machining Data Handbook*, produced by Metcut Research Associates, Inc., of Cincinnati, Ohio. This handbook is also available as *Logistics—Machining Data*, AD636 106, from National Technical Information Service, Department of Commerce, Springfield, Virginia 22151.

11.7 CONVENTIONAL AND CLIMB MILLING

Peripheral milling may be performed in either of two ways: conventional or climb milling. These are illustrated in Fig. 151. Conventional milling rotates the cutter in a direction opposite to the translation of the workpiece, the feed motion forcing the work against the cutter. This method must be used if there is any significant backlash in the table feed. In this method the cutter teeth must first scrape the material until pressure is sufficient to force the cutter to bite into it. Climb milling tends to pull the work into the cutter and therefore cannot be used if there is considerable backlash. Surface burrs

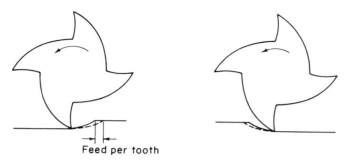

Feed per tooth

Fig. 151 Conventional and climb milling.

produced when the chip breaks off in conventional milling are eliminated by climb milling, and the finish is better. Climb milling also gives better results in the milling of deep, narrow slots—narrow cutters tend to flex under the initial pressure of conventional milling and thus produce a slightly crooked slot. Flexible material too should be climb-milled when possible, because the workpiece must be forced against the worktable or vise.

Climb milling must not be used on castings with surface sand inclusions, because the cutter teeth will be in constant contact with this hard surface. Nor must it be used on lightweight and small milling machines that lack rigidity. Conventional milling, because of its work-hardening effect at the start of each tooth cut, should not be used on work-hardening materials such as the austenitic stainless steels.

Milling must always be performed in the direction to force the work into the fixture or toward the fixed jaw of the vise, never in a direction that would tend to spring or otherwise loosen the work.

11.8 SETTING UP THE MILL

The workpiece to be milled must be clamped to the table or held in a milling vise, angle plate, indexing table, or other device. The rotary indexing table of Fig. 152 is for the setting-up of work that must be rotated in a horizontal

Fig. 152 Indexing table.

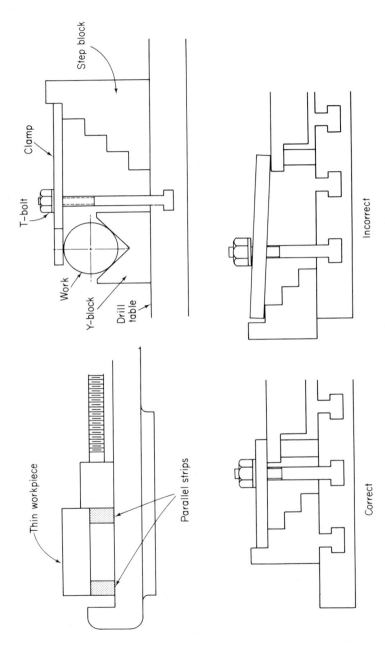

Fig. 153

plane. Indexing tables are also available that can be rotated from the milling machine by gearing; still another type is air-operated and indexed by a pneumatic mechanism. When one is clamping rough or unfinished surfaces to the table, the face of the table must be protected by a sheet of soft metal against abrasion or indentation by the workpiece. Clamping must be carefully set up to resist any tendency of the workpiece to creep from its position. Some clamping methods are illustrated in Fig. 153.

The milling vise must be set up accurately parallel or perpendicular to the arbor. An accurate setup is made with the use of a machinist's square or a dial indicator. The dial indicator may be clamped between two collars on the arbor to read the position of the solid jaw of the milling vise. The vise jaw is then fed across the dial indicator with the hand feed controls of the machine. When the dial indicator reads zero (or some other number) at both ends of the solid jaw, the alignment is satisfactory. In the case of a universal milling machine, the swivel table must first be aligned before alignment of a vise is attempted.

To mount an arbor and cutter, use the following procedure:

1. Select an arbor with the same diameter as the hole in the cutter. The arbor should be the shortest one possible, for the usual reason of rigidity.
2. Wipe arbor and spindle clean with a dry cloth.
3. Insert the arbor in the spindle.
4. Insert the draw-in bolt through the spindle and screw it in by hand as far as possible, then back it off about one turn.
5. Tighten the draw-in bolt locking nut with a wrench until the arbor is secured.
6. Remove the arbor nut on the opposite end of the arbor and as many spacers as necessary and position the cutter reasonably close to the spindle. Check for clearance of the workpiece and vise during the milling cut.
7. Mount the cutter with a key.
8. Add the required spacers so that the arbor nut will clamp the cutter between the spacers.
9. Screw on the arbor nut by hand.
10. Set up the overarm and yoke for support of the arbor.
11. Tighten the arbor nut with a wrench. This nut must not be tightened until the outboard end of the arbor is supported by the overarm.

11.9 CENTERING THE CUTTER

There are many methods of positioning the cutter, the method used depending on the accuracy required. For rough centering, the use of a square and a scale is sufficient, as shown in Fig. 154. When the measurement from the cutter to the square is the same on both sides, the cutter is centered, at least to the precision obtainable in this quick method. The paper shim method, discussed next and illustrated in Fig. 155, is a more precise method.

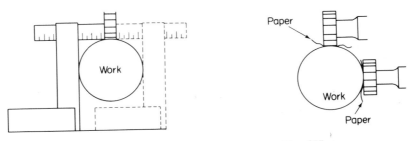

Fig. 154   **Fig. 155**

1. Move the workpiece close to the side of the cutter until it is about 0.010 in. from the side of the cutter.
2. Hold a strip of white bond paper (typewriter paper) or paper tape as used in numerical control between the workpiece and the side of the cutter. Such paper is 0.004 in. thick.
3. Start the cutter rotating slowly. Feed the workpiece carefully toward the cutter until the cutter just tears the paper. By feeding the workpiece over another 0.004 in. the cutter will be in light contact with the work.
4. Lower the workpiece so that the cutter clears the top of the work.
5. Set the transverse micrometer feed collar to zero.
6. Move the workpiece over an amount equal to half the cutter thickness plus half the diameter (or width) of the workpiece. Backlash error must not be included.
7. The cutter is now centered.

The paper shim method can be used also to set the cutter for depth of cut. A paper shim is laid on top of the workpiece. The cutter is rotated slowly, and slowly lowered until it just grabs the paper. The cutter is then lowered further by the thickness of the paper shim to obtain the position of zero thickness of cut.

11.10 MILLING OPERATIONS

The method of squaring rough stock was set out in Sec. 10.2. To repeat this method briefly, machine the first surface, then place this finished surface against the fixed jaw of the milling vise. When the second surface, adjacent to the first surface, is milled, set up for the third surface by putting the first finished surface against the fixed jaw and the second finished surface against the bottom of the vise or against parallels on the bottom of the vise. Finally, mill the third and fourth surfaces.

Plain milling and slab milling are terms that imply the removal of considerable material from a large horizontal surface. Such conditions call for the best in rigidity of setup, for both the workpiece and the cutter. Helical mills with coarse teeth of adequate strength and large helix angles are required for heavy stock removal. The largest possible arbor is preferred, and the distance between column and arbor support yoke should be as small as possible. Where possible, use an intermediate arbor support. Since a helical slabbing mill will exert an axial thrust because of its helical twist, it is preferable to mount two helical mills together with opposite helix angle to balance the thrust.

The dividing head, discussed in the next section, is usually required when one is milling round stock to a square or hexagon section.

The Hexagon. See Fig. 156. The size of a hexagon is measured across opposite flats, dimension H. The diagonal of a hexagon is $1.155H$. This is dimension D in the figure.

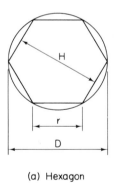
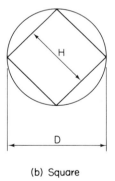

(a) Hexagon   (b) Square

Fig. 156

The length of the flat of a hexagon is equal to the radius of the equivalent round bar, or $D/2$.

The largest hexagon that can be cut from a given size of round bar of diameter D is $0.866D$.

The Square. See Fig. 156. The diagonal of a square is $1.414H$, where H is the distance across opposite flats. The largest square that may be cut from a cylinder of diameter D is $0.707D$.

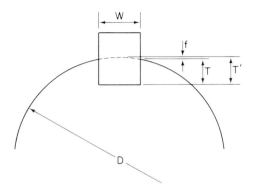

Fig. 157

When one is milling a square from round bar, the depth of cut is equal to one-half the difference between the diameter of the cylinder and the distance across the flats; that is,

$$\text{Depth of cut} = \frac{D-H}{2}$$

Keyseats. When rectangular or square keyseats must be milled in a shaft, the depth T of the keyseat is measured from a line passing through the upper corners of the keyseat, as indicated in Fig. 157. The total depth T' is equal to T plus the additional depth f resulting from the curvature of the shaft. The depth f may be found from handbooks, or calculated from

$$f = \tfrac{1}{2}(D - \sqrt{D^2 - W^2})$$

where D = shaft diameter.
      W = width of keyway.

11.11 THE DIVIDING HEAD

The dividing head, Fig. 158, is an almost indispensable milling attachment. Its function is to divide circles of 360 deg into any number of equal divisions for precision spacing. Hence, the dividing head is used in milling gear teeth, splines, squares, hexagons, or to graduate a micrometer collar. In combination with the longitudinal feed of the table, it can rotate the workpiece so that a helical or a spiral cut can be produced.

The main spindle of the dividing head drives the workpiece by means of a dog and live center or a three-jaw universal chuck. Recent dividing heads use a spindle taper that is a standard milling machine taper. Older

Fig. 158 Dividing head.

models have a Morse or a B & S taper. The spindle can be clamped against rotation by a spindle clamping lever. A separate tailstock or footstock carries the dead center. The center height of the footstock is adjustable, unlike a lathe, so that certain types of tapered cutting may be executed.

The *index plate* of a dividing head is readily distinguished by the pattern of holes drilled into it. The index plate and the index crank (Fig. 158) provide the angular dividing operation. The index crank drives the spindle and live center through a worm and gear with a ratio of 40:1 (5:1 in the case of a few dividing heads). Hence, 40 turns of the index crank will produce one turn of the spindle. Standard and special index plates are available with series of concentric circles of holes with an accuracy of about one minute of arc. The index crank can be turned through some angle and its index pin inserted into one of the holes in the index plate to fix the angular position.

If desired, the worm and gear may be disengaged and the work indexed by hand. A 24-hole (15 deg per hole) plate is located at the headstock for this purpose. This method of *direct indexing* may be used for angles that are multiples of 15 deg.

Three types of dividing head are in use: (1) plain; (2) universal; (3) helical.

The spindle of the plain dividing head rotates about a horizontal axis. This basic pattern of dividing head contains a spindle, worm, worm wheel, index plate, index pin, and sector. These parts are shown in Fig. 159. The index pin is located on the end of the crank attached to the worm shaft. The arm length of the crank can be adjusted so that the index pin can be made to coincide with any circle of holes.

Suppose that the indexing operation is to divide a circle into five equal angles of 72 deg each, a 30-hole circle on the dividing head being used. In this operation six holes must be counted out for each index. Counting

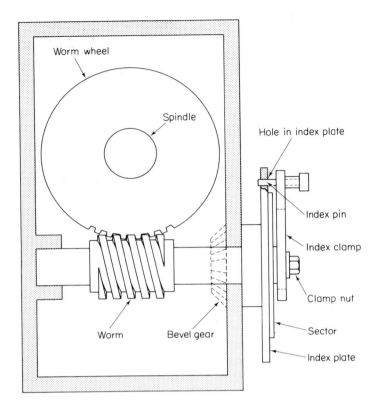

Fig. 159

holes may be a simple enough operation, but counting is not an activity that human beings can do with accuracy. It is surprisingly easy to count five or seven holes instead of six, and if this is done, all the machinist's work on the part is probably wasted.

To prevent such errors, the index plate is provided with two sector arms. The angle between these two arms can be adjusted and locked by a clamp screw to the angular position desired. When the sector arms are used, the index crank is adjusted for the required row of holes and the index pin is dropped into the correct hole in the row. The sector arms are rotated until one arm touches the index pin. The pin is retracted to index, the index handle is rotated, and the pin is inserted at the second sector arm. Finally, the sector is rotated so that the first sector arm is again in contact with the pin. This sequence is repeated around the circle. Note that in this method the angle between the two sector arms includes one hole more than the number of spaces to be indexed. This can be a source of error if not clearly understood.

The *universal dividing head* differs from the plain dividing head by

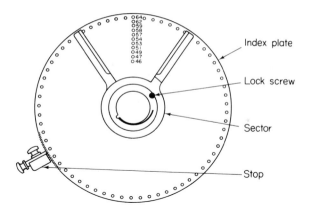

Fig. 160

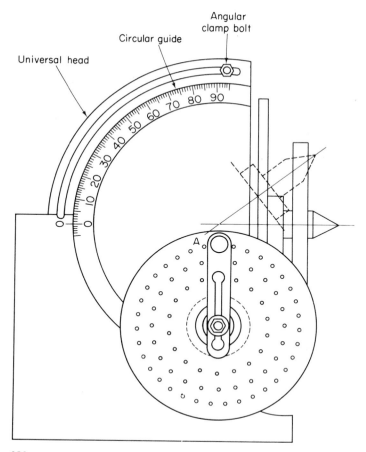

Fig. 161

having a spindle that can be swivelled about a horizontal axis to any angle with the milling table.

In the case of the *helical dividing head* the spindle of the head can be connected to the milling table leadscrew by gearing; thus, the work can be rotated as it is moving longitudinally. This movement results in a helix cut by the milling cutter. The pitch of the helix is determined by the rate of rotation of the workpiece in relation to the movement of the milling table. The helix may be right-hand or left-hand. The drive from the leadscrew is shown in Fig. 162. The gear train is selected to produce the desired helix.

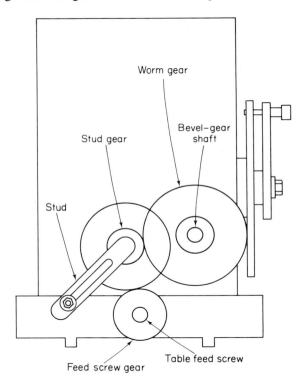

Fig. 162

The headstock of the dividing head is clamped in the center slot of the milling table. After mounting the dividing head, check the spindle for parallelism with the milling table, using a test bar and dial indicator. The tailstock must be in alignment with the headstock.

11.12 PLAIN INDEXING

Direct indexing at the headstock was discussed in the previous section.

Various index plates are available for dividing heads. The Brown & Sharpe Company provides three standard plates with the following numbers of holes:

\#1   15, 16, 17, 18, 19, 20

\#2   21, 23, 27, 29, 31, 33

\#3   37, 39, 41, 43, 47, 49

Cincinnati Milling provides the following hole systems:

On one side of the plate: 24, 25, 28, 30, 34, 37, 38, 39, 41, 42, 43

On the other side: 46, 47, 49, 51, 53, 54, 57, 58, 59, 62, 66

The number of holes in each circle is stamped on the index plate beside one of the holes. Indexing should begin from this readily identifiable hole as a precaution against errors and for checking on errors.

To explain plain indexing, assume a 40:1 gear ratio between index crank and spindle. Then if N is the number of divisions of the circle that are required, and M is the number of turns of the index handle,

$$M = \frac{40}{N}$$

For example, a gear blank must be divided into 20 tooth positions with the dividing head.

$$M = \tfrac{40}{20} \text{ or 2 turns of the crank}$$

It will require 40 revolutions of the index handle to rotate the workpiece a full 360 deg.

Example 1. A six-flute milling cutter is to be produced. Determine the number of crank turns for indexing each position.

$$M = \tfrac{40}{6} = 6\tfrac{2}{3} \text{ turns}$$

or six complete turns plus two-thirds of a turn to be metered off the index plate. Suppose the B & S 15-hole circle is selected. Then two-thirds of a turn is obtained by counting off 10 holes (do not count the hole the pin already is in). If the 18-hole circle is selected, count off 12 holes to obtain two-thirds of a turn. Other possibilities:

21-hole circle: 14 holes

27-hole circle: 18 holes

39-hole circle: 26 holes

etc.

Example 2. One-deg indexing of the work is required. This is $\frac{1}{360}$ of a complete revolution of the work.

$$M = \tfrac{40}{360} = \tfrac{1}{9} \text{ turn of the crank}$$

Select the 18-hole circle and count off two holes, or the 27-hole circle and count off three holes.

Example 3. Twenty-three degrees, twenty minutes is to be indexed.

From the previous example it can be seen that one revolution of the crank produces a rotation of the work of 9 deg ($\frac{360}{40}$ = 9 deg). Twice 9 deg is 18 deg. Subtract 18 deg from 23 deg 20 min, leaving 5 deg 20 min. This requires two revolutions of the crank (18 deg) plus 5 deg 20 min.

Next, 5 deg is $\frac{5}{9}$ of a crank turn, and 20 min is $\frac{1}{3}$ degree, or $\frac{1}{27}$ of a turn of the crank. So

$$\begin{aligned} 5°\ 20' &= \tfrac{5}{9} + \tfrac{1}{27} \\ &= \tfrac{15}{27} + \tfrac{1}{27} \\ &= \tfrac{16}{27} \end{aligned}$$

Select the 27-hole circle. Use 16 holes for the increment. The final result: two complete revolutions plus 16 holes in 27.

Example 4. Determine the indexing for 16 deg 40 min.

$$\begin{array}{r} 16°\ 40' \\ -\ \ 9°\quad\quad \text{(one revolution of the crank)} \\ \hline 7°\ 40' \end{array}$$

But 7 deg = $\frac{7}{9}$ turn.
And 40 min = $\frac{2}{3}$ degree, or $\frac{2}{3}$ of $\frac{1}{9}$ turn, or $\frac{2}{27}$ turn.

$$\tfrac{7}{9} + \tfrac{2}{27} = \tfrac{21}{27} + \tfrac{2}{27} = \tfrac{23}{27} \text{ turn}$$

Suppose the 54-hole circle is selected. Count 46 holes plus one revolution of the crank.

Example 5. Determine the indexing for an angle of 24 deg 41 min.

This angle must again be converted to a number of full turns and a part of a turn.

$$\begin{array}{r} 24°\ 41' \\ -18° \\ \hline 6°\ 41' \end{array} \quad \text{(two full turns)}$$

This angle calls for two full turns plus 6° 41'/9° of a turn.

Convert 6° 41'/9° to minutes, which is $\frac{401}{540}$ in minutes of angle.

To find a suitable circle, divide 401 into 540 or 540 into 401. It is more convenient to divide 401 into 540.

$$\tfrac{540}{401} = 1.3464.$$

Now multiply 1.3464 by any number that gives as a product a number approximating one of the available hole circles:

1.3464	1.3464	1.3464	1.3464	1.3464	1.3464
× 12	× 14	× 15	× 36	× 38	× 32
16.1568	18.8496	20.1960	48.4704	51.4632	43.0848

Multiplying by 32 gives the closest approximation to a hole-circle number, with an error of 0.0848. Select the 43-hole circle.

$$\tfrac{401}{540} \times 43 = 32 \text{ holes in the 43 circle.}$$

There is, of course, a slight error. The amount of the error is found by converting a 32-hole increment in the 43 circle to minutes, and comparing this number with the fraction $\frac{401}{540}$ converted to minutes.

Summary Information for Indexing

1. One turn of the crank = 9 deg.
2. One hole on a 9-hole circle would equal 1 deg.
3. One hole in the 18-hole circle = $\frac{1}{2}$ deg = 30 min.
4. One hole in the 27-hole circle = $\frac{1}{3}$ deg = 20 min.
5. Two holes in the 27-hole circle = $\frac{2}{3}$ deg = 40 min.
6. One hole in the 54-hole circle = $\frac{1}{6}$ deg = 10 min.

11.13 COMPOUND INDEXING

The standard index plates do not permit indexing to a complex number of parts such as 119 by the plain indexing methods just discussed. More complex methods, such as compound indexing and differential indexing, are available for such indexing requirements.

Compound indexing, now to be discussed, exposes the machinist to the possibilities of error if he is not careful or cautious. Differential indexing can substitute for compound indexing if facilities for it are available, and is less open to error.

The compound indexing method obtains the required spindle movement by turning the index crank to a plain indexing setting, and then turning the index plate itself to locate the crank in final position.

Compound indexing is most easily explained with the use of the 19-hole and 20-hole circles. Suppose that the index crank is moved one hole in the 19-hole circle. The stop pin is next disengaged and the index plate is rotated one hole in the same direction in the 20-hole circle. If both operations are in the same direction, the operation is called positive compounding. The result is shown in Fig. 163.

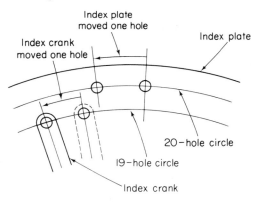

Fig. 163

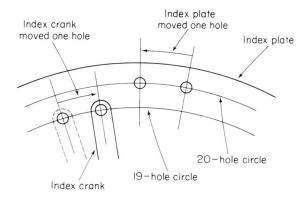

Fig. 164

The two operations have produced the following rotation:

$$\frac{1}{19} + \frac{1}{20} = \frac{20 + 19}{380} = \frac{39}{380} \text{ revolutions of the worm}$$

If the dividing head ratio is 40:1, the spindle rotation is

$$\frac{39}{380} \times \frac{1}{40} = \frac{39}{15,200} \text{ revolutions}$$

In negative compounding the two operations are in opposite directions, as shown in Fig. 164. The rotation of the worm is now

$$\frac{1}{19} - \frac{1}{20} = \frac{1}{380}$$

and the spindle movement is

$$\frac{1}{380} \times \frac{1}{40} = \frac{1}{15,200}$$

Example. Suppose the number 119 must be compound indexed.
Factor the number 119 into its components:

$$119 = 17 \times 7$$

Two hole circles must be obtained that will give 17 and 7 equal divisions. The Cincinnati dividing head offers 34 (17×2) and 42 ($7 \times 3 \times 2$).
Next find the product of 34×42, which is 1428.
Divide 119 into 1428:

$$119 \times 12 = 1428$$

For compound indexing,

$$\frac{X}{34} - \frac{Y}{42} = \frac{12}{1428} = \frac{1}{119}$$

X is some number times 42; Y is some number times 34, and the difference between X and Y is 12. Actually,

$$\frac{10}{34} - \frac{12}{42} = \frac{420 - 408}{1428} = \frac{12}{1428} = \frac{1}{119}$$

Differential indexing is somewhat similar to compound indexing.

except that the index plate is turned by gears connected to the spindle of the dividing head. With the three index plates and the change gears provided, the B & S dividing head can index all numbers from 1 to 382. Tables provided with the dividing head indicate which change gears to use for any ratio. This method will not be discussed.

Sometimes in gear cutting both plain and compound indexing can be used. In such an operation every other tooth is cut by plain indexing, and then compound indexing is used to position the cutter in the center of the uncut areas and the other half of the cuts are made by plain indexing again.

QUESTIONS

1. What is the difference between a plain and a universal milling machine?
2. What is the reason for giving a plain milling cutter helical teeth?
3. Sketch a right-hand helix on an end mill.
4. Set out the step-by-step procedure for mounting a plain milling cutter on an arbor and mounting the arbor in the milling machine.
5. Explain the meaning of (a) straddle milling, (b) gang milling.
6. Why are tracer mechanisms often attached to vertical spindle mills but not often to horizontal spindle mills?
7. What are the differences between the three principal types of dividing heads?
8. A milling cutter has 12 teeth. If a feed of 0.027 ipr is used, what is the thickness of each chip?
9. It is decided to mill a certain material at 80 sfpm with a feed of 0.004 in. per tooth, a four-lipped end mill 1 in. in diameter being used.
   a. What is the theoretical rpm of the spindle?
   b. What is the feed per minute?
10. A certain material is to be end-milled at 150 sfpm with a feed of 0.005 in. per tooth, a two-lipped end mill $\frac{3}{4}$ in. in diameter being used.
    a. What is the theoretical rpm of the spindle?
    b. The milling machine cannot provide this rpm. Do you use the next higher or lower available rpm?
    c. What is the feed per minute?
11. A hexagon must be milled from round bar, and the dividing head of your own shop must be used. Select a hole circle and explain the indexing.
12. Select a hole circle and explain the indexing to obtain 11 divisions of a circle.
13. Explain how to index an angle of 13 deg 20 min.
14. Using your own dividing head, find the best indexing arrangement available for obtaining an angle of 16 deg 49 min.

15. The Kearney & Trecker dividing head uses a 5:1 worm ratio instead of 40:1, with the following hole circles:
Side A: 98, 88, 78, 76, 68, 58, 54
Side B: 100, 96, 92, 84, 72, 66, 60
Determine the indexing to divide a circle into 18 divisions if this dividing head is used.

16. Find a method of obtaining 1 minute of arc by compound indexing, using 27 and 20 hole circles. Worm ratio is 40:1.

17. Under what conditions would you use climb milling?

18. You must operate a very light milling machine with backlash. What will happen if you try climb milling on this machine?

19. Why would you not use climb milling to remove the flame-cut edge of a plate?

20. What is meant by zero rake angle, a positive rake angle, and a negative rake angle?

Chapter 12

Advanced Milling Operations

The cutting of gear teeth, helical grooves and flutes, and cams requires a high degree of skill and experience and some ability with machine tool mathematics and trigonometry. These are the operations to be discussed in this chapter.

12.1 SPUR GEARS

This section provides a basic description of the standard spur gears. The subject of gears, their production and use, is pursued further in Chapter 20.

Although the standard methods of producing gears use specialized machines adapted to such a product, a large number of gears are still produced on milling machines in small machine shops. The milling cutter for this purpose is a standard involute gear tooth cutter, which is stocked by supply houses. The gear blank is first machined or ground, then pressed on a mandrel and carried between the tailstock and the dividing head center for indexing tooth by tooth.

Gears have an outside diameter, but the significant diameter is the *pitch diameter*. The pitch diameter is a calculated diameter such that if the two mating gears were a pair of disks without teeth, one driving the other by friction, the diameters of the two gears would be the pitch diameters. See Fig. 165.

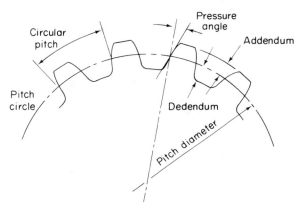

Fig. 165

The *diametral pitch*, often abbreviated "pitch," of a gear must also be known. This determines the size of the gear tooth.

$$\text{Diametral pitch} = P = \frac{N}{D}$$

where N = number of teeth in the gear.

D = pitch diameter.

Thus if the pitch diameter (not the outside diameter) is 2 in. and the gear has 24 teeth, the gear is 12-pitch. Small teeth have a large diametral pitch; large teeth have a small diametral pitch.

Pressure angle is the angle at which the force between mating gear teeth is applied (Fig. 165). This is the angle between a radius drawn through the pitch circle (circle of pitch diameter) and a tangent to the tooth profile drawn at the pitch diameter.

With a few exceptions not discussed here, all gear tooth profiles are a curve called an involute curve. The involute shape is more fully discussed in Chapter 20. Only a few pressure angles are in use. A 20-deg pressure angle is usual for power transmission gears, though some use a 14½-deg angle. The gears used in hydraulic gear pumps often have a pressure angle of 28 deg, for the reason that this large angle increases the pumping capacity.

Although an involute is a curved surface, in the case of teeth on a straight rack the involute becomes a straight line. Therefore, rack teeth have straight sides, though the pinion or gear that meshes with the rack has curved teeth.

A different pressure angle means a different tooth profile. Therefore, if two gears are to mesh, they must have the same pressure angle. Again, a milling cutter suited to a 20-deg pressure angle cannot shape a gear tooth that must have a different pressure angle.

The following are the several American Standard Spur Gear Tooth Systems:

1. American Standard 20-deg involute full-depth tooth.
2. American Standard $14\frac{1}{2}$-deg involute full-depth tooth.
3. American Standard 20-deg involute fine-pitch tooth.
4. American Standard $14\frac{1}{2}$-deg composite tooth.
5. American Standard 20-deg involute stub tooth.
6. Fellows Stub Tooth 20-deg pressure angle.

Only the 20-deg involute full-depth tooth form will be further discussed in this book, though reference will be made to 28-deg pressure angles in the case of gear pumps for fluid power systems.

12.2 CUTTING SPUR GEAR TEETH

The shape of the space between gear teeth depends on the diametral pitch and also on the number of teeth in the gear—a gear with many teeth has a larger diameter and therefore less curvature, if the same diametral pitch is assumed. Therefore, in theory a different milling cutter must be used for each gear in each diametral pitch having a different number of teeth. But this would require at least a hundred different milling cutters for each diametral pitch in each of several gear tooth systems and pressure angles. Therefore, some compromise must be made to reduce the required number of milling cutters; eight different cutters are used for each diametral pitch. Each cutter in the system will cut the number of teeth as listed:

No. 1 cutter	135 teeth up to a rack
2	55 to 134 teeth
3	35 to 54 teeth
4	26 to 34 teeth
5	21 to 25 teeth
6	17 to 20 teeth
7	14 to 16 teeth
8	12 or 13 teeth

Greater accuracy in tooth shape for higher-precision gears is given by the use of half-number cutters:

No. $1\frac{1}{2}$ cutter	80 to 134 teeth
$2\frac{1}{2}$	52 to 54
$3\frac{1}{2}$	30 to 34
$4\frac{1}{2}$	23 to 25
$5\frac{1}{2}$	19 or 20
$6\frac{1}{2}$	15 or 16
$7\frac{1}{2}$	13 teeth

The whole depth of tooth is usually marked on the side of the gear tooth milling cutter.

The first check to be made when one is preparing a gear blank for milling is to ensure that its periphery is concentric with its center or with its mandrel. After it has been mounted on a mandrel, it must be rotated against a dial indicator. If the blank is eccentric, it may be cleaned up with a light cut on a lathe or grinder. Tolerance specifications allow the outside diameter of a gear to be slightly undersize, but it cannot be oversize. When the blank is concentric, the mandrel can be mounted on the dividing head.

The center lines of the blank and the cutter must coincide. The basic method for such a setup is explained from Fig. 166. A precision square is placed on the machine table as shown, with the vertical blade in contact with the side of the cutter and the side of the gear blank. Paper shims can be

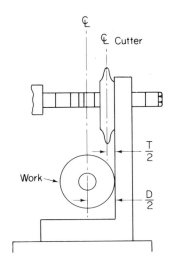

Fig. 166

placed at the contact points between square and blank and square and cutter to test for contact. If both paper shims are held in place with the same pressure, accuracy is assured. From this reference position, the cutter must be moved to center on the blank.

Assume a blank of diameter 3.000 and a cutter 0.208 in. thick. Then to center the cutter over the blank, move it one-half the difference of blank and cutter thickness:

$$\text{Displacement of cutter} = \tfrac{1}{2}(D - T)$$

where D = blank diameter.

T = cutter thickness.

If paper shims are used, the cutter should be moved an additional distance equal to the thickness of the paper. Backlash must be accounted for when one is making these settings.

Centering the cutter may also be done by finding the contact points A and B, Fig. 167, of the cutter against the blank on both sides of the blank at the same table elevation. A paper shim should be used to test for contact. With the cutter rotating slowly, contact occurs when the cutter just catches the paper shim. The center of the blank is halfway between these points.

Small teeth can be cut to full depth in one cut.

12.3 MEASURING GEAR TOOTH SIZE

When the gear teeth are being cut, it is necessary to check that the proper tooth thickness is being produced. If the tooth thickness is oversize, there

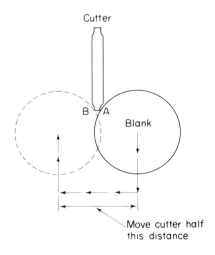

Fig. 167

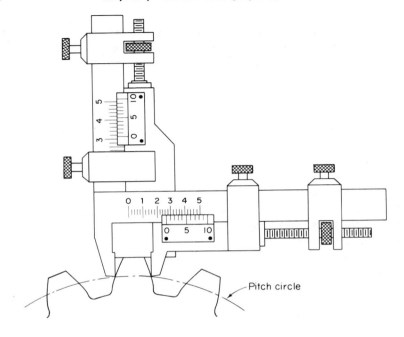

Pitch circle

Fig. 168

may be interference between mating gears; if undersize, backlash and noise will be excessive.

Many methods are used in industry to check tooth thickness. Only the convenient vernier gear tooth caliper is discussed here. This method can give accuracy of almost 0.0001 in., but is limited to diametral pitches of 24 and coarser.

The use of the vernier gear tooth caliper is shown in Fig. 168. The vernier measurement of tooth thickness is made at the pitch diameter by first setting the caliper for depth so that it reads exactly at the pitch diameter. It should be apparent that this method will be uncertain if there is significant total indicator runout of the gear blank.

The tooth depth H in Fig. 168 is called the *chordal addendum*. See Fig. 169. The tooth caliper measures the *chordal* thickness, also shown in

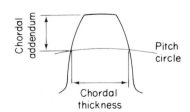

Fig. 169

Fig. 169. Values of chordal addendum or chordal thickness may be obtained from gear handbooks or may be calculated from the following formulas.

$$\text{Chordal addendum} = H = \text{gear radius} \times \left(1 - \cos\frac{90}{N}\right) + \text{addendum}$$

where N = number of teeth in the gear.

$$\text{Addendum} = \text{radial height of tooth from pitch radius to outside radius}$$

$$= \frac{1}{\text{diametral pitch}}$$

$$\text{Chordal thickness} = t_c = \text{pitch diameter} \times \sin\frac{90}{N}$$

where N = number of teeth in gear.

Example. A small gear of 12 diametral pitch with 11 teeth is to be produced. For this gear, find the following:

a. Outside diameter.
b. Pitch diameter.
c. Addendum.
d. Chordal addendum.
e. Chordal thickness.

a. 12 pitch means that if the pitch diameter were 1 in., the gear would have 12

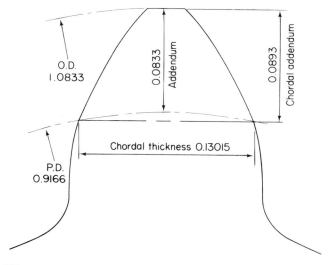

Fig. 170

teeth. Since it has 11 teeth, the pitch diameter of the gear is $\frac{11}{12}$ = 0.9166 in.

b. The addendum, or tooth height above pitch radius, is the reciprocal of the diametral pitch. Therefore, the addendum

$$= \tfrac{1}{12} = 0.08333 \text{ in.}$$

c. The outside diameter of the gear will be the pitch diameter plus two addendums.

$$\text{O.D.} = 0.91666 + 0.08333 + 0.08333 = 1.0833$$

d. Chordal addendum $= 0.5417(1 - \cos \tfrac{90}{11}) + 0.0833$

$$= 0.0060 + 0.0833$$

$$= 0.0893 \text{ in.}$$

e. Chordal thickness $= 0.9166 \times \sin \tfrac{90}{11}$

$$= 0.9166 \times 0.142$$

$$= 0.13015 \text{ in.}$$

12.4 HELICAL SURFACES

A helical curve is a three-dimensional curve that circles a cylindrical surface and advances axially along that cylinder at a uniform rate. The most familiar

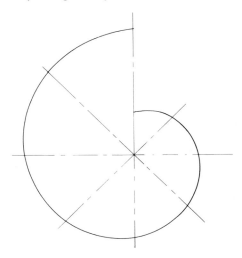

Fig. 171

examples of helical curves are screw threads and cylindrical coiled springs. Unlike the helix, the spiral is a two-dimensional curve (Fig. 171). Spirals are less commonly met in machinery components, though many cams are spiral cams, and the housings of centrifugal ventilating fans are spiral shapes. The spiral has a radius that is proportional to the angle which the spiral has turned through.

There is a tendency to confuse the terms "spiral" and "helical" in machine tool technology. "Spiral-fluted" taps are offered in tool catalogs; actually, it is impossible to imagine what a true spiral-fluted tap would look like. Such taps have helical flutes. In the architectural field we also meet "spiral staircases," which are actually helical. Fortunately, the helix and the spiral are geometrically so different that any confusion in terms can hardly lead to confusion in practice.

Helices are produced on milling machines by rotating the workpiece as it is fed in an axial direction. To cut the helix, a dividing head is driven

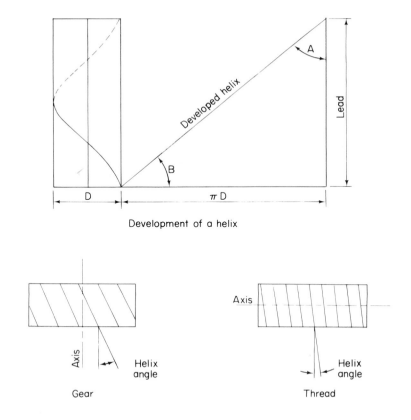

Development of a helix

Gear

Thread

Fig. 172

from the table feed screw with change gears; the gear ratio provides the required relation between axial motion and rotary motion that produces the desired helix. The indexing mechanism of the dividing head is employed to space the several helical grooves around the circumference of the work-piece. A universal milling machine is required to machine a helix, since the table must be swivelled to the required helix angle.

A flat spiral cam may be cut on a milling machine. To cut the spiral, the radial displacement of the table must be related to the rotary movement of the cam blank on the dividing head or rotary table.

A development of a helix is shown in Fig. 172. The axial distance travelled in one complete revolution of the helix is called the *lead*.

Note that the helix angle could be given either by angle *A* or angle *B*. The helix angle for screw threads is angle *A*, which for screw threads is always a small angle of a few degrees. On the other hand, the helix angle for helical gears and milling cutters is angle *B*.

$$\text{Lead} = \pi D \tan B$$

$$= \pi D \cot A$$

In Fig. 173 a number of equally spaced and parallel helices are shown, such as might be cut in a reamer with helical flutes. If the helices are parallel,

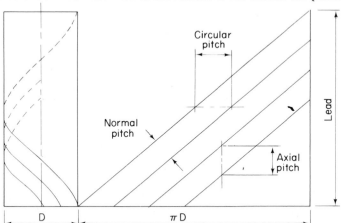

Fig. 173

then they have the same lead angle. The pitch of the helix is defined as the distance between two adjacent helices. This pitch may be defined in several ways:

P_a = axial pitch, measured parallel to the axis of the cylinder on which the helix is cut.

P_n = normal pitch, measured normally, that is, at right angles to the curve of the helix.

P_c = circular pitch, measured on the circumference of the cylinder. Thus if four helical flutes are cut in a spiral (helical) tap with an O.D. of 1.000 in., then the circular pitch is one-quarter of the circumference, which is 3.14156/4 = 0.7853 in.

The relationships between the several methods of defining pitch are simply

$$P_n = P_c \cos A \qquad P_a = P_c \cot A$$
$$P_n = P_c \sin B \qquad P_a = P_c \tan B$$

Since the quantity πD influences the helix angle, helix angle is dependent on the diameter at which it is measured. For helical milling cutters the helix angle is that angle measured at the outside diameter of the flutes. In the case of a helical gear, the significant diameter is the pitch diameter, not the outside diameter, and the helix angle is measured at the pitch diameter.

In order better to understand the concept of helix angle, consider the following example. The case is a 5-pitch helical gear with 8 teeth and a helix angle of 9 deg, measured at the outside diameter. The lead of this helix and also the helix angle at the pitch diameter will be determined.

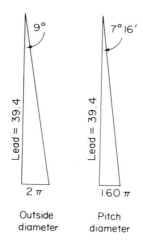

Fig. 174

The geometry of this case is shown in Fig. 174. The helix angle is 9 deg. Cotangent of 9 deg = 6.3138.

$$\text{The lead} = \pi D \times 6.3138$$

To find D, the outside diameter, consider that the pitch diameter of a 5-pitch gear of 5 teeth would be 1.00 in., so that the pitch diameter for 8 teeth is $\frac{8}{5}$ in. or 1.60 in.

$$\text{The addendum} = \frac{1}{\text{pitch}} = \frac{1}{5} = 0.20 \text{ in.}$$

$$\text{The outside diameter} = 1.60 + 0.20 + 0.20 = 2.00 \text{ in.}$$

$$\text{Lead} = 2\pi \times 6.3138 = 39.4 \text{ in.}$$

The lead does not change with a change in diameter; that is, the lead is the same at the pitch diameter of 1.60 in. To find angle C at the pitch diameter:

$$\text{Lead} = \pi D \cot C$$

$$39.4 = 1.60\pi \cot C$$

$$\cot C = 7.84$$

and from trigonometric tables, $C = 7$ deg 16 min = the helix angle.

12.5 HELICAL MILLING

The milling of helical grooves is required in gears, milling cutters, drills, taps, and some types of air rotors. These grooves are produced by rotating the table of a universal milling machine to the required angle and driving the workpiece with the dividing head connected by change gears to the leadscrew of the milling machine. The index pin is engaged during a helical milling operation, but the dividing head is rotated manually for intermittent indexing.

In order to determine the change gears required to rotate the dividing head, the lead of the milling machine must first be known. This lead is the distance that the milling table moves longitudinally when the spindle of the dividing head makes one revolution while being driven by gears, giving a 1:1 ratio.

Most dividing heads have a 40:1 ratio, and most milling machines have a leadscrew with four threads per inch. If the change gears between leadscrew and dividing head have a 1:1 ratio, 40 turns of the driven index crank would turn the workpiece through one revolution and at the same time advance the worktable $40 \times \frac{1}{4}$, or 10 inches. That is, a 1:1 ratio would generate a helix with a 1-inch lead.

$$\text{Lead of the mill} = \frac{\text{dividing head ratio}}{\text{tpi of leadscrew}}$$

$$= \frac{40}{4} = 10$$

The table moves 10 in. in the time required for the dividing head spindle to make one revolution.

To calculate the change gears for a helix:

$$\frac{\text{driven gear}}{\text{driving gear}} = \frac{\text{lead of helix}}{\text{lead of the machine}}$$

Example 1. A helix with a lead of 6 in. is to be produced with a 40:1 dividing head ratio and a leadscrew of 4 tpi. Set up the change gear ratio.

The lead of the mill is 10.

$$\frac{\text{driven gear}}{\text{driving gear}} = \frac{6}{10}$$

The available gears for the machine must provide a ratio of 6 to 10, such as 36 teeth and 60 teeth or some equivalent combination.

Example 2. For the same milling machine lead of 10, the available change gears are 17, 18, 19, 20, 21, 22, 24, 24, 27, 30, 33, 36, 39, 42, 45, 48, 51, 55, 60. Find a suitable gear train for a 27-in. lead.

$$\text{Gear ratio} = \frac{10}{27}$$
$$= \frac{5 \times 2}{9 \times 3} = \frac{(5 \times 4)(2 \times 15)}{(9 \times 4)(3 \times 15)} = \frac{20 \times 30}{36 \times 45} = \frac{\text{driving gears}}{\text{driven gears}}$$

If the workpiece is $1\frac{1}{2}$ in. in diameter, the tangent of the helix angle is $1\frac{1}{2}\pi/27 = 0.17453$. This is the tangent of 9 deg 54 min, the angle to which the universal table is swivelled.

Example 3. The available gears for a dividing head are given in the list in the previous example. Find a suitable gear ratio to produce a lead of 16.330.

Since only a restricted range of change gears is supplied with any machine, it is easily possible that the required gear ratio cannot be set up exactly. In these circumstances a gear ratio must be sought that approximates as closely as possible the lead desired. This ratio may be found by trial calculations, though there are systematic procedures available. Note, however, that an error in helix angle of one or two degrees would not be significant in the case of a spiral-fluted tap. An error in helix angle in a helical gear would, again, not be significant, except that the helix angle of the mating gear must be exactly the same angle.

For the present case, the gear ratio $= 10/16.330 = 0.61237$.

Multiply 0.61237 by trial numbers to try to obtain a number that corresponds to an available gear. Multiplying 0.61237 by 36 gives 22.045, which corresponds reasonably well with 22. Then, if this is the decision, the gear ratio is

$$\frac{22}{36} = \frac{\text{driving}}{\text{driven}}$$

The error in the lead $= 16.363 - 16.330 = 0.033$ in. This can hardly be a significant error.

12.6 CALCULATIONS FOR A HELICAL PLAIN MILLING CUTTER

In this section the calculations for the helical milling of a plain milling cutter will be set out. The calculations are somewhat complex, and of course there must be assurance that they are correct before the machining is undertaken. It is preferable to perform the mathematics on a desk calculator.

     The cutter to be milled is shown in Fig. 175. This is an end view, and therefore the view is not perpendicular to the helix. The 55-deg flute angle shown in the figure would be less than 55 deg if measured perpendicular to the helix. Hence a standard 55-deg fluting cutter would actually cut a flute angle slightly larger than 55 deg, because the milling cutter is angled with respect to the blank to be milled.

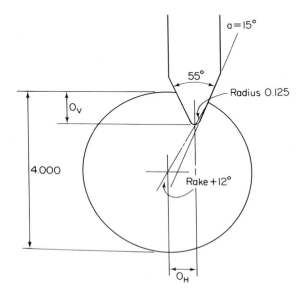

Fig. 175

The finished blank diameter is to be 4.000 in. The blank, therefore, must be oversize by a grinding allowance of several thousandths. The helix angle is to be 25 deg, and the rake angle 12 deg positive. The radius at the bottom of the flute is 0.125, and the depth of cut radially into the unfinished (unground) blank is to be 0.505 in.

1. *Change gears.* Using the finished diameter of the blank, we find that the circumference is 12.56 in.

$$\frac{12.56}{\text{Lead}} = \tan 25° = 0.46631$$

The lead is 27.072 deg. If the ratio between leadscrew and dividing head is 10 as before, then

$$\frac{\text{driven gears}}{\text{driving gears}} = \frac{27.07}{10}$$

and gearing must be set up to approximate this ratio.

2. *Dividing head.* The cutter is to have 10 teeth. Four turns of the crank will index one tooth distance.

3. *Included angle of the flute cutter.* The 55-deg flute angle is 55 deg as measured in a plane perpendicular to the axis of the cutter to be milled. If this angle is measured in a plane perpendicular to the helical flute of the blank, it will be smaller than 55 deg.

   Use the following formula to find the included angle of the fluting cutter that will give a 55-deg flute:

$$\tan f = \tan 55° \cos a$$

where a = angle to which the milling table is swivelled.

f = the required angle in the flute cutter.

If the angle is other than 55 deg, use the actual angle in the formula instead of 55 deg.

   The angle a would be the helix angle of 25 deg if the cutter axis were exactly over the axis of the blank. But the fluting cutter must be offset from this position (Fig. 175), and a slight angular adjustment to the universal milling table is required. But since the gear ratio driving the dividing head is unlikely to provide a 25-deg helix exactly, it is sufficient to call angle a 25 deg.

   Hence the included angle of the fluting cutter is given by

$$\tan f = \tan 55° \cos 25°$$

$$1.43 \times 0.906 = 1.295$$

This corresponds to an angle of 52 deg 20 min. If the cutter is ground to this angle, it will cut a 55-deg flute as measured perpendicular to the axis of the blank. But if a 55-deg cutter is used, it will cut a flute oversize by about $2\frac{2}{3}$ deg.

4. *Swivelled angle of the milling table.* Because the cutter is offset from the center of the blank, the angle of table swivel is not the helix angle of 25°. The angle of table swivel is determined from the formula

$$\tan s = \tan H \cos (r+a)$$

where s = the angle of milling table swivel.

       H = helix angle as usually measured, that is, the angle to the axis of the blank.

       r = radial rake angle of the blank being milled.

       a = side angle of the fluting cutter, the angle a shown in Fig. 175. This is the side angle toward the cutting edge of the blank.

(This formula is not exact, but avoids difficult calculations and is sufficiently close for machining requirements.)

For the present example,

$$\tan s = \tan 25° \cos (12°+15°)$$

$$= 0.46631 \times 0.89101$$

$$= 0.41547$$

and $s = 22° \ 34' =$ angle of table swivel

5. *Cutter offsets.* The offset distances that must be calculated are the distances O_V and O_H shown in Fig. 175. These offsets are calculated by the following formulas, which are closely approximate.

Horizontal offset = $O_H = R_B \sin (r+a) - d \sin a - R_C(\cos a - \sin a)$
Vertical offset = $O_V = R_B[1 - \cos (r+a)] + d \cos a + R_C \cos a$
$(\cot a - 1) - R(\csc a - 1)$

where R_B = finished radius (radius, not diameter) of the cutter being milled.

       R_C = radius of the fluting cutter teeth (see Fig. 175).

       r = radial rake angle to be cut into the blank.

       a = side angle of the milling cutter (see Fig. 175).

       d = depth of the flute being cut.

For the present example,

$$O_H = 2 \sin (12° + 15°) - 0.505 \sin 15° - 0.125(\cos 15° - \sin 15°)$$
$$= 2 \times 0.4539 - 0.505 \times 0.2588 - 0.125(0.9659 - 0.2588)$$
$$= 0.6887$$

$$O_V = 2[1 - \cos 27°] + 0.505 \cos 15° + 0.125 \cos 15°(3.7321 - 1) - 0.125$$
$$(3.8637 - 1)$$
$$= 2[1 - 0.8910] + 0.505 \times 0.9659 + 0.125 \times 0.0659 \times 2.7321 -$$
$$0.125(2.8637)$$
$$= 0.6774$$

Aligning of the cutter with the swivelled blank is an operation that must be done with some thought and care. It is usual to make this alignment before the table is swivelled. First put the center axis of the fluting cutter above the end face of the blank, as in Fig. 176. Place a machinist's square against the end face of the blank and move the table until the collar of the milling arbor is against the square. A paper shim may be used to test for contact. Then move the table a distance equal to half the arbor diameter (plus the thickness of the paper shim). Alignment in the other direction can be done by lining up the largest diameter of the fluting cutter above the center of the blank, then offsetting the distances O_h and O_v.

The thrust of the milling cutter should be directed against the headstock of the dividing head. Since a good finish is required, a rough cut should be made, followed by a finishing cut of perhaps 0.030 in.

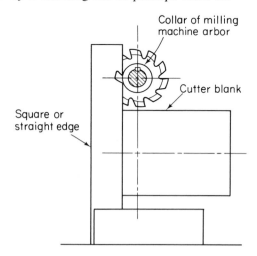

Collar of milling
machine arbor

Cutter blank

Square or
straight edge

Fig. 176

12.7 MILLING A CONSTANT-RISE CAM

A further discussion of cams and their design is given in Chapter 21.

The cam of Fig. 177 has a constant rise, meaning that its radius is proportional to the angle turned by the cam. Such a shape is easily cut by synchronizing the longitudinal table feed with the rotation of the dividing head, an end mill in a vertical-spindle mill being used. The head of the milling machine and the dividing head may be rotated to the same angle in order to mill the cam.

The leads required in such cam milling are short, and a short-lead attachment for the milling machine is usually required.

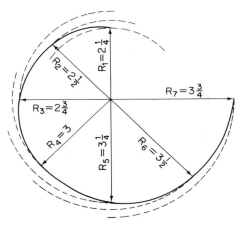

Fig. 177

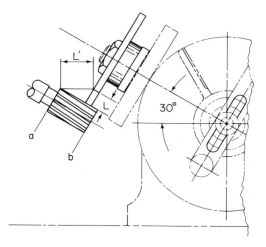

Fig. 178

Consider a cam with a constant rise of 0.600 in. in 120 deg. The lead of the cam in a full revolution is $0.600 \times \frac{360}{120}$ or 1.800 in.; a vertical-spindle mill with the end mill at 90 deg to the horizontal cam blank is used.

Next consider the end mill and the dividing head to be rotated 30 deg to the horizontal, as in Fig. 178. The lead of 1.800 in. is the distance L, but the actual movement of the dividing head is the horizontal distance L'. Since $\sin 30° = 0.500$, this distance $L' = 2 \times 1.800 = 3.600$ in., the actual lead distance that would be set up (if the required gears were available). Note, however, that the end mill must have a sufficiently long flute length, distance ab, since the dividing head is moving away from the cutter. The length of the end mill flute must be at least $0.600 \cot 30° + W$, where W is the thickness of the cam blank.

QUESTIONS

1. Explain pitch diameter of a spur gear.
2. Explain the use of the vernier gear tooth caliper.
3. Define chordal addendum and chordal thickness.
4. Define addendum of a spur gear.
5. How is an addendum calculated?
6. What does the addendum of a spur gear measure?
7. What is the difference between pitch diameter and diametral pitch?
8. What is the pitch diameter of the following spur gears?
   a. 8-pitch gear, 8 teeth.
   b. 8-pitch gear, 15 teeth.
   c. 12-pitch gear, 13 teeth.
   d. 4-pitch gear, 39 teeth.
9. Give the addendum for the four gears of Question 8.
10. What is the outside diameter of the four gears of Question 8?
11. Calculate the chordal addendum of the four gears of Question 8.
12. Calculate the chordal thickness of the four gears of Question 8.
13. Define a helix.
14. Define a spiral.
15. What is meant by the lead of a mill with respect to helical cuts?
16. A helix with a lead of 38 in. is to be milled. What is the ratio of driven to driving gears for the dividing head?
17. A helix with a lead of 23.30 in. is to be milled. The available change gears are 17, 18, 19, 20, 21, 22, 24, 24, 27, 30, 33, 36, 39, 42, 45, 48, 51, 55, 60. Find three possible pairs of gears (driving-to-driven ratios) suitable for the job and giving only a small error in lead.

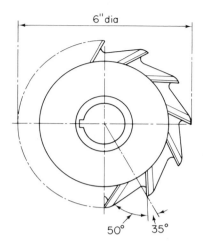

Fig. 179

18. The milling cutter of Fig. 179 is to be produced on a milling machine.
    Data:

Finished cutter O.D.	= 6.000 in.
Number of teeth	= 12
Radial rake angle	= 35 deg
Helix angle	= 25 deg
Side angle of fluting cutter	= 0 deg (angle *a* in Fig. 175)
Radius of fluting cutter teeth	= 0.187
Depth of cut	= 0.400 in.
Included angle of flute	= 50 deg

    a. Determine the angle to which the universal mill table should be
       swivelled.
    b. Calculate the cutter offsets O_H and O_V. For a side angle of the fluting
       cutter of 0 deg, the formulas in the text reduce to

$$O_V = R_B(1 - \cos r) + d$$
$$O_H = R_B \sin r - R_C$$

Chapter 13

Boring Mills

The horizontal boring mill is usually a machine tool of large size and capacity, with ample horsepower, capable of considerable versatility in facing, boring, drilling, and milling, especially of large castings and weldments. It is one of the more interesting machine tools, because of the variety of operations and workpieces that the operator may encounter.

The workpiece may not move in many horizontal boring mills. On a vertical boring mill, which is actually a large vertical-spindle lathe, the workpiece is rotated on a large horizontal table.

13.1 THE HORIZONTAL BORING MILL

The table type of a horizontal boring mill is assembled on a base or runway, with a saddle sliding on longitudinal ways parallel to the spindle and a table sliding on crossways on the saddle. The construction thus somewhat resembles that of a horizontal milling machine.

A heavy headstock column is mounted on the bed. The headstock column has vertical ways machined on its face, on which the headstock slides. The internal taper of the headstock is a gripping type, not a milling machine taper. This taper is intersected by two key slots, one for the insertion of a draw key to draw in the tool tightly, and a rear slot for a cross key to drive the tool by its tang. The rear slot is also used for the drift key that loosens the tool. The head has a sleeve that can be moved in and out of the headstock, either manually or by power feed, for line boring operations. If it is not to move axially, it is clamped.

Fig. 180 A small horizontal boring mill.

In such operations as boring out a long cast iron pipe or a cast blower housing, a long boring bar, called a *line boring bar*, must be used. This line boring bar must be supported at its outboard end. This support is provided by a bushing carried on the backrest or end support column. As the headstock moves up or down, the outboard bearing also moves up or down with the headstock, the two being connected by shafts and gearing.

In the case of the planer-type boring mill, the table can move only perpendicular to the spindle axis. The headstock column is mounted on a slide for movement parallel to the spindle axis. This movement is for setting-up operations only; when one is feeding the tool parallel to the spindle axis, the spindle provides this movement. The end support column is mounted on a slide also.

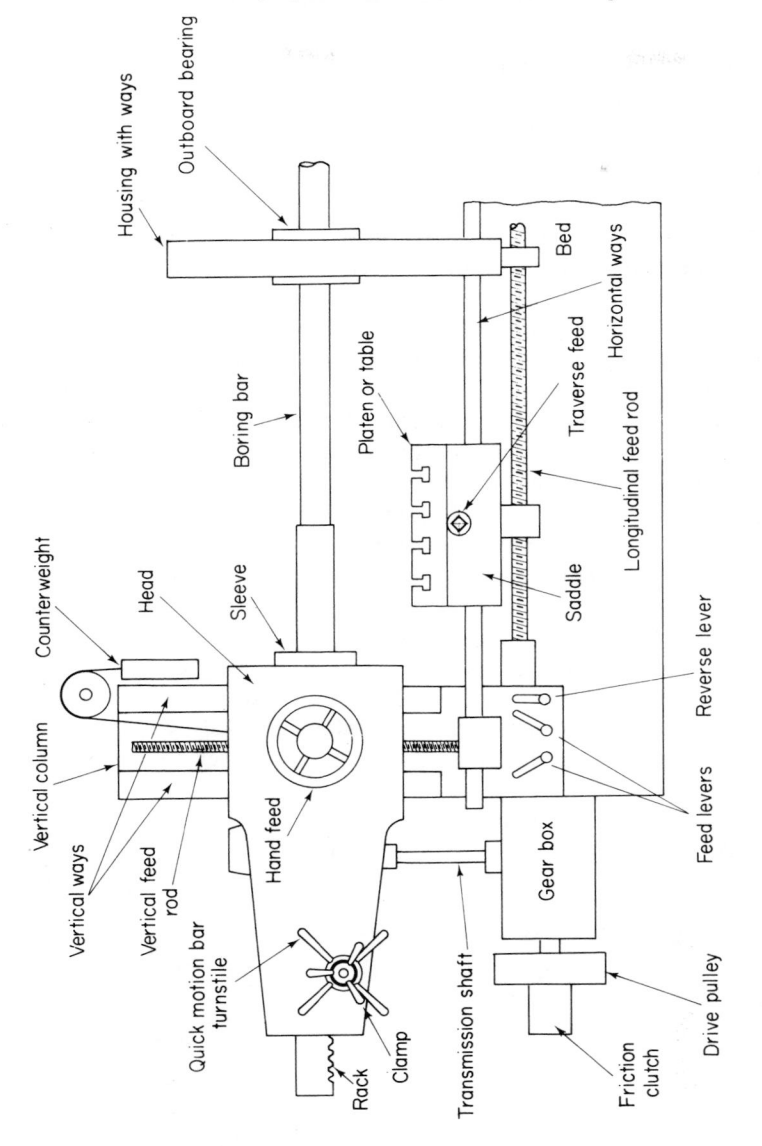

Fig. 181

13.2 OPERATIONS ON THE HORIZONTAL BORING MILL

A horizontal boring mill will provide the following movements:

1. Headstock up or down.

2. Spindle in or out longitudinally.
3. Saddle toward and away from the headstock longitudinally.
4. Table crossfeed.
5. Variable spindle speeds.

Typical heavy operations performed on this mill would be the line boring of the several main crankshaft bearings of a large diesel engine, boring of the internal diameter of large iron pipe, or boring out a series of holes in a complex gear box housing. The boring bars have several slots along their length for insertion of a boring cutter. The tool may have a single cutting edge or two cutters on opposite sides of the bar. Three cutters may be set up in sequence along the bar to provide rough, intermediate, and finishing cuts.

The combination boring and facing head was discussed in Sec. 5.11. Combination heads of large size and heavy construction are used in operations on horizontal boring mills. These are furnished with a range of tooling and cutters for a wide variety of work (Fig. 182).

For milling operations on the horizontal boring mill, almost any type of milling cutter may be used. End mills are used to cut grooves, slots, and holes, and facing cutters for flat surfaces.

Boring and milling at right angles to the spindle are possible with the use of an angular milling head, which is mounted on the headstock and driven by it. Feed for boring at right angles is provided by crossfeed of the table. The angular head has a standard milling taper to receive milling machine tooling.

The workpiece to be machined in horizontal mill operations is often large, heavy, and expensive, and setting up may consume considerable time. Setting up must be done with care and careful checking, since the con-

Fig. 182 Boring and facing head on a small horizontal boring mill.

sequences of a spoiled job are serious. After the workpiece is set up and clamped in position, it is given a final checkout.

Setting up is especially difficult if the workpiece is a large and complex casting. Such a workpiece usually has no truly flat and reliable surfaces. The setup must allow for sufficient cleanup of all machined surfaces and at the same time preserve the required dimensional relationships between surfaces of the casting. This requires careful planning and thinking through the sequence of machining operations. If a previously machined surface is available, the setup operation is made simpler. Combination squares, dial indicators, surface gages, rules, and shims may be needed for the setup operations, and many of the procedures used will follow those used in milling and planer work. To locate a line boring bar in the center of a large hole to be bored, a dial indicator must be used. The spindle with the dial indicator is rotated through 360 deg until a satisfactory reading is obtained on the dial indicator. This operation will have to be performed at the two extremes of a long bore. The position of the boring bar or of the work may have to be adjusted, depending on circumstances.

In face milling operations, frequently the workpiece is supported on a heavy angle plate bolted to the table.

Correct dimensions are more difficult for the operator to achieve in these more difficult setup operations. The operator thinks in X and Y coordinates, usually setting his boring bar from the base of the work and one edge as datum surfaces, or quite often from some more important hole near a bottom corner. Measurements should be made from these zero locations for all operations, and not from hole to hole or position to position successively.

13.3 VERTICAL BORING MILLS

Work that is long with respect to diameter would be machined on a horizontal boring mill, whereas the vertical boring mill is suited to work of large diameter and shorter length. The vertical boring mill can machine inside and outside diameters of large circular shapes and face them.

The basis of the vertical boring mill is a large horizontal rotating table to which the workpiece is fixed. Two vertical housings are mounted at the rear of this table. The housings support a crossrail and toolheads similar in construction to that of a planer. The cutter or cutters can travel vertically or transversely across the table on the crossrail. Since the tool can be fed horizontally, vertically, or at an angle, the work can be faced, bored, turned or contoured. The vertical boring mill, therefore, is actually an oversize lathe with a rotating table as a horizontal faceplate and no tailstock. Small versions of this type of machine tool are actually called vertical turret lathes,

Fig. 183 Vertical boring mill. (Courtesy of the Bullard Co.)

but differ from the large vertical mill in that they are equipped with a tool turret.

The type of work suited to the vertical boring mill includes large ring gears, flanges for large pipes, water-turbine runners, and large circular tables for machine tools.

Various types of thin circular shells for aircraft gas turbine engines present unique machining problems. Such shells have slender sections that are easily deformed, yet must be machined to half a thousandth of an inch on diameters. Adding to the difficulties of machining are the heavy tool forces required to machine complex aerospace alloys of poor machinability. The vertical boring mill is well adapted to the machining of such components, because the vertical mounting on the rotating table offers full all-around support during the cutting operations.

Chapter 14

Grinding Wheels

Many machining operations formerly done with cutters are being performed by grinding. Successful grinding operations depend on wise choice of the grinding wheel and its management. The interesting complexities of the grinding wheel are discussed here.

14.1 GRINDING PROCESSES

A grinding wheel is a self-sharpening cutter removing metal as chips greatly reduced in size. As a machining process, grinding has the following functions:

1. Machining for heavy metal removal rates.
2. Machining for materials too hard for standard machining cutters.
3. Machining to extreme limits of accuracy.
4. Machining to finest surface finishes.

1. *Heavy metal removal.* Where heavy metal removal must be accomplished

by grinding, large vertical-spindle rotary surface grinders such as the Norton, Mattison, or Blanchard grinder must be used. Several smaller workpieces (or a single large one) are distributed over a horizontal rotary table, preferably of the magnetic chuck type, and passed under a large horizontal grinding wheel. Such machines are capable of impressive metal removal rates.

On these large horizontal machines, a hard wheel with a coarse grit is selected. A high rate of downfeed is used for the roughing cut, perhaps as high as 0.250 ipm. The spindle is tilted to a small angle for the

Fig. 184 Mattison vertical-spindle surface grinder.

roughing operation. This applies the heavy motor horsepower to a relatively few grains at the leading edge of the wheel to increase penetration. A harder wheel is used to reduce the breakdown of the grains. When the work is within a few thousandths of an inch of required size, the spindle is returned to the perpendicular position for the finishing cut. The finishing cut is made with the full area of the wheel and a reduced downfeed rate until the wheel sparks out. The roughing cut does not produce a flat surface due to the tilt of the wheel, but the roughing irregularities are removed in the finishing cut. See Fig. 185.

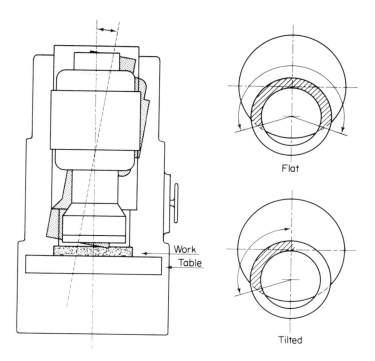

Flat

Work
Table

Tilted

Fig. 185

In both machining and grinding, the finer the chip, the greater the horsepower required to remove a cubic inch of chips. Grinding chips are quite minute; therefore, heavy grinding operations require large spindle motors—250 HP is not unusual. The weight of any machine tool must match its spindle horsepower; these big grinders weigh about 1000 lb per spindle motor horsepower.

2. *Hard materials.* Shafts are frequently required to be turned, then hardened to a high Rockwell, then ground. If the hardening of the shaft is done in a carburizing or induction-hardening operation (see Chapter 17) then the surface of the shaft will have a hardness greater than R_c 55, which is too hard for a turning operation. Therefore, the shaft will be finished by grinding.

3. *Accuracy.* Dowel pins, circuit breaker pins, punches for punch press work, and many other machine and die components require a diameter accurate to 0.0005 in. or better. Such fine dimensions call for a final grinding operation, since practical limits for turning are about 0.002 in.

4. *Surface finish.* For accuracy of fit and for wear and corrosion resistance, certain components such as wrist pins and reverse shafts of engines and gear boxes require a fine surface finish. It is not generally known by

machinists that corrosion resistance is improved by a better surface finish. A surface finish half as rough as the best finish obtainable in standard turning is easily obtainable by grinding; even mirror finishes are possible. A discussion of surface finish is given in Chapter 25.

Certain grinding machines, especially the centerless grinder, are more suited to production operations. For both job and production work the surface grinder and the cylindrical grinder are in use in all machine shops. The tool and cutter grinder is really a maintenance machine; the successful operation of a machine shop depends upon this machine to maintain its cutters.

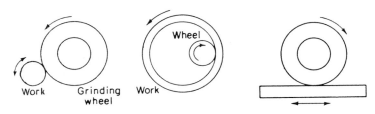

Fig. 186 Precision grinding methods: external cylindrical grinding, internal cylindrical grinding, and surface grinding.

14.2 GRINDING WHEELS

Most abrasive machining is carried out by means of grinding wheels of various shapes. Such wheels are composed of two basic materials:

1. The abrasive grain.
2. The bonding agent.

The grains should be considered as an assembly of single-point cutting tools embedded in a toolholder, which is the bonding agent. Each grain removes a small chip as it touches the workpiece once each revolution. The grains, however, are self-sharpening. As each grain becomes dull, grinding pressure increases (this is, of course, true of all cutting tools as they become dull) and fractures the grain to present a fresh cutting edge. Cutting life of the grain terminates when the bonding agent can no longer hold the fractured grain, which is removed to expose a new sharp grain beneath it.

The size of a grinding wheel is given by three numbers:

1. Diameter of wheel.
2. Diameter of spindle hole.
3. Face width of wheel.

Thus $20-1\frac{1}{2}-\frac{3}{32}$ indicates a 20-in. wheel for a $1\frac{1}{2}$-in. spindle and a wheel $\frac{3}{32}$ in. wide; this is a small abrasive cutoff wheel.

Some of the more frequently used wheel shapes are shown in section in Fig. 187. The type numbers shown in the figure are standard numbers for the abrasive industry.

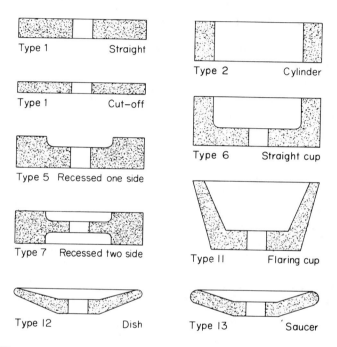

Type 1   Straight

Type 1   Cut-off

Type 5   Recessed one side

Type 7   Recessed two side

Type 12   Dish

Type 2   Cylinder

Type 6   Straight cup

Type 11   Flaring cup

Type 13   Saucer

Fig. 187

The performance of a grinding wheel is governed by five characteristics:

1. The abrasive material.
2. The grit size.
3. The grade.
4. The structure.
5. The type of bond.

1. *The abrasive material.* Abrasive cloths and belts may use many naturally occurring abrasive materials such as garnet, emery, and crocus. Abrasive wheels, however, are always made of synthetic abrasives manufactured in high-temperature furnace processes: silicon carbide, synthetic aluminum oxide (natural aluminum oxide is not used), and diamond (which also

occurs in nature). Selection of the proper abrasive follows these rules:

1. Silicon carbide for gray cast iron, stainless steels, nonferrous metals, stone, rubber, and carbides.
2. Aluminum oxide for steels generally.
3. Diamond for carbides, stone, and for dressing grinding wheels.

Silicon carbide is harder than aluminum oxide, and can be recognized by its blue-black color. It is sometimes called carborundum, as in carpenter's carborundum stones, though this is a trade name. Note that the harder silicon carbide is used to grind soft metals, and the softer aluminum oxide for the steels. Aluminum oxide wheels are white or brown.

2. *Grit size.* Grain sizes for grinding wheels range from 10 to 600. These are mesh sizes, that is, the size of a sieve mesh through which the grit will pass. An 80-grit will pass through a mesh with 80 openings per inch. The many grit sizes may be grouped thus:

   Coarse: up to 24 mesh
   Medium: 30 to 60 mesh
   Fine: up to 180 mesh

Grades finer than 180 mesh are rarely used in wheels. Coarse-grain wheels are usually preferred for rapid metal removal when one is grinding soft metals; medium grades are preferred for steels.

As would be expected, finer grit sizes will supply finer finishes, though surface finish is also dependent on grinding technique. Excellent finishes are obtainable on steels with 60-mesh wheels in centerless grinding operations, so that fine grits are not usually required.

3. *Grade or hardness.* The hardness of a grinding wheel is not the usual meaning of hardness. Though both aluminum oxide and silicon carbide are extremely hard, these materials can be incorporated into wheels that are either hard or soft. The hardness of a grinding wheel refers to the ability of the bonding material to hold the abrasive grains against cutting pressures. A hard wheel contains a large amount of bond, whereas a soft wheel contains a smaller amount. In selecting a wheel for grade, harder materials to be ground require a softer wheel, whereas soft materials require more hardness. The grade is designated by letters from A (soft) to Z (hard). The grades in the range of F to M are most commonly used in precision grinding. Rough grinding and foundry snagging operations may use a wider range of hardness.

A wheel that is too hard for the operation wears its grains down to the bonding material. When this occurs, the bonding material rubs on the work without removing chips, giving a glazed wheel.

4. *Structure.* Wheel structure is designated by numbers from 1 to 15. Structure designates the spacing between grains, as illustrated by Fig. 188. If the grit is very closely spaced, the wheel is referred to as *dense*, and if

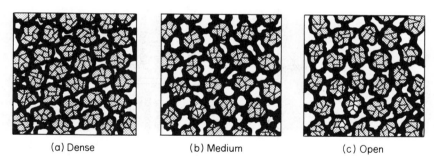

(a) Dense　　　　　　　(b) Medium　　　　　　　(c) Open

Fig. 188

the grains are spaced farther apart, the wheel is referred to as *open-grain*. The gaps between grains are empty spaces, not filled with bonding agent. These gaps, as with any multipoint cutting tool such as a milling cutter, must be sufficiently large for chip clearance and the prevention of "loading," the locking of chips into the voids of the wheel.

A close-grained or dense wheel will produce a finer finish than an open grain. Open-grain wheels are required for soft materials that tend to load the wheel. The most dense structure is designated 1, and the most open is 15.

5. *Type of bond.* The bonding agent determines the strength of the wheel. Five bonding agents are in use for wheels, though a wider variety of bonding agents may be used for abrasive cloths and belts.

The *vitrified* bond, designated V, is the commonest. This bond is made from suitable clays. All clays will become adhesive if heated to their vitrification or glassy range of temperature, which is somewhat above 2000°F. The resulting vitrified bond is a glassy cement. Wheels with this bond are limited to speeds of 6500 fpm.

The *silicate* bond, designated S, is made with sodium silicate, a well-known adhesive. This bond makes a softer wheel, and is generally restricted to large slow-running wheels with a cooler cutting action. Speed is limited to 6500 fpm to prevent destruction of the wheel from centrifugal action.

The *rubber*-bonded wheel, designated R, uses vulcanized rubber. This bond produces a very strong and elastic wheel capable of very high surface speeds and good surface finish in grinding. Thin cutoff wheels and the regulating wheels of centerless grinders are rubber-bonded.

The *resinoid* wheel, designated B, uses a plastic adhesive. This bond is found in rough grinding and some cutoff wheels, and gives a strong and shock-resistant wheel capable of high speeds.

The *shellac*-bonded wheel, designated E, uses shellac. Such a wheel gives a high surface finish to the ground part and offers reasonably high surface speeds.

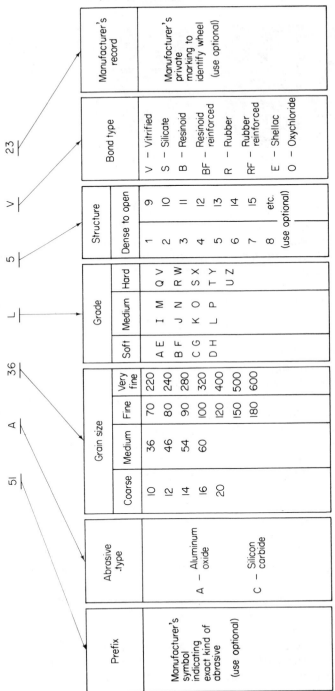

Fig. 189

STANDARD MARKING SYSTEM CHART

FOR DIAMOND PRODUCTS

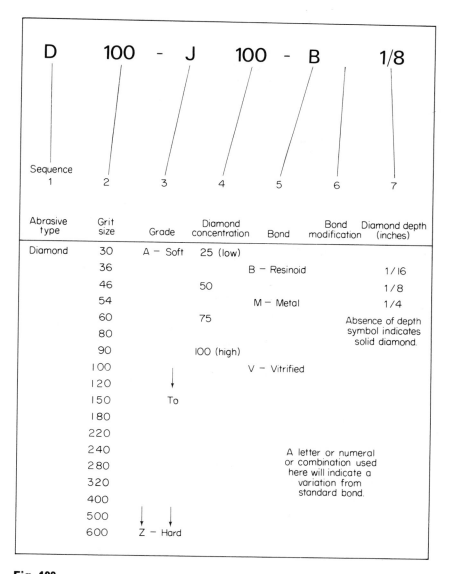

Abrasive type	Grit size	Grade	Diamond concentration	Bond	Bond modification	Diamond depth (inches)
Diamond	30	A — Soft	25 (low)			
	36			B — Resinoid		1/16
	46		50			1/8
	54			M — Metal		1/4
	60		75			Absence of depth
	80					symbol indicates
	90					solid diamond.
	100		100 (high)	V — Vitrified		
	120	↓				
	150	To				
	180					
	220					
	240					A letter or numeral
	280					or combination used
	320					here will indicate a
	400					variation from
	500	↓	↓			standard bond.
	600	Z — Hard				

Fig. 190

The standard system of marking grinding wheels is given in Fig. 189. The manufacturer adds his own coding for wheel characteristics to the end of this marking system. Consider, for example, the following wheel identification:

32A60-H8VG

    32A identifies the abrasive grain (A = aluminum oxide)
     60 grit size
      H grade (hardness) is in medium range
      8 structure is between dense and open
      V vitrified bond
      G manufacturer's symbol

Diamond wheels use a somewhat different classification system. The following are two examples of diamond wheels:

D100 J25V $\frac{1}{8}$

SD220 P50B $\frac{1}{8}$

D means natural diamond and SD synthetic diamond. The grit sizes in the two examples are 100 and 220. In the case of diamond wheels, 100 is a rough grit and 220 is a finishing grit, that is, grit size is generally smaller than for the standard abrasives. The hardness of the two examples is J and P, and the bonding materials are vitrified in the first example and resinoid in the second. The numbers 25 and 50 are the concentration of diamond; 50 means twice as much weight of diamond as 25. The last number indicates the thickness of diamond layer, $\frac{1}{8}$ in. The first wheel is a harder wheel than the second, since if the amount of diamond is low (25), then the amount of bond is high.

Diamond wheels are used for finish grinding only. Thus, when one is grinding a carbide lathe cutter, rough grinding would be done on a silicon carbide wheel and finish grinding might be done on a diamond wheel.

Diamond wheels must be treated with care, since they are easily damaged and are expensive. Excessively high pressures must not be used against a diamond wheel. Because of the high cost of this abrasive, the wheel should be dressed as little as possible.

Diamond wheels should be centered on the shaft by measuring wheel runout with a dial indicator, and tapping the wheel into alignment with a soft hammer. Total indicator reading should be 0.001 in.

14.3 SELECTION AND USE OF GRINDING WHEELS

Grinding wheels must not be operated at peripheral speeds in excess of their ratings. Consider a rubber-bonded wheel rated at 10,000 sfpm. What is the maximum rpm at which such a wheel may be operated at diameters of 18 and 9 in.?

For the 18-in. wheel, maximum rpm $= 10,000/1\frac{1}{2}\pi = 2100$ rpm closely. The smaller wheel may be operated at twice this speed.

The selection of a grinding wheel for any operation is determined by the type of material to be ground, the hardness of the material, the amount of stock to be removed, the speed of wheel and workpiece, and the finish required. The grinding machine requirements dictate such dimensions as wheel diameter and hole size. Since wheels are available in both aluminum oxide and silicon carbide, in at least a dozen common grit sizes, perhaps 20 grades of hardness, at least a dozen structures, and at least five bonding agents, if a grinding machine is to be equipped with wheels for all possible jobs, in theory the shop could stock $2 \times 12 \times 20 \times 12 \times 5$, or about 28,800 varieties of wheel for each grinding machine. It is clearly impractical to maintain on hand a wheel exactly suited to every possible job that may arise. Some less effective choice of wheel must be substituted in almost all cases. The problem is eased by the possibility of varying the cutting action of grinding wheels. These modifications of cutting action can be employed if the operator understands the theory of *grain depth of cut*.

To make the explanation of grain depth of cut easier, consider a single grain in the wheel. The grain rotates around the wheel until it makes contact with the workpiece. At this point the depth of cut is zero. As both wheel and workpiece revolve, the depth of cut must increase to some maximum depth along the arc of contact. The wheel always rotates very much faster than the workpiece; this results in a maximum depth of cut near the end of contact, as is explained next. This maximum depth of cut is termed the *grain depth of cut*.

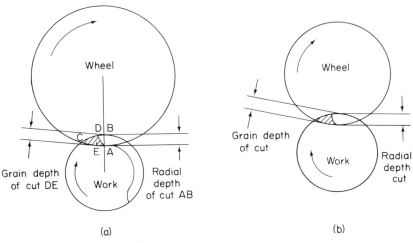

(a)   (b)

Fig. 191

Now consult Fig. 191(a). The radial depth of cut is the distance AB, and the arc of contact is shown as AC. The grain depth of cut is DE.

As the wheel rotates, the grain travels from the initial point of contact with the workpiece to point C in a given interval of time. But in the same time interval point C on the workpiece moves to point D. Since the workpiece rotates much more slowly, the length CD will be less than AD (the proportions shown in the figure are distorted for ease of reading the diagram). During this same interval of time the grain removes the chip with the shape ACD.

Unlike the chip removed by a turning tool, the grinding chip does not have a uniform cross section.

Next consider Fig. 191(b). Here we assume that the wheel has worn to a smaller diameter, but the original sfpm has been maintained by increasing the rpm. Because of the smaller wheel diameter, the arc of contact is reduced. This means that the grain depth of cut is increased for the worn wheel. A grain on the worn wheel removes the same volume of chip as is removed on the larger wheel.

If the grain depth of cut is increased, the wheel will act softer. This statement will be understood by considering that if the arc of contact decreases, then the number of grains in contact with the work has decreased and thus the pressure on each grain is increased (if the radial depth of cut is unchanged). Hence the grains are more readily torn from the wheel.

Increasing the grain depth of cut causes the wheel to act softer; decreasing the grain depth of cut causes the wheel to act harder. Therefore, to modify the grinding action of a wheel, use the following procedures:

1. For a softer wheel (greater grain depth of cut):
   - increase work speed
   - or decrease wheel speed
   - or reduce wheel diameter
   - or reduce work diameter

2. For a harder wheel (reduced grain depth of cut):
   - decrease work speed
   - or increase wheel speed
   - or increase wheel diameter
   - or increase work diameter

If the above discussion is not understood, then these basic aspects of grinding practice may be explained in another way. Suppose that a work speed of 60 sfpm is the ideal speed for grinding. Then at 30 sfpm the grit will have a reduced pressure, insufficient to split it or remove it from the bond. The grit will not cut freely, and the wheel will tend to rub and to glaze the work; that is, it will act too hard. But at 120 sfpm, the chip volume would be larger and the grit would be more torn from the wheel. The wheel would act too soft and would break down too easily.

Note that the work and the wheel run in opposite directions. If they rotated in the same direction, the grit would not take up the full depth of cut gradually but would reach this depth almost on contact with the work. This would produce too soft a wheel and a greatly reduced wheel life with limited metal removal. Such a grinding arrangement might be compared to climb milling.

When one is cylindrical grinding the external diameter of the work, the center of the wheel and the center of the work are on opposite sides of the contact area between the two. In the case of internal grinding, the centers of both are on the same side of the grinding contact. For the same depth of cut, the length of the chip is longer when one is internal grinding. If the grit is to remain sharp, less load must be applied to the grit in internal grinding, and this condition is obtained by a lower wheel speed.

Surface grinding of flat surfaces gives conditions intermediate between internal and external grinding. Surface grinding is actually the external grinding of a cylinder of infinite radius. However, since the workpiece travels back and forth beneath the wheel, it alternately travels with and against the wheel. This means that on the return stroke, the grit goes quickly to full depth, and this is not ideal practice.

For grinding hard materials, use aluminum oxide and a softer bond for materials of higher Rockwell hardness. Use the harder silicon carbide for nonferrous materials, and for cemented carbides. The softer and more ductile the material to be ground, the coarser the grit must be. Coarse grits must, of course, be used for maximum metal removal. Finer grits provide finer surfaces.

Typical selections of grinding wheels are the following:

1. Cylindrical grinding of hardened steel   A60L5V
2. Cylindrical grinding of soft steel   A54M5V
3. Cylindrical grinding of aluminum   C36K5V
4. Surface grinding of hardened steel   A60F12V
5. Surface grinding of soft steel   A46J5V
6. Surface grinding of gray cast iron   C36J8V
7. Tool grinding of high-speed steel   A46K8V

14.4 MOUNTING THE GRINDING WHEEL

Cracked wheels are rarities. To check for a cracked wheel, tap the wheel with a wooden screwdriver handle. A sound wheel gives a ringing sound; a cracked wheel has a flat sound.

All grinding wheels of large size and weight must be balanced. Such wheels are provided with movable balance weights that can be adjusted and locked in place. To balance the wheel, it is supported on an arbor or shaft and rotated slowly on a pair of balancing ways. The weights are adjusted until the wheel no longer stops its rotation at any one position.

Before the wheel is mounted on its shaft, the shaft and flanges must be wiped clean. Wheels for pedestal and bench grinders are mounted with a blotter between the wheel and the flange. The blotter serves as a soft material to distribute clamping pressure evenly over the clamping area. The flanges are

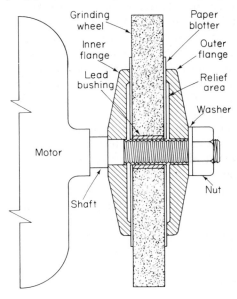

Fig. 192

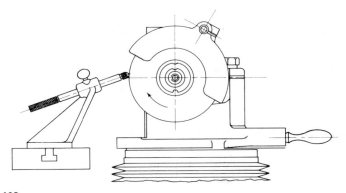

Fig. 193

recessed, and must be at least one-third the wheel diameter. After mounting, dress the wheel.

Most grinding machines are equipped with a fixture for truing and dressing the wheel. Truing means reducing the wheel to uniform diameter and shape, while dressing means the maintenance or cleaning of the grinding surface of the wheel. Both operations are performed by the dressing tool. In these operations, a diamond-tipped tool is traversed across the face of the wheel. The depth of cut per pass must not exceed 0.001 in. with a diamond; a diamond tool is not suited to heavy cutting. Coolant must be used. Turn on the coolant before the wheel truing operation commences; a flow of coolant against a hot diamond will shatter it. The final passes of the diamond should be made without advancing the depth of cut.

On some surface grinders the diamond dresser is held on the surface of the magnetic chuck on the worktable and traversed over the wheel.

14.5 GRINDING MACHINE ADJUSTMENTS

The *traverse speed* is the rate at which the workpiece is moved past the grinding wheel, or the feed. In the case of a surface grinder, the traverse movement or crossfeed is the distance in each stroke of the table that the wheel is fed across the surface of the work.

By increasing the traverse speed, the area of contact is increased. This reduces the pressure on each grain, and thus should make the grinding wheel act harder. Actually, a higher traverse rate increases the force against the grinding wheel, so that the wheel acts softer. Similarly, a decrease in traverse speed makes the wheel act somewhat harder. Slow traverse rates improve the surface finish in all grinding processes.

The *depth of cut* also influences the performance of the grinding wheel. Increasing the depth of cut (infeed) increases wheel pressure, thus producing a softer wheel.

The *work speed* may range from about 20 to 100 sfpm in grinding operations, though soft metal may be ground at higher speeds. Frequently both rough and finish grinding are done at the same speed, though slower workspeeds improve the surface finish.

An increased *wheel speed*, as discussed previously, will make the wheel act harder. The length of cut is shorter at higher wheel speeds. The maximum speed specified by the manufacturer must not be exceeded, however. Grinding speeds depend on wheel diameter. A small wheel will be rotated at a higher speed than a large wheel, and since the number of times that each grain abrades the work is proportional to the rpm, the small wheel will act harder than a large wheel. To compensate for this effect of diameter, wheels of large diameter must be softer than small-diameter wheels when the same type of material is ground.

14.6 GRINDING ALLOWANCES

The usual production sequence for much cylindrical work such as shafting is turn-harden-grind. In the case of soft materials, a grinding allowance of as much as 0.02 to 0.04 in. on diameter is satisfactory for larger-diameter work. Smaller diameters call for a smaller grinding allowance. If too great a grinding allowance is provided on a small-diameter part, the additional heat of the extra grinding passes may cause distortion of the part, as well as greatly increasing the grinding time.

In the case of hardened shafts, a grinding allowance of 0.01 to 0.015 in. is sufficient to clean up the shaft without requiring excessive grinding. A greater allowance may be required to remove warpage produced by the heat-treating operation.

Internal grinding of hardened parts should be restricted to 0.008 to 0.010 in. on diameter.

QUESTIONS

1. Why should the use of a spindle motor of more than usual horsepower improve the life of an abrasive cutoff wheel?
2. State which materials should be ground by aluminum oxide, and which by silicon carbide.
3. Rate diamond, aluminum oxide, and silicon carbide in order of hardness of material.
4. What is the meaning of 80-mesh?
5. What is meant by the grade or hardness of an abrasive wheel?
6. What is meant by structure of an abrasive wheel?
7. A wheel is rated at 6500 sfpm. What is the maximum allowable rpm for a 20-in. wheel?
8. For a wheel to act softer, should the work speed be increased or decreased?
9. Explain the following wheel markings: C36K5V; A60G10R.
10. What is meant by the term "soft" as applied to grinding wheels?
11. Why is the wheel tilted in heavy metal removal on a large vertical spindle grinding machine?
12. What do the wheel sizes 9–1–1 mean?
13. Would a dense or an open grain be used to grind aluminum?
14. Why is it dangerous to operate a grinding wheel at a speed exceeding its rating?
15. Why must a larger-diameter grinding wheel be balanced?

Chapter 15

Grinding Operations

A higher quality of workmanship, accuracy, and surface finish is demanded in a grinding operation. Some machinists say that grinding is 50 percent "witchcraft."

15.1 THE TOOL AND CUTTER GRINDER

The tool and cutter grinding machine serves the important function of sharpening the single-point and multipoint cutters and drills used in all types of machine tools. Hence, it is a machine that belongs in the toolroom. In addition, it can perform cylindrical, internal, and surface grinding if equipped with suitable attachments. Although offhand grinding of lathe cutters on bench and pedestal grinders is frequently seen in smaller shops, in production machining all cutters must be sharpened on a tool grinder.

    The tool grinder is very similar to a cylindrical grinder, which is discussed later in this chapter. The basic grinding attachments are a powered workhead or headstock, a tailstock or footstock, and a wheelhead with grinding spindle. Frequently, a left-hand footstock is substituted for a powered workhead. The wheelhead can be adjusted vertically, but does not traverse toward the workpiece, as would be the case for a cylindrical grinder. The workpiece is moved toward or away from the wheel with a cross slide, on which the sliding table traverses longitudinally. A swivel table on the sliding table permits the grinding of tapered tools such as taper reamers.

Fig. 194 Grinding a spade drill on a tool and cutter grinder.

The wheelhead carries a double-ended spindle for mounting a grinding wheel on each end. Usually a different type of wheel is mounted at either end. By rotating the wheelhead 180 deg, either direction of rotation of the grinding wheel is available.

To support the cutter tooth in contact with the grinding wheel there is a variety of types of tooth rests (Fig. 195). Often these tooth rests are made in the shop to suit the cutters to be ground. Precision arbors are required for the mounting of milling cutters to be ground; the arbor is supported between two footstocks. The milling cutter should be firmly held on the arbor, for accurate grinding cannot be done on inaccurate arbor setups.

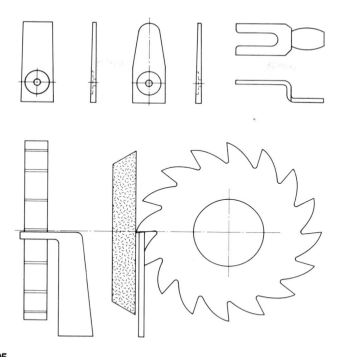

Fig. 195

Straight, dish, and flare-cup grinding wheels are usually employed for tool grinding (Fig. 196). The straight grinding wheel will produce a hollow-ground surface on the tooth equal to the wheel radius. This curvature will not be significant if the tool land being ground is small or if the wheel diameter is sufficiently large. The cup wheel will grind a flat surface. Since the cup wheel can grind the tool at two contact points opposite each other on the wheel, where necessary the wheelhead should be swung one degree about its vertical axis so that only one side of the wheel will come in contact with the tool.

The cutter tooth is held in position against the wheel by a tooth rest blade, as shown in Fig. 196. The tooth rest should clear the wheel by only a few thousandths. The cutter is held in place against the blade by hand.

15.2 GRINDING A MILLING CUTTER

As shown in Fig. 196, a plain milling cutter has a land ground on a small clearance angle, with a larger secondary clearance angle behind it. When one is regrinding the land with a disk-type or cup-type grinding wheel, the wheelhead is raised or lowered a distance *d* above or below the cutter axis.

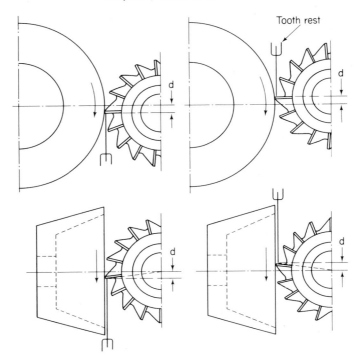

Fig. 196

This distance *d* in inches can be calculated from the following formula if the clearance angle is known or can be estimated:

$$d = 0.0087DC$$

where D = diameter of the grinding wheel in inches.

C = clearance angle of the milling cutter in degrees.

The cutter is arbor-mounted and ground with a 60- or 80-grit K or L wheel of aluminum oxide, if it is assumed that the cutter is of high-speed steel. The centers of wheel, work, and tooth rest are adjusted to the same height; then the distance *d* as calculated is set up by adjusting the wheelhead vertically. These adjustments are made by a height gage or a special centering gage.

The cutter may be ground in either of two ways: *off-grinding* or *on-grinding*. Both methods are shown in Fig. 196. If the wheel rotates off the cutting edge (the cutting edge is the trailing edge) this is off-grinding. In off-grinding, the grinding force holds the tooth firmly against the tooth rest. However, the cutting edge will have a burr which must be honed off. In the off-grinding method the wheel touches the cutting edge first. There is no burr on the cutting edge in this method, but the operator must be careful that the tooth is maintained firmly against the tool rest, since the wheel force can remove it if not restrained.

Before the cutter is ground the grinding wheel is dressed. During the cutter sharpening operation some wheel wear is to be expected, especially because soft grades of wheel are used for sharpening. To compensate for wheel wear, use the following procedure. Grind all teeth in sequence on the first pass. Then index the cutter 180 deg with each additional pass. Only about 0.002 in. is removed on each pass, with a final light pass or passes of 0.0005 in. for finishing. Check that the grinding operation does not taper the cutter.

Repeated sharpenings will increase the land width. The width should not exceed $\frac{1}{16}$ in.; greater widths must be ground back by grinding the secondary clearance.

When the outside diameter of an end mill is sharpened, the diameter of the end mill is reduced. When this occurs, it is preferable to grind off the size markings on the end mill if possible, to leave the cutter unmarked as a warning to the user. If the sharpening of an end mill is to reduce its diameter by the least possible amount, then the front of the teeth inside the flutes must be ground instead of the land.

The grinding of the outside diameter of a reamer would make it, like an end mill, undersize. This is done only in the unusual case where an odd size of hole must be reamed. If the cutting face (front face) of the reamer is ground, this will still have a slight effect on reamer diameter. Usually a grinding operation on a reamer sharpens the chamfer angle on the front of the reamer, which is usually 45 deg. The diameter of a reamer is usually about 0.0002 in. greater at the chamfered front than at the back end.

The grinding of cutters is a critical operation that can be properly learned only by demonstration and practice.

15.3 SURFACE GRINDING

Surface grinding means the grinding of flat surfaces. Hardened ways of machine tools are finished by a surface grinding operation, and, as a matter of interest, are not ground to a high polish because a polished surface does not hold lubricating oils.

The worktable of a surface grinder reciprocates back and forth underneath the grinding wheel. At the end of each longitudinal movement, the saddle on which the table is mounted crossfeeds by a small increment, in the manner of a shaper feed. On some machines the wheel crossfeeds and not the table. Vertical adjustment of the wheel height provides downfeed.

The surface grinder of Fig. 184 uses a vertical spindle and grinds with the face of the wheel. The face of the wheel covers a much larger area than the edge of the wheel, and the whole area of the workpiece can be ground in a single pass.

Fig. 197 Surface grinder.

On the horizontal spindle surface grinder used in standard machining operations, precise adjustments of the downfeed can be made by use of the micrometer graduations of the downfeed handwheel, usually in increments of 0.0001 or 0.0002 in. per graduation. In any surface grinding operation, table travel, downfeed, and crossfeed must be selected to suit the workpiece being ground. Besides the material, the type of wheel and the type of cut—rough or finish—influence these adjustments. An increase of depth of cut (downfeed) requires a reduction in crossfeed; similarly, a decreased downfeed and table speed permit a larger crossfeed. Stop dogs control the terminal positions of table feed and crossfeed.

Most wheels 12 in. or less in diameter are balanced by the manufacturer. Larger wheels require balancing. In surface grinding, as in other types of grinding, coolant must be used. Without coolant, the heat of grinding distorts the workpiece. However, the wheel absorbs some coolant, and this action tends to unbalance the wheel. If wheel and coolant are stopped after the grinding operation is completed, coolant absorbed by the wheel will migrate to the bottom of the wheel, unbalancing it. This condition is, of course, eventually corrected when the wheel is next started up but requires a certain period of time. It is standard procedure at the end of the job to run the wheel for a short time with coolant off so that any coolant will be spun out of the wheel. When starting up, allow the wheel to spin with coolant on for a few minutes before grinding begins.

Wheel dressers are frequently designed to be mounted on the work-table. Mount the dresser about $\frac{1}{4}$ in. forward (to the operator's left) of the center of the grinding wheel. The wheel is traversed across the dresser. Not more than 0.001 in. should be removed in any pass with a diamond dresser.

15.4 MAGNETIC CHUCKS

Most surface grinding is performed on flat pieces of steel, and therefore a flat magnetic chuck is the most convenient work-holding tool, since with its use the whole surface of the workpiece is clear of obstructions. Loading and unloading of the piece is also convenient, since no clamps or jaws are used. The workpiece is secured by a magnetic field. The magnetic chuck cannot hold brass, aluminum, austenitic stainless steels, and other nonmagnetic materials without additional fixturing.

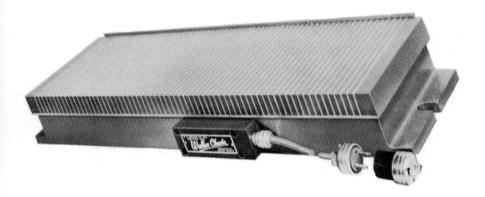

Fig. 198 An O.S. Walker magnetic chuck.

There are two types of magnetic chucks: (1) permanent magnet and (2) electromagnetic. The permanent magnet type is not made in the largest sizes. It requires no rectifier or the other electrical equipment used with the electromagnetic chuck. The magnetic chuck is activated by turning a lever 180 deg.

Electromagnetic chucks are available in 24-, 110-, or 220-volt supply rating. The chuck is activated by an on-off switch.

When a magnetic chuck is first mounted on a surface grinder, absolute parallelism with the worktable cannot be assumed. The chuck surface, therefore, must be ground with the wheel, and reground each time the chuck is removed and remounted. Since these grinding operations mate a certain chuck to a certain grinding machine, the interchange of a chuck between two or more grinding machines is not recommended. In these chuck grinding operations, the table speed should be conservative, with a fine crossfeed, and not more than a half-thousandth depth of cut, with the finishing cut limited to one or two tenths of a thousandth. The grinding operation is concluded by allowing the wheel to "spark out" in a few grinding passes without downfeed. Coolant must be used. The chuck must be turned on during the grinding operation even though no workpiece is mounted on it. The reason for this is that a change in the magnetic state of a chuck or any other part produces a small dimensional change in the part, and the chuck is always used in the magnetized condition. The dimensional change due to a change in magnetization would not exceed about three "tenths" of a thousandth at the most. Only the minimum metal is removed in order to level the chuck. Final flatness may be checked by a coat of machinist's blue or other marking compound.

The ground surface of the chuck should have a smooth, dull surface. It should not be highly polished, since a frictionless smooth surface is not able to hold the workpiece against the thrust of the wheel.

15.5 SETUP PROCEDURES FOR SURFACE GRINDING

1. Select a suitable wheel for the material.
2. Mount the wheel.
3. Dress the wheel.
4. Clean the surface of the magnetic chuck and the part to be ground. Remove any burrs that could interfere with the seating of the part on the chuck.
5. Align the part on the magnetic chuck.
6. Turn on the chuck and check that it holds the workpiece.
7. Turn on spindle, coolant, and hydraulic system motor. Rotate the wheel for about a minute.
8. Set up the automatic crossfeed to about 0.020 per pass.
9. Set up the table speed.
10. Adjust the length of stroke of the table. This is controlled by the position of the two dogs on the side of the table, which activate the table reverse lever. The stroke should allow the wheel to pass off the end of the part about an inch at each end.
11. Stop the coolant.
12. Start the table travel.
13. Position the wheel over the far edge of the workpiece.
14. Carefully lower the wheel until it just touches the workpiece. A slight

spark and the characteristic sound of grinding indicate contact of wheel and work. A light cut is desired for the first grinding pass.

15. Turn on the coolant again.

16. Take a cut across the part by means of the automatic crossfeed.

17. The surface of the part may not be level. The wheel may lose contact with the work, or the depth of cut may gradually increase. If the wheel loses contact, start the next cut with an additional downfeed of one to three thousandths of an inch. If the wheel cuts too heavily, back it off and remove the high spot on the work.

18. At the end of the first grinding pass, stop the crossfeed.

19. Set up the downfeed for an additional pass.

20. Take a second pass with the automatic crossfeed.

21. Stop the crossfeed. Inspect the part and measure the thickness to find the amount of stock to be removed.

22. Return the workpiece to the position it occupied on the chuck.

23. Complete the roughing cuts, leaving a tenth of a thousandth or slightly more for finishing cuts.

24. It may be desirable to dress the wheel for the finishing cuts.

25. Make the finishing passes at a somewhat higher table speed, 0.0001 in. downfeed, and about 0.1 in. crossfeed.

26. Make two or three spark-out passes over the work with no additional downfeed.

27. Raise the wheel.

28. Shut off the coolant.

29. Run the wheel for a minute or more before shutting it down, if no more work is to be ground.

30. Clean the chuck.

31. Clean the machine.

Irregular scratches are caused by a dirty coolant or too soft a grinding wheel. Waviness of the work surface is usually the result of an out-of-round wheel that needs truing. Chatter or vibration marks are caused by a loaded or glazed wheel.

15.6 CYLINDRICAL GRINDING

Cylindrical grinding is the grinding of cylindrical or tapered surfaces held between centers. Cylindrical grinding resembles a lathe turning operation, and replaces turning when the workpiece is hardened, or when the superior precision and surface finish results of the cylindrical grinder are required.

The cylindrical grinder (Fig. 199) is equipped with a headstock and a tailstock with centers. The workpiece rotates between centers as the grinding wheel on the wheelhead machines it. The headstock center can be made to rotate or not to rotate with the workpiece. When the spindle and center do not rotate, a driving plate driving a dog revolves around the spindle. The tailstock center is dead, that is, does not rotate. With both centers dead, precision is not prejudiced by any runout of the headstock center.

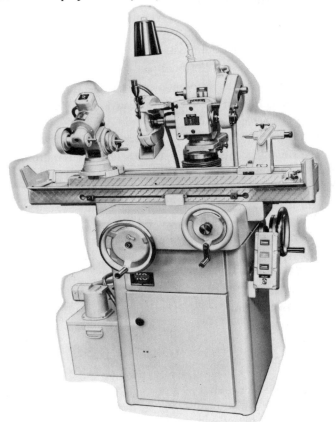

Fig. 199 B6060 universal grinder. (Courtesy of the K.O. Lee Co.)

There are two basic types of cylindrical grinding machines: the plain and the universal cylindrical grinder. The plain machine is somewhat more rigid, while the universal machine offers more flexibility in operation. On the plain cylindrical grinder the headstock and wheelhead cannot be swivelled. The headstock and the wheelhead can be swivelled to an angle on a universal grinder, and the wheelhead slide can be angled to the table. The table on both types of machine reciprocates back and forth to traverse the workpiece longitudinally across the grinding wheel. This table traverse should be about half the wheel width for each revolution of the workpiece. An adjustable taper table, located on top of the sliding table, is used to grind long tapers of small angle. The motor-driven workhead and workholding devices are mounted on the taper table. No vertical movement of the wheelhead is provided, since in cylindrical grinding the axis of both work and wheel are in the same horizontal plane. Manual and automatic control of table traverse speed and grinding wheel infeed are available.

15.7 CYLINDRICAL GRINDING OPERATIONS

The two basic cylindrical grinding methods are traverse grinding and plunge grinding. As in plunge cuts in lathe work, the wheel may be dressed to any contour that is desired in the part.

About 60 sfpm is a suitable average work speed for external cylindrical grinding. To reduce the heating effect of grinding, a sufficiently high work speed and wheel traverse speed are needed, together with coolant. It would seem that the maximum volume of metal removal would be obtained by a large crossfeed, but this is not entirely true. Best production is obtained from a fast traverse of half to two-thirds of the wheel width per revolution of the work and a reduction in diameter of 0.0005 to 0.002 in. for each reversal of the machine. Too heavy a crossfeed will cause rapid wear of the wheel. In high-production operations, however, the approach to abrasive cylindrical grinding is entirely different: Maximum production is obtained with very wide wheels contoured to the part shape and with plunge grinding being used.

The grinding technique at the ends of the table traverse is important if variations in diameter at the ends of the part are to be avoided. The dwell time at the end of each stroke must be related to the traverse speed. For a slow traverse, a long dwell time is used; for a faster traverse speed, a shorter dwell time is suitable. The table traverse must allow the face of the grinding wheel to extend beyond the end of the workpiece a distance of one-quarter to one-half the wheel width. If the other end of the traverse should bring the wheel up to a shoulder on the work, the table should reverse when the wheel is not closer than 0.010 in. from the shoulder. If several pieces of the same part are to be ground, it cannot be assumed that this shoulder setting for the first part off is suitable for the next part. Consider that the center holes could be drilled to different depths in the several pieces. Therefore, each piece must be set up for shoulder distance.

If the part must be ground over its full length, it is first rough-ground and finish ground up to the driving dog. The part is then reversed, and the remaining short end is ground to size. The machine centers and the center holes must be accurate and grinding technique carefully controlled if the two diameters so ground are to have the same axis. Use as little as one-eighth of the wheel width per revolution of the part for finish grinding.

Long slender shafts should be ground on a centerless grinder if at all possible. If a cylindrical grinder must be used, then back rests (steady rests) are necessary to support such slender work against deflection. Use a back rest for every 6 to 10 part diameters. The back rest is equipped with two shoes, a horizontal and a lower shoe. The surface of the part against which the back rest bears must be trued before the rest is adjusted to it. This calls for skill on the part of the operator. The workpiece may be trued by means of a light cut over it, or if very slender, a back rest surface may be ground by a very slow plunge cut. After the back rests are set up and carefully adjusted to the workpiece, they may require resetting if considerable metal removal is required to reach final size. As the workpiece approaches final size, the diameter must be checked for uniformity along the length, and final adjustments must be made to the back rests.

15.8 SHOULDERS AND TAPERS

Shoulders present special problems in cylindrical grinding, and are usually more easily produced on a centerless grinder. It is preferable not to grind the shoulder, but instead to machine the shoulder square on a lathe, with an undercut of the surface adjacent to the shoulder, so that the grinding does not require to be brought against the shoulder.

A simple method of shoulder grinding is to grind the bar to finished size up to 0.010 in. or more from the shoulder. The table is then manually traversed to bring the side of the grinding wheel against the shoulder. The shoulder is machined to size with the side of the wheel. The reverse procedure, that of grinding the shoulder first, is practical.

Where surface finish of the shoulder must be excellent, or where the shoulder is very wide, the wheel may be angled and dressed as shown in Fig. 200.

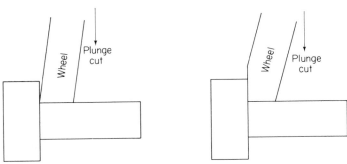

Fig. 200

To grind a taper, set the swivel table to the taper angle as closely as possible, using the angular scale at the end of the swivel table. Then grind a trial taper, allowing the wheel to spark out. Spray a layer of blue dye over the taper, or make four chalk lines along the length of the taper 90 deg apart. Fit a taper gage or the matching taper to the taper as ground, then remove it and observe the areas of marking material removed. If the marking material is removed at the small end, then the taper is not steep enough. When an equal amount of marking material is removed over the whole length of the taper, then the taper is correct.

Flat surfaces may be face-ground on a universal grinder in a face-grinding operation. The headstock is rotated to an angle of 90 deg to the table ways. The workpiece may be held on a faceplate, a chuck, or a magnetic chuck.

15.9 INTERNAL GRINDING

Wheel speeds for internal grinding are in the range of 10,000 to 16,000 rpm, higher than those customary in external grinding. The grinding wheel is usually of small diameter in order to enter the hole; therefore, wheel speeds are higher in order to obtain the required surface feet per minute. The area of contact between wheel and work is comparatively large.

Grinding is the machining process adopted when dimensional accuracy of 0.001 in. or better is demanded. But this level of precision is obtained only on heavy and rigid machines with heavy and rigid components. Internal grinding of holes a half-inch in diameter and smaller is not unusual; it is clear that the grinding spindle for such a hole will have no acceptable rigidity. The internal grinding of deep holes will require a long spindle, and doubling the length of a spindle will increase its deflection by eight times for the same force on the spindle. Hence there are internal grinding jobs that can tax the machinist's skill as no other operation can—the slightest pressure between work and wheel will deflect a light spindle, in an operation where "tenths" matter.

This problem of rigidity explains the bell-mouthed holes that an internal grinder can produce (the opening of the hole has an enlarged diameter). When the grinding wheel reaches the outside end of the hole, the pressure between wheel and work changes, and therefore the spindle deflection changes. Bell-mouths of holes can be reduced by taking lighter cuts, by reducing the dwell time at the end of the cut, or by reducing the amount of the wheel that is allowed to pass out of the hole. If bell-mouthing cannot be prevented by any such methods, then still another solution to the problem is to drill and grind an extra-long piece and cut off the bell-mouthed end.

When one is grinding to the bottom of a blind hole, the possibility

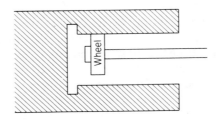

Fig. 201

of running the spindle into the bottom of the hole arises. To prevent this, the end of the hole should be recessed before grinding (Fig. 201).

15.10 CENTERLESS GRINDING

The centerless grinder is a production machine for external cylindrical grinding. Certain difficulties of the cylindrical grinder, such as the springing of long slender shafts, are avoided in the centerless grinding method.

It is often remarked, "Grinding is 50 per cent witchcraft." This statement is an exaggeration, of course; yet every experienced grinder operator has to learn the important tricks that help him get out his work. The centerless grinder too has its "witchcraft"; it is an interesting machine to set up, but when it misbehaves, it can present problems that may completely baffle an inexperienced operator. If improperly set up, this machine can kick the workpiece vertically out of the machine, and in addition to a flying workpiece, a piece may be cracked out of an expensive $100 grinding wheel. These little excitements, of course, do not happen to experienced operators, and when working properly, this grinder can produce a short workpiece perhaps every second, with accuracy of perhaps 0.0002 in. on diameter.

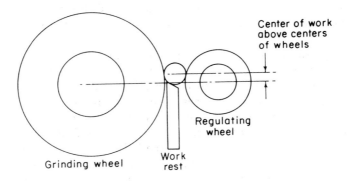

Fig. 202 The centerless grinder method.

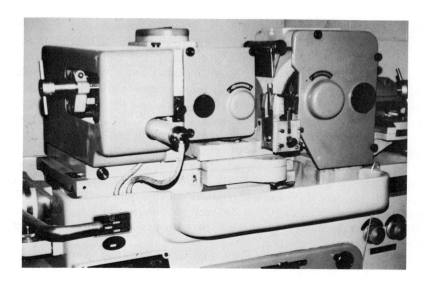

Fig. 203 Centerless grinder. The regulating wheel is on the left side. The adjusting handles for the wheel dressers may be seen at each end of the machine. For infeeding or plunge cuts, the L-shaped handle in the lower left-hand corner is used.

The centerless grinder (Fig. 202) uses a grinding wheel five inches or more wide, a rubber-bonded regulating wheel of smaller diameter than the grinding wheel, and a work rest between the wheels to support the workpiece between the wheels. The top surface of the workrest is sloped about 30 deg toward the regulating wheel. Because the workrest supports the length of the workpiece that is in contact with the wheels, even a slender rod cannot deflect while being ground. It is possible to grind a long rod 0.070 in. in diameter on a centerless grinder, if a sufficiently narrow workrest is used.

The regulating wheel pulls the workpiece across the face of the grinding wheel at a controllable rate of feed. This feed rate is controlled by the diameter of the regulating wheel, its rpm, and its angle of inclination. The spindle of the regulating wheel must be tilted to a slight vertical angle in order to pull the workpiece into the grinding wheel. This angle may be 2 deg for slow feeds or as much as 6 deg for fast roughing feeds.

$$\text{Feed rate} = CN \sin \theta$$

where θ = angle of inclination of regulating wheel.

N = rpm of regulating wheel.

C = circumference of the regulating wheel.

An angle scale is marked on the machine for these settings.

The workpiece is restrained over its length by the pressures of the grinding wheel, the workrest, and the regulating wheel. Very heavy and rigid construction is necessary in a centerless grinder if chatter is to be eliminated; centerless grinders, therefore, are heavy machines even in the smaller sizes. Chatter is possible in an imperfect setup, however, especially if the workrest is long and narrow with too steep a top angle. The chatter can result from deflection of the thin workrest, and the solution is usually to reduce the top angle in order to reduce the side deflection of the workrest.

Note from Fig. 202 that though the grinding wheel rotates in the same direction as on other types of cylindrical grinders, the work rotates in the "wrong" direction. The two wheels and workpiece therefore appear to rotate in the relation of three meshed gears in a gear train. This is only apparently so, since if it were true, the workpiece would not be ground. The regulating wheel rotates at 20 to 200 feet per minute and acts as a brake to hold the workpiece back from the high velocities that it would receive if driven by the grinding wheel.

The depth of cut, or the diameter which is to be ground, is set by adjusting the distance between the two wheels. The distance between the two wheels is not the diameter produced, because the axis of the workpiece is either above or below the axes of the wheel spindles.

15.11 SETUP OF THE CENTERLESS GRINDER

A new wheel for a centerless grinder must be carefully balanced, mounted, and then dressed. Both the grinding wheel and the regulating wheel require periodic dressing. The dressing diamond for either wheel is traversed slowly across the face of the wheel by a hydraulic mechanism. If the workpiece is to be contoured by a shaped wheel and plunge grinding, then the wheel must be trued to the required shape. It is possible to grind billiard balls, or even threads, on a centerless grinder.

A workrest somewhat narrower than the work diameter must be used. If the workrest surface is not absolutely level, a slight taper will be ground into the workpiece.

The axis of the workpiece must be slightly higher than the level of the axis of the two wheel spindles. Both spindles are at the same level. Slightly bent long bars may be ground with the bar axis below rather than above. This distance above the wheel centers is in the range of $\frac{1}{8}$ to $\frac{1}{2}$ the work diameter: perhaps half the work diameter for very small work and a much smaller fraction of diameter for workpieces of large diameter. Distances over half an inch would be unusual even for large diameters. This distance is set up from a known reference level on the machine.

The reason for the level of the workpiece's being higher than the level of wheel axes is the pressure of the regulating wheel. Suppose that work and wheels are all three at the same level. Suppose also that a slightly high spot on the workpiece comes into contact with the regulating wheel. This will result in the whole length of the bar's being pushed into the grinding wheel. There will be a high spot opposite the regulating wheel and a low spot opposite the grinding wheel. The high spot and the low spot will be opposite each other on the circumference of the bar. When the workpiece rotates 180 deg, the low spot just ground will come against the regulating wheel, so that the high spot that was the cause of the fault cannot be ground away and thus remains in the bar. When the high spot rotates to bear against the workrest, the piece is elevated slightly, so that the work center is higher than wheel centers; this results in a slight increase in the diameter ground into the bar. Actually, a second high spot will be produced at 120 deg from the initiating high spot. The two high spots 120 deg apart will then produce a third one at another 120 deg. The bar will be ground to the shape of the lobed or three-arc circle of Fig. 204.

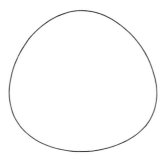

Fig. 204. Three-lobed circle produced by an imperfectly adjusted centerless grinder.

Now if the workpiece is elevated by some fraction of its diameter, the high spot will cause the grinding wheel to grind a low spot as before. But the high and low spots now are not diametrically opposite. As the piece is rotated, the high and low spots not being opposite, the bar will gradually be rounded by the grinding wheel.

15.12 METHODS OF CENTERLESS GRINDING

Three grinding methods are possible with this machine:

1. *Through-feed.* So far in our discussion of the centerless grinder, the through-feed method has been assumed. The part is gripped between the two wheels and spirals along the workrest until it is discharged out the opposite side. Depending on the amount of material to be removed, one or more passes may have to be made. This is the method used to

grind drill rod, centerless-ground bar stock, dowel pins, and automotive wrist pins.

2. *In-feed.* Many parts have shoulders or heads at the end of the diameter to be ground. Such parts can be placed manually or automatically on the workrest, with the head or shoulder off the workrest, and the grinding can be performed in a plunge cut. For this purpose a handle is used to móve the regulating wheel toward the grinding wheel, a stop terminating the grinding operation when the required diameter is obtained. The regulating wheel is then withdrawn and the finished piece is extracted. The end of the workpiece bears against an adjustable stop, and the regulating wheel is angled just enough to give the workpiece a slight pressure against the end stop. The length of cylinder that may be ground by the in-feed method is limited to the width of the grinding wheel.

   If the head on the part is unbalanced, the workpiece must be rotated somewhat slowly by the regulating wheel to prevent setting up sufficient centrifugal force to flip the part off the workrest.

3. *End-feed.* In the end-feed method the workpiece is pulled forward by the regulating wheel up to a fixed stop. This method is used for the grinding of tapers, using a suitably dressed wheel.

   The K.O. Lee Company offers a centerless grinding fixture that may be used with their universal grinder (Fig. 199) to convert it to the centerless method. This fixture is illustrated in Fig. 205. The fixture consists essentially of a regulating wheel and workrest. The regulating wheel spindle is mounted between centers of the cylindrical grinder and

Fig. 205 K. O. Lee centerless grinding attachment.

Fig. 206 Centerless grinding operation of a K.O. Lee cylindrical grinder.

driven by the headstock, as shown in Fig. 206. Despite the limitations of a narrow cylindrical grinding wheel and lightweight machine, this fixture is effective in grinding small diameters. Through-feed, in-feed, and end-feed methods may be used with this fixture.

QUESTIONS

1. What is the chief difference between the plain and the universal grinding machine?
2. Why should shoulders ground on a cylindrical grinder be ground with wheel pressure directed toward the headstock?
3. Explain why internal grinding tends to produce a bell-mouthed hole.
4. What advantages does centerless grinding offer?
5. What is the function of the regulating wheel in a centerless grinder?
6. Why is the spindle of the regulating wheel canted slightly?
7. Why is coolant required in a grinding operation on a shaft?
8. Explain how coolant can unbalance a grinding wheel.
9. Why is it not a good procedure to interchange magnetic chucks between two surface grinding machines?
10. Why should a magnetic chuck be active when it is ground for parallelism?

11. In Sec. 14.5 a standard operating procedure (SOP) for setting up a surface grinder is given. Such a procedure gives step-by-step instructions in sequence for a machine operation, in clear and simple language that cannot be misunderstood. Modify this standard operating procedure to suit your own surface grinder and where possible improve on it.

12. Set up a standard operating procedure for your own cylindrical grinder.

13. What is the advantage of operating both centers dead on a cylindrical grinder?

14. Why is the work center placed above the wheel centers in a centerless grinding setup?

15. What is the difference between off-grinding and on-grinding of tools and the disadvantage of each method?

Part III

Advanced Practice

Chapter 16

Metallurgy

Metallurgy, the science of metals, is one of the most interesting and helpful areas of knowledge for the machinist. This chapter discusses only those aspects of metallurgy that are of concern to the machinist and only those metals which he will commonly encounter: the low carbon, medium carbon, tool, stainless, and machinery steels, and the aluminum alloys. A brief introduction to the plastics is included. While the brasses and bronzes are also commonly machined, they do not usually present problems, and their metallurgy is not discussed.

ABBREVIATIONS OF THE MORE COMMON METALS

Al — aluminum
Cd — cadmium
C — carbon (not a metal, but an essential component in steels)
Cr — chromium

Co — cobalt
Cb — columbium
Cu — copper
Au — gold
Fe — iron
Pb — lead
Mg — magnesium
Mn — manganese
Mo — molybdenum
Ni — nickel
P — phosphorus (not a metal; usually an undesired element in steels)
Si — silicon
Ag — silver
Ta — tantalum
Sn — tin
Ti — titanium
W — tungsten
V — vanadium
Zn — zinc
Zr — zirconium

16.1 STEELS

For at least the last hundred years, ours has been a steel civilization. In this country, or any other country, the annual tonnage of steel alloys consumed exceeds by a wide margin the sum of all other metals and the plastics combined. It is possible that by the year 2000 the tonnage of plastics annually consumed may exceed that of the steels. Should this happen, we will at last have begun to live the much talked-about Plastics Age. But, of course, in order to shape plastics, we still require steel alloys for molds and dies. The engineering of plastics is chiefly a matter of designing and machining the plastic molds.

It is probably not known how many steel alloys are currently in use. Certainly the number is in the thousands. For convenience these alloys based on steel are referred to as *ferrous metals*; all other metals and alloys are termed *nonferrous*.

16.2 CARBON IN STEEL

Pure iron has few commercial uses, the chief one being for small machine parts such as gears, pawls, and ratchets, made of sintered iron powder. Most iron is used in alloy form as steels.

Perhaps it is a little difficult to define exactly what steel is, but the following definition will probably do. Steels are made of iron alloyed with carbon, manganese, and silicon in small amounts, plus other alloying elements where special properties are required. Of the alloying elements in steel, none has the importance of carbon. Carbon is very powerful in its effect on steel characteristics. Few steels require more than one per cent of carbon, and most steels contain only about a fifth of one per cent, or two parts of carbon per thousand parts of iron by weight. Those steels in which carbon is the only important alloying element are called *carbon steels*. Those steels which contain other alloying elements in addition to carbon, such as chromium or tungsten or nickel, are called alloy steels. The manganese and silicon alloying additions noted above are required to correct certain problems in steelmaking at the steel mill, and will not be discussed here.

Low carbon steel, usually called *mild steel*, is produced in greater tonnages than all other steels combined. It is cheap, soft, remarkably ductile, and is readily welded without cracking. It cannot be heat-treated. This mild steel is the material used for most of the structural products of our civilization, including the ships, storage tanks, car bodies, building frames, household appliances, bridges, and culverts.

Steels are designated according to their carbon contents in the following classification:

1. Low carbon steel   0.01–0.30% carbon   For structural shapes and plate. Weldable, but cannot be heat-treated
2. Medium carbon steel   0.35–0.55% carbon   For machine parts
3. High carbon steel   0.60–1.5% carbon   For tools and tooling
4. Cast iron   over 2% carbon   For iron castings

The medium carbon steels are used for reinforcing rods for concrete, harrow teeth, shafts, gears, and the whole range of machine parts. High carbon steels are employed in knives, shears, cold chisels, punches, and dies.

A small increase in the carbon content of a steel, even as little as a tenth of a per cent, has a powerful effect on all the properties of the steel. If the carbon is increased, these are some of the effects:

1. The melting point is lowered.
2. The heat-treating temperature is lowered (for hardening).
3. The steel becomes more difficult to weld.
4. The steel is less easily machined.
5. The steel becomes more brittle.
6. The steel has a higher tensile strength.

In the processing of steel, a breakpoint occurs at about 0.30 per cent carbon. Below this carbon content, the steel presents few problems for the weldor. Above this carbon content, the steel becomes hardenable by heat treatment. The explanation is that if a steel is hardenable, then it could crack when welded, since the heat of welding can harden it.

The effect of carbon content on the hardness of steel is shown in Fig. 207. The hardness of any steel may be varied by suitable heat treatment;

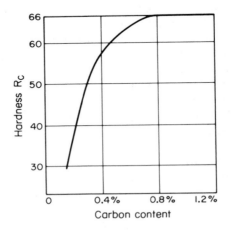

Fig. 207 Maximum hardness of steels of varying carbon content.

this graph shows the hardest possible condition at any carbon content. The maximum hardness is reached at 0.8 per cent carbon: a Rockwell C of 65. Carbon contents above 0.8 per cent are sometimes used, the principal reason being that still higher carbon contents provide increased wear resistance.

Welding rods are limited to a carbon content of 0.1 per cent to prevent any brittleness from occurring in welds.

In order to estimate the maximum hardness obtainable in machinery and tool steels, the following rule may be used:

$$0.4\%—Rc \; 60$$

$$0.8\%—Rc \; 65$$

Some hardening is possible even in mild steels, but the results are unpredictable. If you are lucky, you will obtain a hardness in a mild steel of Rc 35, but usually a lower hardness is obtained. Mild steel bars for machining have a Rockwell C hardness of less than zero, and should actually be tested on the Rockwell B scale.

16.3 ALLOYING ELEMENTS IN STEELS

A great many alloying elements are added to steels, but only those will receive mention here that have special interest for machining and welding operations.

The following rough rule is offered for understanding and remembering the effects of these alloys in steels. The rule does not apply to nonferrous metals. To recall the purpose of alloying elements, consider them to be of two kinds: those which combine with carbon to form carbides in the steel, and those which are added to give special properties to the steel.

1. *Carbide-formers.* These are chiefly chromium, tungsten, molybdenum (often abbreviated to "moly"), vanadium, columbium, and titanium.

Carbides are required in those steels that require great strength, high hardness, resistance to heat, and resistance to wear. Balls and rollers for bearings must be very hard, and are alloyed with chromium. End mills and high-speed steel lathe cutter bits must retain their hardness at high cutting temperatures, and contain substantial amounts of tungsten, molybdenum, chromium, and vanadium. Since these alloy additives will normally be in the form of carbide particles in the steel, the steel must also contain sufficient carbon to combine with these alloys, generally from 0.5 to 1 per cent.

Iron itself will form carbides without the addition of alloying elements. But without alloy carbides, a plain carbon steel will lose hardness above 300°F; alloy carbides will maintain the hardness of the steel to as much as 1100° F. Every machinist knows these characteristics from his own experience; it is very easy to burn a plain carbon drill bit, while a high-speed steel bit is much more resistant to the heating effect of a drilling operation. The plain carbon steels have other limitations, one being that they will not harden to a depth of more than about one-quarter inch. During heat treating operations the plain carbon steels can distort considerably.

The stainless steels contain 12 per cent or more of chromium. Ordinarily such a steel would be a tool steel rich in chromium carbides. The stainless steels, however, are not tool steels because their carbon content is held at levels low enough to prevent carbide formation. Instead, the chromium is dissolved in the iron and provides not hardness, but corrosion resistance and heat resistance.

As an example of a heavily alloyed tool steel, consider 2.25 per cent carbon, 12 per cent chromium. The carbide content of this steel would presumably be about 14 per cent if all the carbon and chromium combine as carbides. Such a tool steel would be highly resistant to wear and abrasion.

This tool steel may be compared with stainless steel 410, which also contains 12 per cent chromium. But 410 has only 0.1 per cent carbon. Only limited amounts of chromium carbides can be produced in this stainless steel, just enough for heat treating. (Most stainless steels cannot be heat treated.) The 12 per cent chromium tool steel can be hardened to Rc 65, while stainless 410 has a maximum possible hardness of only Rc 40 if heat treated.

Perhaps the most popular tool steel for general-purpose tool, punch, and die work is 0–1, containing 0.9 per cent C, 0.5 per cent Cr, 0.5 per cent W. The high carbon and the two carbide formers indicate this steel analysis to be a tool steel.

As an example of a steel analysis that cannot be a tool steel, consider 1330, with 0.30 per cent C and 1.60–1.90 per cent Mn. Manganese is not one of the designated carbide formers (it has a slight tendency to form carbides, but is not added for this purpose), and the carbon content is only medium.

2. *Manganese.* Sulfur makes a steel brittle, and since sulfur is found in all steels as an undesirable impurity, manganese is added to remove this brittleness. The manganese combines with the sulfur as manganese sulfide inclusions. Such inclusions are not harmful, except in a few special steel products, such as ball and roller bearings or the shafts of large electric generators.

3. *Nickel.* Nickel provides toughness in steels, especially at low temperatures. Nickel also prevents grain growth and may for this reason be added to

Fig. 208 Gray cast iron, magnified about 300X.

steels that must be subjected to long heating cycles, such as those that occur during carburizing.

4. *Cobalt.* Cobalt is a heat-resisting metal. Some of the best grades of high-speed steels include cobalt. This metal is also an ingredient in carbide cutters for the same reason.

5. *Machinability additives.* A number of special additives are used to improve the machinability of steels. The manganese sulfide inclusions previously mentioned assist machining because of their softness; machinability, therefore, can be improved by adding sulfur. However, this makes for difficulties if such a steel must be welded.

   Lead provides even better machinability. The lead does not actually alloy or mix with the steel, but appears as microscopically small globules in the steel which lubricate the cutting tool.

   Graphite in gray cast iron has the same effect as lead on the machinability of the cast iron. However, graphite is a necessary component in gray cast iron, and the improved machinability due to graphite is a coincidental effect.

16.4 THE AISI-SAE LOW ALLOY MACHINERY STEELS

The American Iron and Steel Institute (AISI) and the Society of Automotive Engineers (SAE) have catalogued by number the large group of machinery steels. These machinery steels are low-alloy medium carbon steels which are converted into machine parts for the automotive, railway, aerospace, farm equipment, hand tool, and other industries. The numbering system for these steels is a four-digit system:

10xx	plain carbon steels
11xx	sulfurized free-machining carbon steels
12Lxx	leaded free-machining steels
13xx	manganese 1.75%
23xx	nickel 3.50%
25xx	nickel 5.00%
3xxx	nickel-chromium steels (not stainless steels)
40xx	molybdenum 0.20–0.30%
41xx	low chromium-molybdenum
4xxx	nickel 1–4%, chromium to 0.55%, moly 0.20–0.30%
5xxx	up to 1% chromium
6xxx	low chrome-vanadium steels
7xxx	not used
8xxx	low nickel-chromium-molybdenum
9xxx	usually nickel-chromium with low molybdenum

The last two digits indicate the carbon content of the AISI steel. Thus 1040 has 0.40 per cent carbon, 8620 contains 0.20 per cent, 5160 has 0.60 per cent, and 52100 has 10.0 per cent carbon. The first two numbers are a kind of alloy coding, as the above table indicates, though in general most of these steels are low nickel-chrome-moly alloys, with the 5xxx and 6xxx series containing no nickel. The 2xxx and 3xxx series are virtually obsolete nowadays.

There is little value in attempting to memorize or remember this coding system. Certain of these steels are very popular and therefore important; others are not. If the analysis of any of these steels is required, it can always be looked up in a handbook. The following is a selection of current uses:

1015	mild steel welded tubing
1022	piston pins of automobiles, often carburized
1040	connecting rods, gear puller parts, shafts for farm combines
1055	gardening tools, such as hoes
1065	spring wire
4140	socket wrenches
4130	small rocket motors for solid rocket fuels
4340	aircraft undercarriage parts
52100	ball and roller bearings
8620	snowmobile shafts, automobile gears, often carburized

The AISI alloys perhaps most frequently encountered and specified on machine drawings are 1020, 1040, 1080, 4130, 4340, 8620, and 12L14. These are all stocked in steel warehouses and are excellent general-purpose machinery alloys. Machinability becomes poorer with increased carbon content, and, of course, so does weldability. A 1080 bar would be turned at about two-thirds the cutting speed of a 1020.

16.5 THE TOOL STEELS

Though some hand tools, such as socket wrenches, crescent wrenches, and gear pullers, are made of machinery steels such as 1040 (gear puller screws) and 4140 (socket wrenches), most tooling requires the higher carbon content of the tool steels.

The tool steels are a group of high-carbon alloy steels with an alloy composition suited to the demands of tooling. (A few tool steels are medium-carbon.) But the requirements to be met by tooling vary greatly. Machining cutters must be resistant to wear and to heat. Punches must be both hard and wear-resistant, but do not require heat-resistance. Pneumatic tools such as concrete breakers must be shock-resistant. Glass cutters require only to be hard. Some tooling parts must be dimensionally stable and must not distort during heat-treating, such as gages. Other tooling parts must be convenient to machine. Because of this diversity of requirements, a great many alloy formulations are required for tool steels, and a competent machinist must be familiar with those in common use.

The American Iron & Steel Institute classifies the tool steels by letter and number thus: O1, W5, S4.

The carbon content of a tool steel determines both its hardness and its wear resistance. A carbon content of 0.4 per cent provides a maximum Rc of 60; carbon contents of 0.8 per cent or higher gives Rc 65, the highest Rockwell obtainable in steels. Carbon contents greater than 0.8 per cent provide maximum hardness with extra wear resistance, due to the presence of additional iron and alloy carbides in the steel.

The alloy content in tool steels is chiefly the carbide-forming elements chromium, tungsten, molybdenum, and vanadium. These elements give the tool steel improved resistance to softening at high temperatures—this quality is called "red hardness"—resistance to red-hot temperatures, less distortion during heat-treating, and greater carbide content. These also increase the corrosion resistance of the tool steel, though this is not usually of importance.

The curves of Fig. 209 show the decrease in hardness of several tool steel types as the operating temperature is raised. These curves are actually curves of hardness obtained at various tempering temperatures. The importance of alloying is apparent by comparing the curves. A plain carbon steel

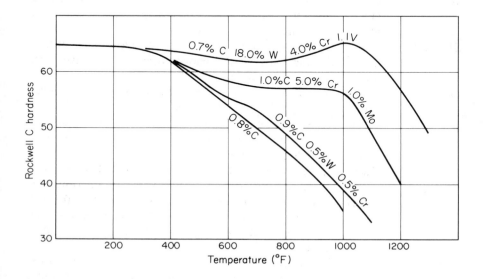

Fig. 209

loses hardness at a temperature of 300 to 400 deg. Most cutting tools, such as drills and mills and lathe cutters, operate at higher temperatures than this range.

As a rough rule of thumb, the plain carbon steels, or W tool steels, require a water quench to be fully hardened; the low-alloy tool steels, or O steels, can be fully hardened by a slower oil quench, and the high-alloy steel or A and other types will harden when cooled in air. A high-alloy steel will contain at least 5 per cent of alloying elements.

W tool steels   plain carbon, water quench. Distort when hardened.
O tool steels   less than 3 per cent alloy elements, oil quench. Little deformation when hardened.
A tool steels   high alloy, usually 5 per cent chromium, air quench. Little deformation when hardened.
S tool steels   shock-resisting. Medium carbon, low alloy.
D tool steels   high-carbon, high-chromium tool steels for cold-working applications, air hardening.
H tool steels   hot work applications, such as forging and plastic molds, air hardening.
T and M tool steels   high-speed steels for machining cutters and other heavy-duty applications.

The following tool steels are perhaps the more commonly met steels.

W1   0.60 to 1.40 per cent carbon. Used for blacksmithing tools, cold chisels, rivet sets, sledges and hammers, arbors and mandrels, glass cutters, and woodworking tools.
S1 to S7   These are shock-resisting tool steels, for pneumatic chisels, bolt header dies, pipe cutters, knockout pins, screwdriver bits, lathe collets, and chuck jaws.
O1   This is the standard punch and die steel for punch press work. It contains 0.9 per cent C, 0.5 per cent W, 0.5 per cent Cr.
D2   1.5 per cent C, 1 per cent Mo, 12 per cent Cr. A wear-resistant steel for such applications as knurling tools and lathe centers. Rather difficult to machine.
H10 to H19   These are hot-working chromium steels, with 0.4 per cent carbon, 5 per cent chromium, and some contain tungsten, molybdenum, and vanadium. They are die steels for die casting and plastic molding, but are recommended also for components that must not warp when heated, such as long slender shafts.
T1   This is the standard tungsten high-speed steel, used for drills, taps, reamers, lathe and planer tools, and milling cutters, containing 0.7 per cent C, 18 per cent W, 4 per cent Cr, 1 per

M1   cent V. For more severe duty and still better red hardness, cobalt is added, as in T4 and T5.

This is the molybdenum equivalent of T1 and used for much the same purposes. It analyzes 0.8 per cent C, 1.5 per cent W, 8 per cent Mo, 4 per cent Cr, 1 per cent V, and the similarity of the analysis to that of T1 should be noted. Other M tool steels contain cobalt for better red hardness.

The student machinist can obtain general information on heat-treating the tool steels from handbooks. However, he is cautioned not to assume that he can heat-treat high-speed steels from handbook information without the help of an experienced heat treater.

The higher-alloy tool steels require high furnace temperatures for hardening. As a result, their surface is easily decarburized, especially if they are high in carbon. The decarburized layer must be removed by grinding or other means.

16.6 THE STAINLESS STEELS

The stainless steels represent a large group of high-alloy steels which are familiar, but often not well understood. A vague knowledge of these steels is of little value and results in some regrettable errors in materials selection. They are often thought of as the standard solution for all steel troubles, especially for corrosion troubles. When an ordinary steel fails in service, a stainless steel may be substituted. Sometimes the substitution is successful, but there are occasions when the stainless steel does not perform as well as the cheaper material.

The stainless steels are somewhat costly, but their advantages and market acceptance often outweigh their additional costs. They offer the significant advantages of attractive appearance, low maintenance and ease of cleaning, oxidation resistance, high strength, toughness, heat resistance, and great corrosion resistance against oxidizing chemicals (but not reducing chemicals or chlorides).

They have a few unfavorable characteristics. The nickel-chromium grades of stainless steels have a thermal expansion about a third higher than that of the standard carbon steels. Hence, when heated or welded, they produce more warping. The straight chromium grades, which have no nickel, have about the same expansion coefficient as carbon steels, but nevertheless will tend to warp when heat-treated. The thermal conductivity of all stainless steels is very low, about one-third that of carbon steels. This low thermal conductivity makes these steels more damaging to machining cutters because of their inability to remove the heat generated during machining.

The chromium-nickel grades offer a third disadvantage for machining or forming. They work-harden very severely. Heavy feeds are necessary when drilling or cutting these materials. Light finishing cuts serve only to harden such metals and to burn out the point of the tool. In an extreme case, work-hardening effects may change the Rockwell C hardness from about zero to 45.

The stainless steels, like the tool steels and construction steels, are not included in the AISI-SAE steel coding system. Instead, they have a numbering code of their own, which uses three digits instead of four. With the exception of a few 200 and 500 series stainless steels, all stainless compositions are assigned numbers in either the 300 or 400 range. The 300's are chromium-nickel steels; the 400's have chromium but no nickel or almost no nickel. Hence, all stainless steels are very rich in chromium.

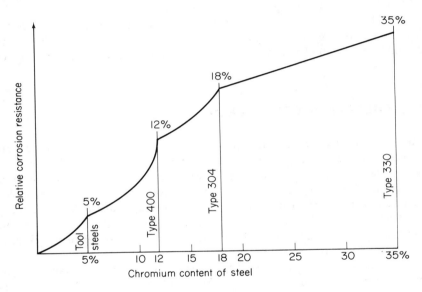

Fig. 210

Chromium provides the corrosion resistance of these steels. Little corrosion resistance is developed with chromium additions of less than 5 per cent. At 5 per cent, a considerable improvement in corrosion resistance results, though not enough to merit the designation "stainless." With increased chromium above 5 per cent, little improvement in corrosion resistance results until the chromium reaches 12 per cent. See Fig. 210. A chromium content of 12 per cent or more characterizes all stainless steels. Above 12 per cent chromium, there is little improvement in corrosion resistance until a level of about 18 per cent chromium is reached. Further improvement in corrosion and heat resistance results with additional chromium above 18 per cent. No stainless steel contains more than 35 per cent chromium (stainless steel 330), this high level being used for applications characterized by exposure to extreme temperatures. Alloys with chromium contents above 35 per cent, such as the Inconels, can scarcely be called steels.

The 12 and 18 per cent steps in corrosion resistance, as displayed in Fig. 210, are the significant ones for stainless steels. The 400 series, with no nickel, contain a minimum of 12 per cent chromium. The 18 per cent level is the minimum chromium used in the 300 series, which also contain nickel.

The stainless steels, therefore, are distinguished by their chromium content. But chromium is a carbide-former, and carbide-formers in the alloy content imply a tool-steel composition, based on chromium carbides. Chromium carbides, however, are harmful to stainless steels, since if the chromium is combined as carbide it is not available as elemental chromium for corrosion resistance. The stainless steels are prevented from becoming tool steels by keeping the carbon content at such low levels that there is insufficient carbon for carbide formation. Hence the alloy description of a stainless steel must be "a high chromium, very low carbon steel."

The first stainless steel to be developed was stainless 302, containing 18 per cent chromium, 8 per cent nickel, 0.12 per cent carbon. This alloy was satisfactory for general stainless applications until the welding of stainless steels became common practice. But the carbon content of 302 was sufficiently high that under the influence of the welding heat chromium carbides formed in the heat-affected zone of the weld. This depleted the elemental chromium and resulted in corrosion in the heat-affected zone adjacent to the weld. The weld itself did not corrode, thus giving the weldor the false impression that the welding procedure was not at fault.

Because 302 is difficult to weld without carbide precipitation in the heat-affected zone, it is becoming an obsolete steel. Stainless 304 is generally used instead of 302, with a composition of 18–20 per cent Cr, 8–10 per cent

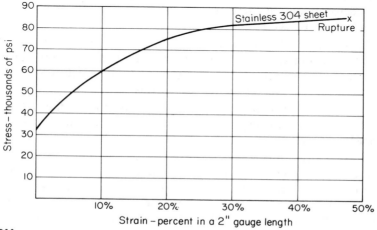

Fig. 211

Ni, 0.08 per cent C maximum, 1 per cent Si, 1 per cent Mn. This is the standard 300 series stainless steel, and, as we shall see, the other 300 series steels are simply variants of 304 to adapt them to special applications.

Stainless 304 has a yield strength of 35,000 psi and an ultimate tensile strength of about three times the yield strength (Fig. 211). In other words, it can be work-hardened to a strength of three times its yield strength. These are stronger steels than low-carbon steels, and this must be borne in mind when processing such steels. For example, a mechanical shear rated at $\frac{1}{4}$-in. steel plate will not safely cut $\frac{1}{4}$ in. of stainless steel. The large number of broken shears are sufficient proof of this statement, and perhaps next week another shear somewhere will be wrecked for the same reason.

The peculiarities of the 300 series may be thus summarized:

1. They are all very low carbon steels, generally less than 0.1 per cent C.
2. They contain a minimum of about 18 per cent chromium and about 8 per cent nickel.
3. All are austenitic steels and therefore nonmagnetic.
4. They are not heat-treatable (though they may be annealed if work-hardened).
5. They work-harden when formed, shaped, or cut.
6. They have an expansion coefficient a third higher than carbon steels.

The following are the most important grades of the austenitic stainless steels.

304. 0.08 per cent C, 18–20 per cent Cr, 8–10 per cent Ni. The basic 300 stainless.

302. Higher carbon than 304, giving unsatisfactory results when welded.

301. A cheaper grade of 304, the nickel being reduced to 6–8 per cent. Used for automotive trim, automobile wheel covers, and other sheet steel applications.

305. This again is a 304, but with the nickel content increased to 10–13 per cent. The higher nickel content provides a lower work-hardening tendency. This steel, therefore, is suited to such applications as deep-drawn kitchen sinks, stainless steel rivets, etc.

303. This is a free-machining grade of 304, modified by adding sulfur. The sulfur additive combines with manganese in the steel to give soft manganese sulfide inclusions.

308. This modification is familiar as stainless steel welding rod and welding wire. If a stainless 304 welding rod were used to weld stainless 304 sheet, some of the chromium would be oxidized in transfer across the arc, and the weld deposit would then be low in chromium. Therefore, the chromium content of 308 welding wire is increased to 19–21 per cent to compensate for such losses.

316. This is a 304 modified by the addition of 2 to 3 per cent molybdenum for greater resistance to the attack of acids. This steel is used in the meat packing, food, and pulp and paper industries for such equipment as pumps, piping, and handling equipment. It is required by the meat packing industry because blood is saline and highly corrosive.

304L and 316L. These are extra low-carbon grades with a maximum carbon of 0.03 per cent for insurance against carbide precipitation in the heat-affected zone during welding. Such low-carbon levels are difficult for the steel mill to produce; hence, these steels are more expensive.

321 and 347. Type 321 is a 304 with a small amount of titanium; type 347 contains columbium or tantalum instead of titanium. These two variants of the basic 304 are termed *stabilized steels*, and will be explained below.

THE AUSTENITIC STAINLESS STEELS

Type	C (per cent)	Cr (per cent)	Ni (per cent)	Mn (per cent)	Other
301	0.15 max	16–18	6–8	2	—
302	0.15 max	17–19	8–10	2	—
303	0.15 max	17–19	8–10	2	sulfur
304	0.08 max	18–20	8–10	2	—
305	0.12 max	17–19	10–13	2	—
308	0.08 max	19–21	10–12	2	—
316	0.08 max	16–18	10–14	2	2–3% Mo
321	0.08 max	17–19	9–12	2	titanium
347	0.08 max	17–19	9–13	2	Cb+Ta

16.7 CARBIDE PRECIPITATION

If the 300 series stainless steels are heated into or used in the temperature range of 800–1600°F, there is a rapid combination of chromium and carbon to form chromium carbides. These carbides may be dispersed through the grains of the steel, but tend to deposit in the grain boundaries. The effect is termed "carbide precipitation." Such loss of chromium impairs the corrosion resistance of such steels. There may be only 0.1 per cent carbon in the steel, yet this small amount can combine with a relatively large amount of chromium. Carbide precipitation is significant only if corrosion resistance is critical. It would not be a matter of serious concern in stainless steel architectural facings on a commercial building or a kickplate on a door.

Carbide precipitation can occur as a result of welding operations. The molten metal of the fusion zone of the weld heats and cools through the temperature range of carbide precipitation very quickly, so that carbides are not to be expected in the fusion zone. The heat-affected zone surrounding the weld, however, may be held in the temperature range that produces carbides for many seconds of time, hence the appearance of carbides in this zone. See Fig. 212.

One obvious method of preventing carbide precipitation is to employ the minimum possible carbon content. This is the explanation for the use of low-carbon grades 304L, 316L, 308L, etc. These are also designated ELC (extra low-carbon). Carbon precipitation is not usually found in stainless steels containing 0.05 per cent carbon or less.

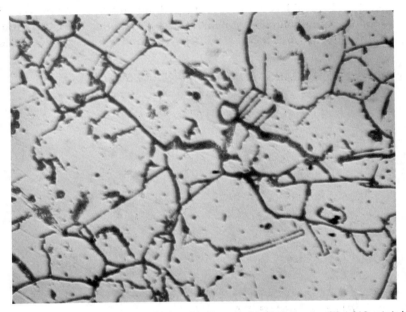

Fig. 212 Black chromium carbides in an overheated austenitic 316 stainless steel. Conversion of chromium to carbides depletes the steel of chromium and reduces the corrosion resistance.

A second method of preventing carbide precipitation is to include in the composition of the stainless steel an alloy ingredient with a greater attraction for carbon than chromium has. Such ingredients take up the carbon instead of the chromium's doing so. Of all the metals, titanium has the strongest affinity for carbon, and is used in stainless 321. The carbides precipitated in this steel, therefore, are titanium carbides. Columbium is used instead of titanium in stainless 347. Stainless 347 welding wire is used for the welding of 321 and 347. Stainless 321 cannot be used as a filler metal, because titanium is extremely reactive when molten. It would combine with nitrogen or oxygen or any other available substance in the arc, and virtually no titanium would be available in the deposited metal.

16.8 THE 400 SERIES STAINLESS STEELS

The 300 stainless steels are austenitic (nonmagnetic) because of the presence of considerable nickel in the alloy. Such steels cannot be hardened by heat treatment.

The 400 series of stainless steels in general contain no nickel. These are magnetic stainless steels. They do not work-harden as severely as do the austenitic stainless steels, nor do they possess the high levels of corrosion and heat resistance exhibited by the richer 300 series. The 400 group actually includes two series of steels, *ferritic* and *martensitic*.

The ferritic stainless steels cannot be heat-treated. These are low-carbon, high-chromium steels containing 16 per cent or more chromium, commonly used in sheet form. The most commonly used ferritic stainless steel is 430, with 0.12 per cent carbon and 16–18 per cent chromium.

The other 400 group is more important to the machinist. It is the group of martensitic stainless steels. Martensite is the hard phase of steel that results from heat treatment, and the word "martensite" implies that a steel may be hardened by heat treatment. Martensitic stainless steels contain more carbon, and during heat treatment form chromium carbides. They are used for machine parts that must combine some degree of corrosion resistance with high strength levels or high hardness.

The basic martensitic stainless steel is 410, containing 0.12 per cent carbon and 12 per cent chromium. This steel machines and grinds well, and may be hardened to a level of Rc 40. However, it scales badly when heated and tends to deform or warp when quenched. A free-machining grade of 410 is offered; this is 416, containing sulfur. The author, however, finds little difference in machinability between 410 and 416.

Type 420 is the basic 410 with about 0.2 per cent carbon. It may be hardened to a Rockwell C of about 50. Type 420 is used in cutlery. Type 440 contains 0.4 per cent carbon or more, with a richer chromium content to match the higher carbon for forming chromium carbides.

As a rule of thumb, consider 410, 420, and 440 to contain 12 per cent chromium. Again, as a rule of thumb only, 410 contains 0.1 per cent C, 420 0.2 per cent C, and 440 0.4 per cent carbon; that is, 410 means 0.1 per cent carbon, 420 means 0.2 per cent carbon, and so on. While not exactly true, such rules of thumb give some meaning and system to the designation numbers of these alloys.

The austenitic stainless steels remain tough down to extremely low temperatures. The 400 series, both ferritic and martensitic, become brittle at low temperatures.

QUESTIONS

Most students of metallurgy find the stainless steels to be their favorite group to investigate. Try the following simple investigations and questions; you cannot understand these steels merely by reading about them.

1. Obtain a small scrap of any 300 stainless in at least 16-gage. Measure the Rockwell C hardness. Hammer it thoroughly with a hammer. Measure the Rockwell C hardness on the hammered zone. The cold working has converted some of the austenite to martensite.

2. If your shop has an induction generator, heat a length of $\frac{3}{4}$-in. round bar in both 304 and 410 alloys. Can you explain why the 410 heats so much faster?

3. Heat a piece of 410 in a furnace set at 1800 deg and quench it in water. (This is a bad practice normally; 410 should be air-cooled.) What is the highest hardness you can obtain?

4. Select a stainless steel for the following purposes:
   a. The head of a golf club.
   b. A kitchen knife.
   c. A surgical instrument.
   d. A hard and corrosion-resistant pin.
   e. A pump shaft.
   f. An austenitic stainless part that must be tapped $\frac{1}{4}$–20. (Hint: The 300's are extremely difficult to tap.)
   g. A stainless cup-shaped part.
   h. A stainless rivet for a highway trailer.
   i. The hull of a naval minesweeper that must sweep magnetic mines.
   j. A stainless consumer article that must be sold at rock-bottom price.
   k. A welded stainless steel acid tank.
   l. A stainless door hinge.

There may be more than one acceptable answer to some of these. Consult the answers given at the back of the book. If you do not agree with them, see if you can defend your own answers. In any case, there is no "right" answer. Engineering solutions are never correct, because they are always compromises.

5. Look through steel handbooks and try to find a steel containing from 6 to 10 per cent chromium. Presumably you will not find such a steel. Why?

6. In Question 3 above, you determined the maximum hardness of stainless 410. Is this a suitable steel for a stainless knife?

16.9 ALUMINUM ALLOYS

Pure aluminum is a very soft metal, almost too soft for easy machining, with one-third the density of steel.

The machinist will process aluminum only in its alloyed forms. These alloys will not be discussed in detail here. It may be noted that new aluminum alloys are put on the market every year, though many standard alloy formulations persist. The following summary makes a quick method of understanding the aluminum alloys:

1. The copper alloys of aluminum are the most machinable.
2. The magnesium or magnesium-silicon alloys are preferred for welding. These are readily machined.
3. Silicon alloys are preferred for castings. The presence of 5 per cent or more silicon makes for some difficulty in machining such alloys, and carbide cutters may be necessary.

The copper alloys have excellent machinability, are hard, and can be hardened by heat treatment. Such alloys are numbered 2xxx. Thus 2024 is a commonly met alloy including $4\frac{1}{2}$ per cent copper. The special free-machining alloy of aluminum is 2011, with 5 to 6 per cent copper.

Magnesium alloys of aluminum are numbered 5xxx and magnesium-silicon alloys 6xxx. The machinist will likely meet 6061. Most extrusions, used for aluminum windows, blackboard trim, and trim on transit buses, are 6063.

The casting alloys have three-digit numbers. Perhaps the most commonly met are the 300 series, with silicon and manganese.

16.10 THE PLASTICS

The plastics as materials are divided into two broad groups: thermoplastics and thermosetting plastics. The thermoplastics may be softened by heating, and most of them are more ductile than the thermosets. The thermoplastic group includes polyethylene, polyvinyl chloride (vinyl), polymethyl methacrylate (plexiglas, lucite, or acrylic), polystyrene, and many others. The group also includes polytetrafluoroethylene (teflon), famous for its resistance to high temperature. The thermosetting plastics cannot be softened by heating, and most of these are more brittle than the thermoplastics. Typical thermosets are Bakelite, epoxies, silicones, polyurethane, and rubbers. Rubbers, of course, are not characterized by brittleness.

All the plastics are poor conductors of heat, and can be damaged by temperatures of a few hundred degrees. If machined at too high a speed, heat may concentrate at the tool point and melt the plastic. Since machinability is the ability to be cut at high cutting speeds, the plastics and rubbers cannot be considered as highly machinable, even though they are easily cut. The plastics, and particularly the rubbers, are best machined with a large back rake angle on the cutting tool.

(There is an interesting relationship between heat conductivity and machinability: Materials that conduct heat readily, such as aluminum, copper, and brass, are readily machinable. Materials with limited heat conductivity, such as plastics and stainless steels, must be machined more slowly. If the machined material retains the heat of machining, then the tool must overheat and lose its edge more quickly.)

QUESTIONS

1. Consider two steels: (a) 1.40 per cent C, 12 per cent Cr, and (b) 0.1 per cent C, 12 per cent Cr. Explain why the first steel is not a stainless steel, but the second is.
2. Define the terms: (a) steel, (b) tool steel, (c) low-carbon steel, (d) medium-carbon steel.
3. Why would you not select a steel with 0.8 per cent carbon for a machine shaft?
4. Why would you not select a steel with 0.4 per cent carbon for a ball bearing steel?
5. Why do welding rods have a low carbon content?
6. What is the highest Rockwell C hardness obtainable in steels?
7. Why do lathe and milling machine cutting tools contain tungsten, molybdenum, and chromium?
8. Give the alloy numbers of the following:
   a. A free-machining mild steel.
   b. A free-machining austenitic (300) stainless steel.
   c. A free-machining martensitic stainless steel.
   d. A free-machining aluminum.
9. Why are the following used in steel alloys? (a) nickel, (b) cobalt, (c) lead.
10. Why can you not produce a continuous chip when machining gray cast iron?
11. Why is a coolant not needed when machining gray cast iron?
12. What is the carbon content of the following AISI steels? (a) 8640, (b) 1045, (c) 52100, (d) 4340.
13. What is the difference between the W, O, and A tool steels as to general alloy content and method of hardening?
14. Classify the following steels as water, oil, or air hardening:
    a. 0.4 per cent C
    b. 0.4 per cent C, 5.5 per cent Cr
    c. 0.7 per cent C, 18 per cent W, 4 per cent Cr, 1 per cent V, 5 per cent Co
    d. stainless 410
    e. 0.8 per cent C, 0.55 per cent Ni, 0.5 per cent W
    f. 0.8 per cent C, 9 per cent W

15. State the two methods used to prevent carbide precipitation in the 300 series austenitic stainless steels.

16. Suggest a simple method of differentiating a 300 from a 400 stainless steel. Try your method on the stainless steels available to you.

17. What alloying element is added to aluminum for
    a. Machinability?
    b. Weldability?
    c. Castability?

18. Why should a material show poor machinability if it does not conduct heat well?

19. Why should soft materials such as the thermoplastics be machined with a generous back rake in the cutter?

Chapter 17

Heat Treating
of Steels

Heat treating refers to the heating and cooling operations performed on a metal for the purpose of altering such characteristics as hardness, strength, or ductility. A tool steel intended to be machined into a punch may first be softened so that it can be machined. After being machined to shape, it must be hardened so that it can sustain the punishment that punches receive. Most heating operations for hardening leave a scale on the surface, or contribute other surface defects. The final operation must, therefore, be grinding to remove surface defects and provide a suitable surface finish.

Modern heat-treating methods require both knowledge and experience for successful results. Some steels, such as the plain carbon steels, are relatively easy to heat-treat, whereas others are rather tricky. The inexperienced machinist should not attempt to heat-treat those steels that require unusually high furnace temperatures, such as the high-speed steels.

To understand heat-treating processes and their results, some examination of steels under the microscope is necessary. Microscopic examination at magnifications from about 20 to 300 discloses a wide range of information about the steel and its processing, including grain size, carbon content, defects, microcracks, previous fabrication and heat-treating history, and sometimes may even identify the particular steel alloy if the type of steel is not known. However, little of significance is disclosed by examining a piece of unprepared metal under the microscope; instead, the metal sample has to be prepared for examination by special grinding, polishing, and etching techniques. These techniques may be found in manuals on the subject of metallography.

Figure 213 shows three microscopic views of steels under a magnification of 300 powers. Figure 213(a) is the appearance of a mild steel. This is a typical grain structure for metals. Figures 213(b) and (c) are two views of a 1080 plain carbon steel, (b) showing the soft or machinable condition, and (c) showing the hardened condition.

A complete understanding of the principles of heat treating steels requires a rather extensive presentation of the metallurgical theory of steels.

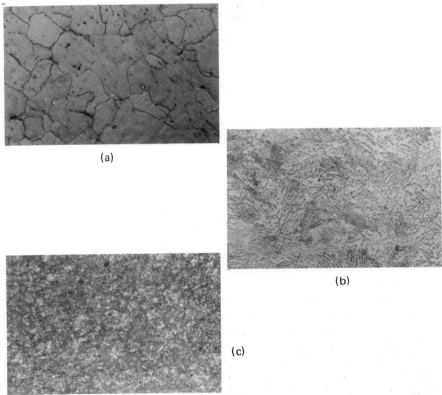

(a)

(b)

(c)

Fig. 213 Phases of steel. (a) Mild steel. (b) Annealed steel, 0.8 per cent carbon (pearlite). (c) Hardened steel, 0.8 per cent carbon (martensite.)

Such a presentation is not attempted here; instead, this chapter will present certain short cuts directed only toward the achieving of successful results in hardening plain carbon and low-alloy steels. No one can be trusted to attempt the hardening of high-alloy steels who has not had successful experience with the simpler steels, and the author believes that much harm has resulted from the attitude that anyone can become a heat treater who has a furnace and a quench tank.

17.1 CRITICAL TEMPERATURES FOR HEAT TREATING

Pure iron in the solid condition exists in two conditions, or phases as they are termed. At low temperatures the phase is called *ferrite*. Above a temperature of 1666°F, iron changes to a different phase called *austenite*. Iron in the austenitic condition is nonmagnetic, whereas in the ferritic condition it is, of course, magnetic. The temperature of 1666°F at which the change from one phase to another occurs is called the *transformation temperature*, or *critical temperature*. Here we will use the term critical temperature, and understand it to be the minimum possible furnace temperature for hardening and softening steels.

The critical temperature of 1666°F applies only to pure iron, a material that the machinist rarely, if ever, sees. Steel is iron alloyed with small amounts of other elements, including always carbon and manganese. Let us consider plain carbon steels first, and we can safely assume that small

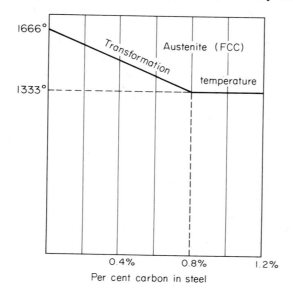

Fig. 214

amounts of manganese present in all carbon steels do not influence the heat-treating principles to be discussed.

As the carbon content of steel increases from 0 to 0.8 per cent, the critical temperature falls. At 0.8 per cent, this temperature is 1333°F. For carbon contents in steel greater than 0.8 per cent, the critical temperature remains at 1333°F. In order to select a furnace temperature for hardening or softening a carbon steel, the heat treater must use the critical temperature graph of Fig. 214. It is an easy graph to commit to memory, since it is based on only three items of data: 1666°F, 1333°F, and 0.8 per cent.

Cast irons contain more than 2 per cent carbon. None of these observations, however, applies to cast irons.

If a plain carbon steel is to be either hardened or softened, its temperature must be taken above this critical temperature line; that is, the steel must be austenitized. Usually a temperature of 50 to 100 deg above the critical temperature is selected, to ensure that the steel part reaches a high enough temperature to be completely austenitized, and also because furnace temperature control is always a little uncertain. For example, in the case of a 1080 tool steel, 0.8 per cent carbon, the furnace temperature would be set at about 1425 deg, or almost 100 deg above the critical temperature.

The same steel could be heated to a higher temperature than 1425 deg, say 1625 deg, and still be in the austenite region. But going to higher temperatures than the minimum necessary temperature produces many possible defects: loss of carbon through oxidation, loss of steel through severe scaling (which increases very rapidly with increase in temperature), and severe warping of the part when it is cooled from the unnecessarily high temperature.

The steel must be held at furnace temperature for sufficient time to dissolve the carbides in the austenite, after which the steel can be cooled. How much residence time in the furnace is required is to some degree a matter of experience with any particular steel. Usually, for a ¾-in. bar, 20 minutes or slightly more will do. Double the time for twice the diameter. Alloy steels may require a longer furnace time; many of these steels are best preheated in a lower-temperature furnace before being charged into the hardening furnace.

When the heating time is completed, the steel must be cooled down to room temperature. The cooling method determines whether the steel will be hardened or softened. If the steel is quickly removed from the furnace and quenched into cold water, it will be hardened. If it is left in the furnace to cool slowly with the heat turned off, or cooled in air (small pieces of plain carbon steel cannot be air-softened, however), it will be softened. High-alloy steels may be hardened by air-cooling, but plain carbon steels must have a more severe quench, almost always water.

There are several softening methods for steels, and the word softening therefore does not indicate what softening process or purpose was used. The method of softening by slow cooling from austenite is called *annealing*, not softening. Annealing leaves the steel in the softest possible condition (dead soft).

Note, then, that the difference between hardening and annealing is not in the heating process, but in the *cooling process*. To harden or to anneal, the steel must be heated into the austenite region and held there for a sufficient period of time. To harden, quench; to anneal, cool quite slowly.

You cannot ever assume that a hardening operation is successful. Suppose the hardening of a 1080 steel is attempted. The steel will probably be harder after heat treating, but how hard ought it to be? You must know what Rockwell hardness is possible with any steel, and test the heat-treated steel against this maximum hardness. Maximums are dependent on carbon content:

$$0.4\% \text{ carbon} \quad \text{Rc 60}$$
$$0.8\% \text{ carbon} \quad \text{Rc 65–67}$$
$$1.0\% \text{ carbon} \quad \text{Rc 65–67}$$

It is not always possible to obtain a Rockwell of 60 in a 0.4 per cent carbon steel; Rc 55 is acceptable for this material.

In an emergency, a file can be used to test for hardness, but there is some degree of uncertainty with a file.

Suppose your hardened steel showed a Rc of 35 after quenching. This hardness indicates that the steel was only partially hardened. What has gone wrong? The most likely possibility is that the heat treater was too slow in transferring the piece from the furnace to the water. Or perhaps the part when in the water was insulated by a covering of hot steam; to prevent this the part must be moved about in the water. Perhaps the quenching water was too hot because of previous quenching operations. The steel also can be softer if carbon is burned out of the steel; this can happen if the furnace temperature is too high or the heating time too long. The steel will not harden if the heating time is too short also. Occasionally, but only occasionally, the steel itself is at fault, but this is difficult to prove, and certainly cannot be assumed simply because the heat treatment was unsuccessful.

17.2 TEMPERING

A quenched steel is in its hardest possible condition. Unfortunately, this is also the most brittle condition. Such a steel would certainly break if put into service as a punch, a cutter, or a chisel. A second heat-treating operation must follow quench-hardening, to give the metal sufficient ductility for service applications.

This second heat-treating operation is a softening operation called *tempering*, often called "drawing." In tempering, we sacrifice some hardness in order to gain some ductility. This is done by reheating the steel to some temperature that is always below the critical temperature (tempering is never carried out in the austenite range of temperatures) and cooling it back to room temperature. Neither the time of heating nor the rate of cooling is very critical.

Hardening and tempering can be illustrated by the case of a cold chisel. To make a cold chisel, saw off a suitable length of 1080 steel in a hexagon bar. Heat and forge to shape. Harden the chisel at 1425°F and water-quench it. This should give a Rc of 65. But the chisel at this hardness is as brittle as glass, so it must be tempered. It is reheated to 550°F for 10 to 15 minutes and cooled. Its hardness after tempering should be not higher than Rc 55, which is the maximum hardness for resistance to impact and hammer blows.

Because a full-hardened steel may crack at any time, it is important that after the hardened steel has cooled very nearly to room temperature it be immediately tempered. Do not harden today and temper tomorrow, since the steel might crack overnight. If there is not time enough to complete the tempering operation, then do not harden.

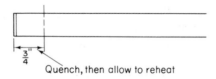

Quench, then allow to reheat

Fig. 215

The blacksmith of former times had an interesting method of hardening and tempering in one operation. This method is still used in emergencies, but does not give an acceptable quality of heat-treating for commercial work. The blacksmith heated the chisel to a cherry red, then quenched the first $\frac{3}{4}$ in. or inch of the chisel end in water. When the chisel end was black and cold, he withdrew the chisel from the water. The red-hot mass of the rest of the chisel then reheated the chisel end for tempering. A succession of temper colors appears at the chisel point: straw yellow, then yellow, brown, purple. When the brown or the purple appeared at the end of the chisel, the whole chisel was quenched. See Fig. 215.

Certain tools, such as screwdrivers, require considerable toughness. Others, such as scribers, need not be tough, but must be hard. The correct balance of toughness and hardness is obtained by selection of a suitable tempering temperature. The tough screwdriver needs a tempering temperature of about 700°F, whereas the hard scriber needs less ductility, and for it a tempering temperature of about 400°F will suffice. The higher the tempering temperature, the lower the hardness and the better the toughness. Figure 209 shows the variation in hardness with tempering temperature for a 1080 steel.

17.3 THE TACTICS OF SUCCESSFUL HEAT TREATING

A hardened steel is in a certain hard condition or phase [Fig. 213(c)], and annealing the steel results in an entirely different phase [Fig. 213(b)]. The difference in results is due entirely to the rate of cooling the metal from the austenite condition. If you do not cool the part fast enough, you reach a soft condition. This leads to the question: How fast is fast enough?

When the steel is cooling, it can choose either the annealed or the hardened condition. The heat-treating problem is that of setting up the conditions in such a way that the steel will go to the phase desired and not the other. To set up such conditions, what is required is a tactical "map" that will predict at all temperatures exactly what a steel will do. Such a "map" for a 1080 steel is given in Fig. 216.

Before we discuss the use of this diagram, an explanation of the hardening process is necessary. The hard phase of steel is called *martensite* [Fig. 213(c)]. Martensite under the microscope often looks like a pile of straw, whereas the annealed condition gives a fingerprint effect in some or all of the grains of steel. (This laminated phase found in annealed steels is called *pearlite*.) When a steel part is removed from the furnace and quenched, it might be thought that it changes to the martensitic condition as soon as the

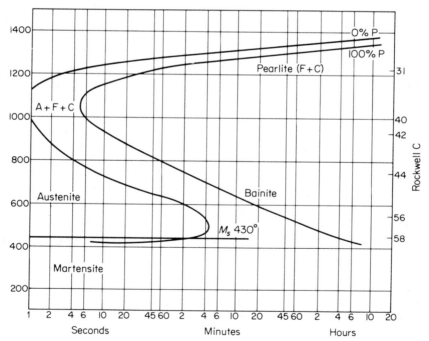

Fig. 216 Isothermal transformation diagram for heat-treating operations on 1080 steel (0.8 per cent carbon).

temperature drops below the critical temperature. But this does not happen. The critical temperature applies only to heating and *slow* cooling, but not to rapid cooling. Thus Fig. 214 applies only to slow cooling, whereas Fig. 216 is the phase diagram for fast cooling rates. During quenching, the austenite condition holds for several hundred degrees below the critical temperature, until at a certain temperature martensite begins to form from austenite. The temperature at which martensite begins to form is called M_s (start of martensite transformation). But this transformation of austenite to martensite does not occur at a fixed temperature, as most transformations do, but over a range of temperatures. As the temperature falls below M_s, more and more martensite forms, and less austenite remains, until at room temperature the transformation is complete or nearly so. It is always possible that a few per cent of austenite never transform.

The greater the carbon and alloy content of the steel, the lower M_s is. For a 4140 steel (0.4 per cent C, 0.77 per cent Mn, 1 per cent Cr, 0.2 per cent Mo), which is used in socket wrenches, M_s is about 600 deg. The lower M_s is, the narrower the range between M_s and room temperature, and the higher the amount of untransformed austenite.

Now turn to Fig. 216. This is called an isothermal transformation diagram. Such diagrams are available for all commonly used steels; this particular I-T diagram applies to a 1080 steel. Note the critical temperature line at 1333 deg. This line is usually identified on such diagrams as A_s. Note also the M_s line at about 430 deg. Note also the "nose" shape formed by the two phase boundary lines. This I-T diagram is a tactical "map" for executing a wide range of heat-treating operations, and a complete explanation of its use may be found in any basic metallurgy textbook. The intent here is simply to show how to keep from heat-treating troubles by the use of this diagram.

Consider first an annealing operation, done by leaving the workpiece in the furnace to cool. Suppose two hours is the cooling time to room temperature. The time scale on the bottom of the diagram is in seconds, so two hours is about 7200 sec. We can show a cooling rate from 1333 deg at zero seconds to room temperature at 7200 sec by drawing a straight line between these two points on the graph (though actually the part will cool rapidly at first and more slowly after an hour). The straight line on the graph will pass through the two phase boundary lines into the phase area marked F + C [ferrite and cementite mixed, the two phases that laminate into the fingerprint effect of the annealed steel of Fig. 213(b)].

To harden the steel will be more difficult. For full hardening the steel *must* remain austenitic until it cools to M_s. This means that the cooling line for hardening must remain to the left at all times of the leftward phase boundary line. But this line allows only about one second to get past the nose at 1000 deg. (1000 deg is just under a red-hot condition.) One second is very little time; hence the need for haste in getting the steel out of the furnace and into the quench tank. Once the cooling has dropped below the 1000-deg nose, the steel can cool more slowly; from this point to M_s there is a full minute allowable.

Suppose that you are just a little slow in getting the steel into the quench. What happens? In this case the leftward phase boundary is crossed into the region marked A + F + C (austenite plus ferrite plus cementite). The fraction of the steel that is A will harden to martensite; the fraction that is F + C will be soft. The steel will show an intermediate hardness, perhaps in the range of Rc 20 to 35.

Successful and predictable heat treating requires the use of this I-T diagram for the steel to be heat-treated. The diagram tells the heat treater how much time he has to get past the dangerous nose, which for any plain carbon steel is at about 1000 deg, or just below a red heat. If the hardening operation fails, it is almost always because too much time was occupied in dropping the temperature below this "nose" temperature.

The I-T diagram provides the three temperatures that the heat treater must know if the heat-treating operation is to be under control:

1. Critical temperature, above which the furnace temperature must be set.
2. The "nose" temperature, where the heat-treating operation may fail by insufficiently rapid cooling.
3. The M_s temperature, where the transformation to martensite begins.

This is the temperature below which the steel may crack. Cracking may often be prevented by water-quenching below the "nose," followed by slower air-cooling. The slower air-cooling is less risky.

Low-alloy steels allow more time past the nose, which means that a slower cooling rate is possible. The low-alloy 4140 steel allows just over two seconds past the nose. Such low-alloy steels can usually be oil-quenched. Oil gives a slower cooling rate with less distortion and less tendency to crack the steel. Very high-alloy steels, such as stainless 410 or the hot-working and high-speed steels, may allow a minute past the nose. Such steels are air-hardened. However, the higher-carbon high-alloy steels require very high furnace temperatures in the range of 2000 deg, and at these high soaking temperatures some carbon is burned out of the surface of the steel. This loss of carbon makes the surface soft, though the interior may be hard. High-alloy steels may require considerable skill for proper heat-treating.

17.4 DISTORTION IN HEAT-TREATING

When a steel alloy is quenched to martensite from austenite, dimensional changes will occur. In martensite the iron atoms are not so densely packed as in austenite. The volume increase is of the order of 4 per cent or so. In a plain carbon steel, the quenched part may increase in length as much as

0.002 in. per foot in some cases. The plain carbon water-hardening steels show the largest dimensional changes and the most warpage, while the oil-hardening low-alloy steels are much better in this respect, often being referred to as "nondeforming" steels. The least warpage and dimensional change are found in certain high-alloy air-hardening steels. Probably the best is the 12 per cent chromium D2 tool steel used for plastic molds. However, it is not true that all air-hardening steels are nondeforming; stainless 410 deforms severely.

A competent heat treater must know what to expect in deformation after heat treatment. A good test piece for assessing deformation is shown in Fig. 217. The piece should measure about 6 in. × 2½ in. × ½ in. before heat-treating. Before heating and hardening, it should be coated with some suitable

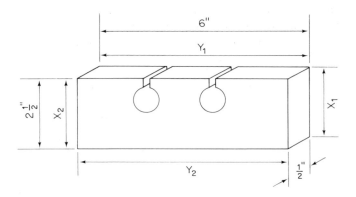

Fig. 217

protective paste to prevent oxidation. After quenching and tempering at 400 deg, the dimensions X_1, X_2, Y_1, and Y_2 are measured and compared with their original lengths.

Distortion of long slim shafts, large flat shapes, or flat shapes with large holes in them results from these dimensional changes, and is an indication of residual or internal stress within the part (see Sec. 18.2). Residual stresses may be removed by stress-relieving heat treatments; dimensional change can be controlled only by selection of a suitable low-distortion alloy.

When long and slender bars, originally straight, are heat-treated, they usually bend into a shallow arc. For a ¾-in. diameter bar a foot long, total indicator runouts (TIR) are frequently in the range of 0.006 to 0.020 in. The TIR is measured with a dial indicator as the total movement indicated on the dial indicator when the bar is rotated through 360 deg. See Fig. 34. For any except very critical applications, a TIR of 0.005 in. is acceptable in a shaft.

17.5 SURFACE HARDENING TREATMENTS

Many machine parts requiring a hard surface cannot be hardened throughout, because through-hardening would make the part too brittle. Other machine parts require a hard and wear-resistant surface, or *case*, combined with a softer and tougher interior or *core*. Typical machine parts that need not or should not be hardened throughout, but require a hard and wear-resistant case, include splined shafts, piston pins, cams, shafts, gears, sleeves, ratchets, clutch dogs, ejector pins for plastic injection molding machines, collets, and valve stems.

Five methods of case-hardening are in general use:

1. Carburizing.
2. Nitriding.
3. Cyaniding, also called carbonitriding.
4. Induction hardening.
5. Flame hardening.

The first three methods change the chemical composition of the case. Carburizing adds extra carbon to the case, to produce a high-carbon analysis capable of being hardened by heat treatment. Nitriding adds nitrogen to the case to produce hard metallic nitrides. Cyaniding adds both carbon and nitrogen. Since carburizing and cyaniding add carbon to the case, low-carbon steels are employed in these processes. Flame hardening and induction hardening do not alter the chemical composition of the case, but are essentially shallow hardening methods. Therefore, for these two methods sufficient carbon must be available in the steel for hardness. A minimum of 0.35 per cent carbon is necessary.

1. Carburizing

Low-carbon steels may be case-carburized by a carburizing gas or a liquid. Carburizing must be performed at some temperature above the critical temperature to ensure that the steel is austenitized. Let us discuss carburizing in terms of 8620 steel, a popular steel for this purpose. A typical analysis for 8620 is

0.20% C, 0.80% Mn, 0.25% Si, 0.55% Ni, 0.50% Cr, 0.20% Mo

Typically for carburizing steels, the carbon content is 0.20 per cent. A small amount of the carbide formers, chromium and molybdenum, is present; these provide extra strength to the core, and are necessary also for those applications where this steel is not carburized, for example, in snowmobile shafts. The necessity for the small amount of nickel will be explained presently.

From Fig. 214, this steel does not become austenitic until a temperature of at least 1580°F is reached, or say 1600°F. To ensure that the steel is well inside the austenite range, carburizing would not be done at a temperature of less than 1650°F. The time required to carburize a steel is several hours, and it is desirable to reduce such long carburizing times. This is possible by going to higher temperatures, since all chemical processes proceed more rapidly at increased temperatures. At a very high temperature of, say, 2000 deg, carburizing would be a reasonably rapid operation. But at such a temperature, several damaging effects would appear: heavy scaling of the steel, severe warping during cooling, and severe grain growth. Indeed, the minimum possible temperature of 1650 deg will produce all these damaging effects to some degree. All things considered then, carburizing cannot be safely executed at temperatures above 1700 deg. At this temperature, the carburizing operation will require at least two hours.

Two hours of heating at 1700°F will result in some grain growth and a resultant loss of steel properties, especially toughness. With a hard case, the steel must possess a tough core. To reduce the extent of grain growth, a little nickel is added to the steel, nickel being a grain refiner.

Carburizing may be done in an atmosphere furnace containing substantial carbon monoxide in its atmosphere. The iron reacts with the carbon monoxide, extracting carbon from it. More commonly, carburizing is performed in a heated bath of molten salts containing sodium cyanide as carburizer.

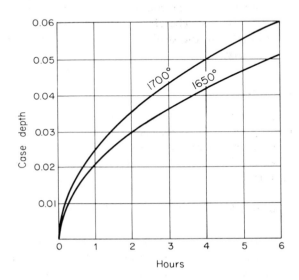

Fig. 218

The depth of carburizing is controlled by the length of time of the carburizing operation. Case depth d as a function of carburizing time in hours is given by the following formulas:

$$\text{At } 1650°F, d = 0.021\sqrt{t} \quad \text{and} \quad \text{at } 1700°F, d = 0.025\sqrt{t}$$

where t = hours. For example, two hours at 1650°F will give a case depth of 0.030 in.

A machine designer must know how deep a case to specify. This is often a matter for experience, though 0.030 to 0.035 in. case depth will suffice for most applications. Too thick a case specification increases costs. But too thin a case specification may lead to part failures. A thin case can be worn away by abrasion, or can be cracked by penetrating loads.

The suggested case depth is the final depth after all manufacturing operations are completed on the part; it is not the case depth supplied in the heat-treating operation. Consider how a carburized shaft is manu-factured. After carburizing, the steel must be hardened and tempered to produce the required case hardness. For example, if good wear resistance is needed, a case hardness of not less than Rc 55 must be specified. After being carburized, hardened, and tempered, the shaft will be warped. It must be straightened, usually within a total indicator runout (TIR) of 0.005 in. The shaft must then be ground to straightness and concentricity on a center grinder or centerless grinder. A grinding allowance of at least 0.010 in. will

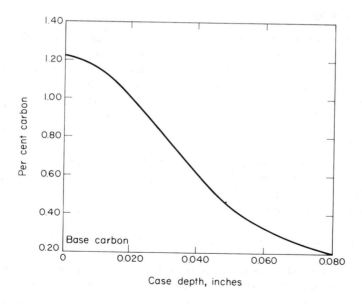

Fig. 219

be needed. Therefore, to obtain a final case depth of 0.035, probably the carburizing operation must provide a case depth of 0.050.

The carbon analysis through a case will resemble Fig. 219. A maximum carbon of 1.2 per cent will appear at the surface, gradually falling as the case is entered, until the core carbon of 0.2 per cent is reached. How much of this depth should be measured in determining case depth? Probably the effective depth should be the depth to 0.40 per cent carbon.

Look again at Fig. 219 and consider what happens when the case depth is too shallow and the grinder removes an unexpectedly large amount of case. In addition to being too shallow, the case may not have sufficient carbon for hardness. The grinding operation removes the best portion of the case.

2. Cyaniding

Cyaniding provides a thin case of high hardness and wear resistance. Cyanide salts are used, but the salt composition is different and a lower salt bath temperature is employed. The cyanide case is lower in carbon and contains considerable nitrogen. Cyaniding is widely employed for producing cases of about 0.010 in. on small parts.

Carbonitriding, also called gas cyaniding, uses an atmosphere of ammonia and hydrocarbons to produce a cyaniding effect.

3. Nitriding

Nitriding is performed in an atmosphere furnace using ammonia at a temperature between 900° and 1150°F. Note that this temperature is below the transformation temperature of the steel; hence there is little distortion of the part in this process. Ejector pins for injection molding of plastics, aviation engine parts, cylinder liners, and gages are examples of parts usually nitrided. Because of the absence of distortion, the parts may be finish-ground before nitriding. The parts are usually tempered at a temperature somewhat above the nitriding temperature.

Nitriding produces only a very thin case after considerable process time. Typically, 10 hours of nitriding will produce a case depth of 0.007 in. The case, however, is extremely hard, with Rockwell C hardness above 70.

The following is a typical analysis of a nitriding steel:

$$0.40\% \text{ C}, 0.60\% \text{ Mn}, 0.30\% \text{ Si}, 1.60\% \text{ Cr}, 0.35\% \text{ Mo}, 1.05\% \text{ Al}$$

Nitriding steels are often called nitralloy steels, and like the above analysis are medium-carbon steels with small amounts of aluminum, chromium, and molybdenum. The aluminum combines with nitrogen from the ammonia to produce extremely hard aluminum nitrides.

4. Flame Hardening

In a flame-hardening operation, a medium- or high-carbon steel is rapidly heated with an oxy-gas torch and quickly cooled with water or an air blast. If the core is to remain soft and tough, the heating rate must be very rapid. Special care must be taken with sharp corners and other changes of section, in order to prevent cracking.

Flame-hardening is quite difficult to execute by manual methods, though sometimes simple punches and dies may be successfully flame-hardened manually.

5. Induction Hardening

The induction hardening process really has to be seen to be believed and understood. A photograph of a simple induction-hardening setup is given in Fig. 220. The bar to be heated is circled by a water-cooled copper coil, and the coil is connected to a high-frequency electric generator. The coil must be water-cooled, because the large currents it carries would melt it in a few seconds. The workpiece becomes the secondary in the induction setup, with the coil as primary, and a very large high-frequency current (10,000 to 450,000 cycles per second) is induced in the surface areas of the workpiece facing the coil. Only that portion of the bar encircled by the coil is heated. The work is heated to hardening temperature in a few seconds.

Fig. 220 Induction hardening of the end of a bar. The work coil will melt if not water-cooled.

It must, of course, be quenched. Tempering is not usually necessary after induction hardening; the hardening is only to a depth of 0.1 in. or less, and the softer core of the workpiece provides toughness. Plain carbon steels of 1035 or 1040 composition are preferred for induction hardening. Because of the rapid rate of heating and the short heating time, the workpiece temperature must be raised at least 100 deg above the critical temperature in this method if the steel is to be austenitized. Because the part is not through-hardened, distortion is not usually a problem, except for the more troublesome steels, such as stainless 410.

The planetary pin of Fig. 4 is an example of a component ideally suited to the induction hardening process, especially because this component is required in production quantities. The planetary pin could be induction-hardened at the rate of about 120 pieces per hour with a suitable induction generator.

QUESTIONS

1. Suggest the maximum Rockwell C hardness you would permit in a cold chisel or a perforating punch.
2. What is the critical temperature for hardening the following steels, all plain carbon?
   a. 0% carbon.
   b. 0.2% carbon.
   c. 0.4% carbon.
   d. 0.6% carbon.
   e. 0.8% carbon.
   f. 1.0% carbon.
   g. 1.2% carbon.
3. To what temperature would you set a hardening furnace for hardening each of the steels of Question 2?
4. You have properly heated a 1040 steel shaft to 1575°F and quenched it into water. Its Rockwell C, however, is only 35. List all the things that come to mind that you could have done wrong. (The failure is not in the heating operation.)
5. It requires an hour in the furnace to austenitize a 1040 steel shaft 2 in. in diameter. Why would you not speed up the operation by raising the furnace temperature to 1800°F?
6. (a) What is the difference between hardening and annealing? (b) What is the difference in procedure?
7. What maximum Rockwell C can be obtained from the following plain carbon steels? (a) 1040, (b) 1080, (c) 10100, (d) 10120.
8. The part print specifies a minimum case depth of 0.050 in. after carburiz-

ing and grinding. How much case depth must be included for the grinding operation?

9. What is the difference between annealing and tempering?
10. What is (a) martensite? (b) austenite?
11. What is meant by M_s?
12. The lower the M_s temperature, the less martensite has transformed from austenite in cooling back to room temperature during the quench. Why should this be so?
13. For any steel, three temperatures are critically important for the control of heat treatment. Name them and explain their importance.
14. What kind of a diagram gives you these three temperatures for any specific steel?
15. What influence does the alloy content of a steel have on the time allowed to pass the "nose" when quenching?
16. What is meant by case-hardening?
17. What is the advantage of a little nickel in the alloy content of a carburizing steel?
18. Is a carburizing steel suited to induction hardening? Why?
19. What carburizing time is required to obtain a case depth of 0.04 in. (a) at 1650°F; (b) at 1700°F?
20. What advantages does the nitriding process offer?
21. A bar of 1080, hardened but not tempered, is severely warped, with a runout of 0.060 in. Can you straighten this bar with a press? If it is induction-hardened and untempered, with the same runout, can it be straightened with the press?
22. What is a generally acceptable TIR for a shaft?
23. Make a graph of the following tempering data for stainless 410. Plot temperature horizontally and Rockwell C vertically.

Tempering temperature	Rockwell C
0°F (no temper)	38
400°F	38
600°F	36
700°F	37
800°F	38
900°F	38
1000°F	35
1100°F	21

a. Suppose this steel is to be used for the shaft of a fan moving high-temperature air. What maximum air temperature can it sustain?
b. Is this a temperable steel?

24. Plot on a graph furnace temperature setting vertically and total carbon and alloy content horizontally for the following tool steel compositions. From this graph answer the following questions:
   a. If the alloy content of a steel increases, does the hardening temperature increase?
   b. Can you predict the hardening temperature from the total alloy content? (If there is not a simple prediction method, then you cannot.)

Analysis *(per cent)*	*Furnace temp.* *(°F)*
0.8 C, 0.25 Mn, 0.20 Si	1450
1.05 C, 0.20 Mn, 0.20 Si	1450
0.40 C, 1.10 Mn, 0.20 Si, 0.15 Mo	1525
0.40 C, 0.75 Mn, 0.60 Cr, 1.25 Ni, 0.15 Mo	1550
0.20 C, 0.80 Mn, 0.25 Si, 0.55 Ni, 0.50 Cr, 0.20 Mo	1600
0.30 C, 0.80 Mn, 0.25 Si, 1.65 Cr, 0.40 Mo	1550
0.15 C, 1.0 Si, 1.0 Mn, 12 Cr	1800
0.60 C, 0.50 Mo, 17 Cr, 1 Si, 1 Mn	1850
1.60 C, 0.3 Si, 0.25 Mn, 12.5 W, 4.75 Cr, 5 V, 5.5 Co	2250
0.78 C, 0.25 Mn, 0.30 Si, 18.5 W, 4.25 Cr, 1.9 V, 8 Co, 0.85 Mo	2375
1.05 C, 0.30 Si, 0.25 Mn, 6.25 W, 4 Cr, 6 Mo, 2.5 V	2200
0.85 C, 0.25 Mn, 0.30 Si, 6.5 V, 4 Cr, 1.9 V, 5.0 Mo	2225
0.75 C, 0.25 Mn, 0.3 Si, 18 W, 4 Cr, 1.1 V	2300
0.35 C, 0.3 Mn, 0.3 Si, 9.5 W, 3.25 Cr, 0.4 V	2100
0.45 C, 0.75 Mn, 1 Si, 5 Cr, 3.75 W, 1 Mo, 0.5 V, 0.5 Co	1850
0.35 C, 0.4 Mn, 1 Si, 1.2 W, 5 Cr, 0.3 V, 1.4 Mo	1800
2.25 C, 0.3 Mn, 0.25 Si, 12 Cr, 0.25 V, 0.8 Mo	1800
0.9 C, 1.2 Mn, 0.3 Si, 0.5 Cr, 0.5 W, 0.2 V	1450
0.6 C, 0.75 Mn, 0.3 Cr, 0.2 Mo, 2 Si	1600
0.45 C, 0.25 Mn, 0.3 Si, 2 W, 1.5 Cr, 0.25 V	1700

If there is too much scatter in the points, draw a line through the lowest points and another through the highest points. By this means all the points lie in a "scatter band" between the maximum and minimum line. You can also add a line to give an average or mean relationship.

Chapter 18

Welding

Welding is so much a part of metal processing that the machinist must have some familiarity with the methods of welding. Much of the tooling and fixturing that the machinist either uses or makes requires welding joints; many of the components produced by machining are later welded to other components.

This chapter is a short discussion on the planning, management, and control of welding and welded joints so that the machinist will have an intelligent knowledge of the welding operations that relate to his machining operations.

The machinist should know that the free-machining alloys so helpful to his metal removal operations present difficulties to the weldor. Sulfur added for machinability will tend to cause cracking if the steel is welded. Lead added for machinability will boil off during arc welding to leave voids in the steel. There are special techniques for welding such free-machining alloys, but they are the business of the weldor, not the machinist.

18.1 WELDING EFFECTS ON METALS

The welding of metals requires that they be heated and cooled, and, as
Chapter 17 indicates, the heating and cooling of metals, especially steels, may
produce changes in the condition of the steel with distortion, hardening, or
other problems. A heat-treating operation is done deliberately and for a
specific purpose, but in welding operations the steel may be heat-treated
whether we wish it or not.

Usually in heat treating, the whole part is uniformly heated. In a
welding operation the heat put into the metal is to be used for a joining
operation and the heat therefore must be localized. Metals generally conduct
heat well; therefore, those metals that are easiest to weld are generally those
with the lowest conductivity for heat, since such metals retain most of the
heat in the region of the weld. Recall that in machining the opposite effect is
desired: Those metals which best conduct heat away from the cutting tool
are usually the easiest to machine. Copper is the most heat-conductive of the
structural metals; it is machinable, but comes close to being unweldable.
Aluminum is also highly conductive; it is easy to machine but not easy to
weld.

Besides thermal conductivity, the thermal expansion of metals has
an effect on the results of the welding operation. When metals are heated and
cooled, they change in dimension and warp. Welding operations on aluminum,
which expands considerably with temperature, result in considerable warpage.
Warpage from the welding of steels is more controllable, since steel expands
only half as much as aluminum in the same temperature rise.

These and other considerations suggest that the management of
welding operations requires the knowledge to predict the reaction of the
metal to the operation. As an example of the surprises that metals can offer
if the person doing the welding is not acquainted with metal characteristics,
the reader is urged to try the following simple investigation.

Deposit a welding bead from a mild steel welding rod on any scrap of
stainless 300, such as 304 or 316. Both the deposited mild steel and the
stainless are soft metals, with Rockwell C hardness less than zero, and
neither can be heat-treated. But now take Rockwell C readings over and
around the weld deposit. Some Rockwells may be as large as Rc 45, an
impossible figure for either metal. The explanation for this unusual result is
that there are now three metal alloys, not two: the rod alloy, the stainless
alloy, and the fused metal deposit. In the weld deposit, both the mild steel
and the stainless steel have melted and blended to form a third alloy. Carbon
in the mild steel has met chromium in the stainless steel, and the two have
combined to produce chromium carbides. The welding operation has combined two soft steels to produce a tool steel! The experienced weldor, of
course, has met a hundred metallurgical problems like this one and knows
how to avoid them.

Most fusion welding methods melt and deposit metal in the place where it freezes. A fusion weld, therefore, must be considered to be a casting and can have any of the defects of a casting. Slag inclusions and blowholes (gas pockets) can appear in welds as easily as in castings.

The weight of metal melted is usually quite small in a welding operation, and it is surrounded by a larger mass of metal that serves as a mold in which the deposited metal freezes. This surrounding metal has a very high heat conductivity, so that the weld metal is cooled very quickly. A rapid cooling from the austenite region produces hard martensite. If the weld metal has enough carbon to be heat-treatable, the deposited metal will be hardened. Usually, however, the deposited metal is quite low in carbon; welding rods for welding mild steels contain only about 0.1 per cent carbon.

Surrounding the welded area is an area of parent metal that was heated from the weld puddle but did not reach the melting point. This area is cooled very rapidly by the mass of metal in the weldment, and therefore this area is often found to be hardened after welding. If the deposited metal is not hardened, but this surrounding heated area is hardened, then cracks would

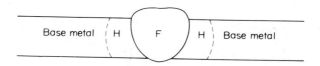

Base metal   H   F   H   Base metal

Fig. 221 Heat effects in a fusion weld: F. fusion zone; H. heat-affected zone.

be more likely to appear in this surrounding area than in the deposited metal. This heat-treated region surrounding the fusion zone is called the heat-affected zone, sometimes abbreviated HAZ.

Low-hydrogen electrodes (electrodes containing no hydrogen in the flux) must be used to weld heat-treatable steels, or steels containing over 0.3 per cent carbon. If there is hydrogen in the rod coating, this hydrogen tends to migrate to the hardened heat-affected zone and cracks it by internal gas pressure.

The rate at which a weld cools is proportional to the thickness of the plate being welded. Clearly, a thicker plate must conduct more heat from the fusion zone than a thin plate. Therefore, the thicker the material being welded, the greater the risk of hardening and cracking the region of the weld. Thicker plates, over one inch, may have to be preheated before welding begins. If the plate is hot, then it draws less heat from the weld, and the cooling rate is less.

To sum up, a welding operation can produce a number of metallurgical effects. When one is welding uncomplicated metals such as mild steel, few difficulties will arise from these metallurgical effects, but the successful welding of machinery, tool, free-machining, and stainless steels requires some knowledge of metallurgy and heat-treating. To avoid such difficulties, remember that a fusion weld produces three major effects:

1. A casting (the melted metal).
2. A heat treatment (the heat-affected zone).
3. A dilution (the creation of a new alloy by combination of the parent metal and the filler rod).

A machining operation does not produce changes in the condition of the metal; a welding operation does. It serves no useful purpose to deposit a beautiful weld seam only to have it or the heat-affected zone crack or fail for lack of metallurgical knowledge.

18.2 RESIDUAL STRESS

Weld metal always contracts or shrinks. If two plates are held at an angle of 90 deg to each other for the deposit of a fillet weld (Fig. 222), the weld metal

Fig. 222 Distortion of the flanges of a heavy beam caused by large fillet weld deposits.

on cooling will pull the two plates out of alignment toward the side of the weld.

Any deformation of a material, such as this, is called a *strain*. A pull on a rope produces a lengthening of the rope. This lengthening is a strain of the rope. The pull on the rope is the *stress* that caused the strain. If the rope is twice as long, we expect the strain (lengthening) to double also. Since strain is affected by length, strain is expressed numerically as inches per inch or feet per foot of original length, For example, if a steel bar 1.000000 in. long is heated 1°F, at the higher temperature it will measure 1.0000065 in.

The thermal strain is, therefore, 0.0000065 in. per inch of length. If the steel is 2.000000 in. long, it will expand twice as much, or 0.000013 in., but the strain is still 0.0000065 in./in.

Similarly, the stress or force must have a useful numerical unit. Stress is given in pounds per square inch. For example, the common welding rods for welding mild steel will sustain a tensile stress of 70,000 psi (pounds per square inch) before they break (they are guaranteed for only 60,000 psi, but will exceed this figure). This means that if the welding rod had a cross section of 1 sq in., 70,000 lb pull would be required to rupture it.

It seems apparent that a stress (force) will cause a strain (deformation). What is not so apparent is that a strain can cause a stress. The following simple investigation illustrates the case for a strain causing a stress, and serves to explain an important concept, that of *residual stress*.

Obtain a piece of 16-gage steel about 4 in. × 6 in. Lay a small arc welding deposit with a 6013 rod down the middle of the sheet parallel to the long edge of the sheet. Do not weld out to the very edges of the sheet (Fig. 223).

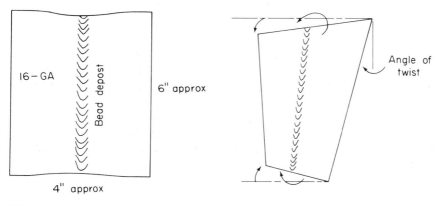

Fig. 223   **Fig. 224**

After the sheet is cooled back to room temperature, it will be twisted to the shape shown in Fig. 224. Why should it twist? (Occasionally the sheet will bow instead of twisting. If it bows, flatten it in a vise. This will change the bow to a twist.)

A weld always upsets or shrinks. The length of the sheet, measured along the axis of the weld, has shrunk a thousandth of an inch or so, but the rest of the sheet has not. The edges of the sheet, being longer, must adopt a curve to accommodate their extra length as compared with the welded center of the sheet.

If the sheet is bent, it is strained. If it is strained, there must be a stress accompanying this strain, since stress always accompanies strain.

The strain due to this weld deposit is too small to measure, but can be determined in the following manner. Lay one long edge of the sheet against a flat surface. The opposite edge will then be warped away from the flat surface. Measure the angle between the flat surface and the opposite edge with a protractor (Fig. 225). Suppose that this angle is 4 deg. This is 2 deg of

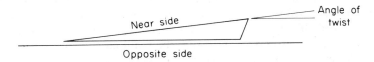

Fig. 225

warp for each side of the weld. The cosine of 2 deg is 0.9994. The shrinkage due to the deposit is (1.0000 − 0.9994) or 0.0006 in./in. length of sheet.

To calculate stress from strain in steel, use the formula

$$\text{Stress} = 30,000,000 \times \text{strain}$$
$$= 30,000,000 \times 0.0006$$
$$= 18,000 \text{ psi}$$

The weld is pulling on the rest of the sheet with a compressive stress of 18,000 psi, and the rest of the sheet is imposing a tensile stress of the same amount on the weld. This type of locked-in or self-imposed stress is called a *residual stress*.

Most residual stresses result from heating. A heat-treated bar that has warped during heat-treating has a residual stress in it. A bar that cracks during heat-treating had such a high residual stress that it exceeded the tensile strength of the bar.

18.3 THE WELDING ARC

Welding arcs are low-voltage, high-current, short-circuiting arcs, typically in the range of 20 to 40 volts, 100 to 1000 amps. A short circuit is an electrical path of nearly zero resistance to the flow of current. The opposite effect, an extremely high resistance such that no current flows, is called an open circuit. The use of the arc for machining purposes in the electric discharge machining process is discussed in Chapter 24.

The welding arc contrasts with the arc across a spark plug in an engine. In the case of the spark plug, a very high voltage is used, together with a very small current; this is almost an open circuit. The difference between the welding arc and the spark-plug arc is easily explained, however. The arc across the spark plug is not sustained, but is only a momentary arc that is at once extinguished. The welding arc is sustained. An arc is an unusual kind of resistance to the flow of current. Initially it offers an extremely high resistance, but once the current flow is established, the arc resistance drops almost to zero.

The welding machine cannot initiate an arc, as can the high voltage applied to the spark plug. Welding machines have a maximum voltage output of 75 to 80 volts; the ignition circuit for an engine provides well over 10,000 volts. To start the arc, the weldor must short-circuit the rod to the work and then draw out the arc. The two methods of starting are shown in Fig. 226.

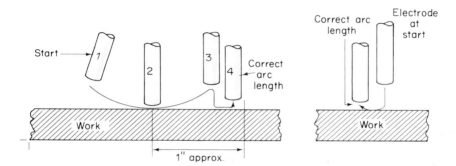

Fig. 226

The arc may be initiated by stubbing or by scratching. In the stubbing method the rod is touched to the work and then withdrawn to the proper arc length. In the scratch method the rod is rotated slightly to touch the work and to draw the arc, and the correct arc length is then established. The change in arc voltage when one is striking an arc is graphed in Fig. 227.

When one is striking an arc, the electrode tends to stick to the work or "freeze." Certain rods tend to freeze more than others. To break the rod loose, snap the electrode holder to one side. If the rod will not break free, shut off the welding machine. Do not release the rod from the holder with the machine running; this will cause arcing at the jaws of the holder and damage to the rod holder.

The electric arc emits ultraviolet radiation of some intensity. It is important that the weldor's face, eyes, and arms be protected from this radiation. There have been rare cases of skin disease produced by the arc, though damage to the retina of the eye is more common. The serious possibilities of eye damage are best indicated by the fact that the dark glass in the welding helmet transmits only about 0.01 per cent of the radiation of the arc. Stating the case differently, we can say that an arc flash on the unprotected eye is 10,000 times too powerful for the eye to receive. The dark protective glasses are numbered from 9, the lightest, to 14, the darkest. A no. 9 glass is suitable for manual arc welding.

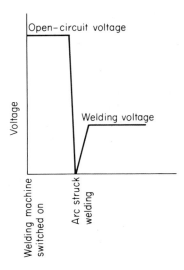

Fig. 227

18.4 ELECTRIC ARC EQUIPMENT

The welding machine may be an engine-driven electric generator or a welding transformer. A welding transformer reduces line voltage to a lower voltage suited to the welding operation. The transformer welding machine may be an alternating-current or a direct-current machine; if direct-current, it must include a rectifier to convert the alternating current from the secondary of the transformer to direct current. Some welding rods are suited to either direct current or alternating current; others will weld only on direct current. The electrical characteristics of welding rods are discussed in Sec. 18.7.

The welding circuit must be completed by connecting a cable between the rod holder and the machine and a second ground cable to the ground clamp. The ground clamp is clamped to the work or to the welding bench. If it is connected to the welding bench, the bench becomes part of the welding circuit. If an arc cannot be started, this usually indicates that the electric circuit is not completed. Perhaps the work does not make proper contact with the ground clamp or with the welding bench. Electrical connections must be checked throughout the circuit.

If direct current is used for welding, there are two possible polarities or connections. If the workpiece is positive, that is, if the workpiece and ground clamp are connected to the positive terminal of the welding machine, the connection is termed *straight polarity*, abbreviated DCSP. If, instead, the electrode cable is connected to the positive terminal of the machine, this second connection is called *reverse polarity*, or DCRP. Alternating current, since it reverses 120 times each second, may be considered as an alternating direct and reverse polarity.

The proper current for burning off an electrode must be found by trial. The weldor makes an approximate setting, tries the arc, and if it is too hot or too cold, cranks the current down or up. An approximate current may be estimated from the diameter of the rod thus:

$$\tfrac{1}{8}\text{-in. rod} = 0.125 \text{ in. Use } 125 \text{ amps}$$

$$\tfrac{5}{32}\text{-in. rod} = 0.156 \text{ in. Use } 150 \text{ amps}$$

$$\tfrac{3}{16}\text{-in. rod} = 0.187 \text{ in. Use } 180 \text{ amps}$$

$$\tfrac{1}{4}\text{-in. rod} = 0.250 \text{ in. Use } 250 \text{ amps}$$

Thus the rod diameter in decimals is a rough indicator of the required current. These estimates are subject to final adjustment, and are more in error in the larger diameters of rod.

Direct-current welding has one disadvantage not present in AC welding: *arc blow*. When a current flows in any conductor, a magnetic field is formed around the conductor and at right angles to the current. Since there is current through the cables, workpiece, ground clamp, etc., magnetic fields exist around all these components. The current is very large; therefore, these magnetic fields can be quite powerful. In welding with direct current, the arc sometimes wanders and lacks control as though it were being blown to and fro by the influence of these complex magnetic fields. This is arc blow. It is more of a problem when one is welding with very high or very low currents, and especially when one is welding in corners or other confined spaces. In addition to the problem of control of the arc, arc blow may cause atmospheric gases to be pulled into the arc, resulting in porosity in the weld.

To correct an arc blow condition, try the following remedies:

1. Weld away from the ground clamp.
2. Change the position of the ground clamp.

Arc blow is not a problem with alternating current.

18.5 TYPES OF WELDS

Welding may be done in any of the four positions shown in Fig. 228: flat, horizontal, vertical, and overhead. Any welding rod will deposit metal in the flat or horizontal position. Some rods are not suited to vertical and overhead welding, since these positions require a fast freezing rod. Flat welding is the easiest to perform and yields the best quality; the other positions are used when conditions make them unavoidable. Some manufacturers of machinery

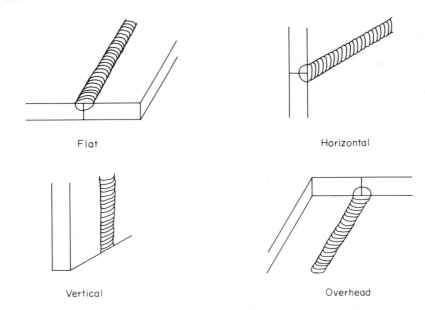

Flat   Horizontal

Vertical   Overhead

Fig. 228

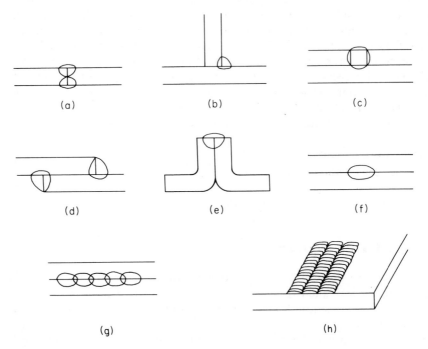

(a)   (b)   (c)

(d)   (e)   (f)

(g)   (h)

Fig. 229

specify that all welds on machine frames must be made in the horizontal position, since this position gives superior welding conditions and fewer faulty welds.

Most arc welds are either butt welds, lap welds, or fillet welds (Fig. 229). The meaning of the *throat* and the *leg* of a fillet weld is explained by Fig. 230. The throat of a butt weld will usually measure 70 per cent of the leg, since sin 45 deg or cos 45 deg = 0.707. In making a butt weld, the two plates may be butted tight together if the thickness of the plate does not exceed about $\frac{1}{8}$ in. For thicker work a small gap is left between the plates in order to obtain full penetration.

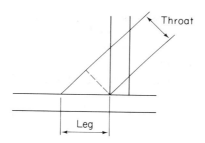

Fig. 230

This chapter and the preceding one have explained at length the problems created by heating metals. To avoid these difficulties as far as possible, do not overweld. Overwelding puts an unnecessary amount of heat into the metal. A little extra weld metal just for good measure is a bad thing, and it is unfortunate that so often the quality of the welding is judged by the amount of metal deposited. Quality welding means the least amount of metal deposited that circumstances require. It is never necessary, for example, to make the leg of a lap weld as thick as the plate it joins, and particularly in toolmaking this would be very poor practice.

18.6 DISTORTION

If the amount of weld metal deposited is the least possible, then heat distortion in the weldment will be the least possible. Many factors influence the distortion produced by a weld.

1. Distortion is proportional to the coefficient of thermal expansion of the metal. Aluminum has twice the thermal expansion of steel, and distorts twice as much.

2. Overwelding has been mentioned as a prime cause of excessive distortion.

3. Thin gages warp more than heavy gages. Do not use light plate for the base and frames of jigs and fixtures.

Fig. 231

4. Distortion is less if both sides of a joint are welded, rather than welded from one side only.
5. A stringer bead produces less distortion than a weave bead (Fig. 231). The weave bead is laid down by oscillating the electrode across the direction of travel to produce a wide bead. A stringer bead is laid down without this cross oscillation.
6. The fewer the number of passes to complete the welded joint, the less the distortion will be.
7. The use of clamps and welding fixtures can be a considerable help in controlling distortion.

18.7 ARC WELDING RODS FOR MILD STEEL

The standard rods for arc welding mild steel are all made of a mild steel of approximately 0.1 per cent carbon. The difference between one rod and another is in the flux coating.

The coating of flux over the rod shields the arc against atmospheric gases and provides slag to protect the weld pool from these same gases and to remove impurities from the pool. Suitable materials are incorporated into the flux to shape the weld, delay the cooling rate, control the penetration of the weld, stabilize the arc, and make possible the use of alternating current for welding.

The characteristics of an arc welding rod for welding mild steels are given by a four-digit number designation, such as E6010. The E indicates electric arc. The first two digits indicate the guaranteed strength of the deposited rod; thus 60 means 60,000 psi tensile strength. Higher strengths are given by 70xx, 80xx, or higher-numbered rods.

The third digit indicates the suitability of the rod for position welding. If the third digit is a 1, as in E6010, then the rod is an all-position or fast-freezing rod, suitable for all four welding positions. If the third digit is a 2, as in E6020, then the rod is suited only to flat and horizontal welding.

The fourth digit conveys information on the rod coating, the penetration, and the electrical and other characteristics of the rod. The information conveyed by this last digit is displayed in the following table.

FOURTH DIGIT FOR WELDING RODS

	0	1	2	3	4	5	6	7	8
Power supply	DCRP	AC or DCRP	AC or DC	AC or DC	AC or DC	DCRP	AC or DCRP	AC or DC	AC or DCRP
Type of arc	digging	digging	medium	soft	soft	medium	medium	soft	medium
Penetration	deep	deep	medium	low	low	medium	medium	medium	medium
Type of slag	cellulose (hydrogen)	cellulose (hydrogen)	rutile (TiO_2)	rutile (TiO_2)	rutile with iron powder	low hydrogen	low hydrogen	mineral	low hydrogen

Consider first the 6010 rod. This rod is distinguished by the coarse ripple it produces in the weld. The 6010 rod cannot be used with alternating current; it requires direct current reverse polarity. It is deep-penetrating and thus cannot be used on thin materials. Since it has cellulose in the flux, which releases hydrogen, it should not be used to weld tool steels. The hydrogen in the flux coating gives this rod its deep-penetrating characteristic, but hydrogen can cause cracks in hardenable steels.

The 6011 rod is a 6010 modified for use with alternating current power supplies. The 6012 rod has less penetration, and is suited to either AC or DC welding. Straight polarity is preferred with direct current. This is a good rod to use if the fit-up between plates is rather poor.

The 6013 rod is used for welding thin sheet metal, down to about 16-gage. Thinner gages than this should be welded by the oxyacetylene or the tungsten inert gas (TIG) method.

The low-hydrogen types such as 6018 and 7018 are suited to welding hardenable steels or for circumstances that may cause weld cracking, such as cold weather.

To reduce all this information, here is a fast summary:

6010	DCRP, deep penetration, for thicker materials, butt welds
6011	AC or DC, deep penetration, for thicker materials, butt welds
6012	AC or DC, medium penetration, butt welds
6013	AC or DC, for thin gages
6018, 7018	AC or DCRP, for critical welds
6024	AC or DC, for fillet welds

18.8 OXYACETYLENE WELDING

Gas welding uses acetylene, C_2H_2, burned in pure oxygen to create the unusually high flame temperature of about 6000°F. This flame temperature is about 3000 deg above the melting point of steels, but well below welding arc temperatures, which exceed 10,000°F. Oxyacetylene and other varieties of gas welding such as oxypropane, etc., are extremely versatile and convenient and require little equipment. The same gas flames are used for thermal cutting of steel and for brazing operations. Gas welding, however, has some limitations. It requires a great deal of heat to produce the weld; this heat is not concentrated in the area of the weld and therefore produces warping and, in the case of higher-carbon steels, hardening of the metal. Although often used to weld light sheet, oxyacetylene is not suited to heavier sections of plate.

The standard oxygen cylinder is 9 in. in inside diameter and usually contains 244 cubic feet of oxygen compressed to about 2400 psi when full.

Oxygen is the most dangerous of all gases if misused, and the following safety precautions must be observed:

1. Oxygen is no substitute for compressed air.
2. Grease and oil can be ignited in the presence of pure oxygen without the assistance of a flame.
3. Do not use a flame or an arc close to an oxygen cylinder.
4. In the case of a leaking oxygen valve, do not attempt repairs, but move the cylinder outside.
5. Do not move an oxygen cylinder unless the cap is on the cylinder.

The standard acetylene cylinder is 12 in. in inside diameter and shorter than the 9-in. oxygen cylinder. Acetylene gas must be loaded into the cylinder in an unusual procedure to prevent its exploding under certain conditions. The gas is dissolved in acetone, this liquid being absorbed in the acetylene cylinder in a porous material such as asbestos or balsa wood.

Both the oxygen and the acetylene cylinder must be equipped with regulators to reduce the high cylinder pressure to a low pressure suitable for welding or cutting. The discharge pressure is adjustable by the operator. Pressure gages indicate cylinder pressure and discharge pressure.

The gas hoses are connected to the regulator. Although welding hose has a rugged construction to withstand the normal abuse it receives in welding operations, it should not be given abnormal punishment, as this leads to

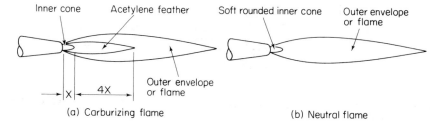

(a) Carburizing flame   (b) Neutral flame

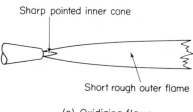

(c) Oxidizing flame

Fig. 232

leakages. Acetylene hose is red in color, and the connecting nuts have left-hand threads and a groove cut around the middle of the nut. Oxygen hose is green with right-hand threads.

The welding torch mixes the two gases and shapes the flame. There is a control valve to adjust the flow of each gas. The acetylene is turned on first and ignited. Then the oxygen is opened slowly. The oxygen flow is adjusted until the correct flame is obtained; a proper flame is judged by its appearance. Depending on the operation, a carburizing, neutral, or oxidizing flame may be required. Adjustment of the flame must be learned by demonstration.

A range of interchangeable torch tips is used with any torch. Larger tips must be used on heavier material to be welded.

18.9 OXYACETYLENE CUTTING

The oxyacetylene cutting process actually proceeds by a combustion reaction between red-hot steel as the fuel, and oxygen, in addition to the combustion of acetylene in oxygen. The steel is first heated by an oxyacetylene preheat flame to ignition temperature of about 1600°F, about a thousand degrees below the melting point of the steel. Then a stream of cutting oxygen is directed against the hot steel, which oxidizes.

Fig. 233 Cutting torch body, showing the three tubes for preheat oxygen and acetylene and for cutting oxygen.

An unusual property of iron makes oxygas cutting possible. The oxides of most metals have melting points very much higher than that of their metal. For example, if oxygas cutting of aluminum were attempted, the aluminum with a melting point of about 1000°F would convert to aluminum oxide with a melting point of about 3700°F. This oxide actually could not be melted by the flame and would remain in the cut. But the melting point of iron oxide is about the same as that of iron or steel; the oxide melts and flows out of the cut.

The cutting torch has three parallel tubes, two supplying preheat oxygen and fuel gas (usually acetylene) and the third supplying cutting oxygen to an orifice in the center of the cutting tip. The preheat flame surrounds the cutting oxygen. The size of the cutting tip must suit the thickness of steel to be cut.

A neutral preheat flame gives best results in cutting. To make a clean cut that does not require cleaning up on a grinding wheel is not easy and requires some practice. Oxygen pressure must be neither too low nor too high, and the preheat flame must not be too long. The correct tip size must be used. Finally, a steady hand is needed.

The steel being cut is heated to hardening temperatures, and the surrounding metal withdraws heat from the cut at such a rapid rate that a quenching effect is produced. The edge of the steel, therefore, is hardened. Even mild steel is hardened by the cutting process, to a Rockwell C of about 35. In addition to this hardening effect, the surface of the steel is oxidized, and iron oxide is an extremely hard material. If the flame-cut edge must be machined, a deep cut should be made on a husky machine tool such as a planer, so that the nose of the tool is not in contact with surface oxides. Removal of a flame-cut edge with high-speed steel milling cutters must not be attempted.

QUESTIONS

1. Why is polarity not important when one is using an AC welding machine?
2. Explain reverse polarity.
3. Explain the meaning of heat-affected zone.
4. Why does welding harden a hardenable steel?
5. Why do welding rods for steel contain very little carbon?
6. Why are 6010 and 6011 rods not recommended for welding hardenable steels?
7. Why is a thick plate more likely to harden than a thin plate in a fusion welding operation?
8. A mild steel plate containing 0.24 per cent carbon is butt-welded to a stainless plate of 0.08 per cent carbon, 20 per cent chromium, 10 per cent nickel. Assume that no welding rod metal is deposited in the welding seam, but that as much of one plate is melted as of the other plate. What is the analysis of the fusion zone? Is the fusion zone hardened by the welding operation?
9. What is a residual stress?
10. Estimate the required current for a $\frac{3}{32}$-in. rod.
11. A fillet weld was originally specified to have a leg of $\frac{1}{8}$ in. The specification is changed to a leg length of $\frac{1}{4}$ in. How much more metal must be deposited for the larger leg?
12. What is the difference between a 6010 and a 6011 rod?

13. Suggest a welding rod for the following applications:
    a. Butt welds, $\frac{1}{4}$-in. plate, horizontal welding.
    b. Fillet welds, $\frac{1}{4}$-in. plate, horizontal welding.
    c. Butt welds, 16-gage sheet.
14. What is the color of (a) oxygen hose; (b) acetylene hose?
15. Why is oxyacetylene cutting restricted to carbon and low-alloy steels?
16. Why is the flame-cut edge of a mild steel hard?
17. Explain why high conductivity for heat in a metal is desirable for turning and drilling, but a disadvantage when welding.
18. Someone has broken a 2-in. shaft of 0.4 per cent carbon steel, and wishes it to be repaired by welding. Why should this repair not be made?
19. "A weld is a casting surrounded by a heat treatment." Explain.
20. What is the difference between stress and strain?
21. Sketch the throat and leg dimensions of a fillet weld.
22. What causes arc blow?
23. What is the difference between a weave and a stringer bead?
24. Two plates are clamped at an angle of 90 deg to each other and joined by a fillet weld. After welding, will the angle be less or more than 90 deg?

Chapter 19

Toolmaking

Almost all production machines are general-purpose machines, capable of producing more than one product or component. A punch press can be used to blank out any shape within its capacity, or to punch holes of any size, to shear sheet, or to do shallow forming operations. The punch press, or any other production machine, must be adapted to make it suited to any specific product. The equipment that adapts a machine to the requirements of a specific product is called *tooling*. The subject of tooling, therefore, encompasses a very wide range of components, from universal tooling such as chucks, milling vises, and clamps, to perishable tooling such as drills, reamers, and lathe cutters, to punches, drilling jigs, welding jigs, extrusion dies, forging dies, injection molding dies, inspection templates, and inspection gages. The full scope of such an advanced and responsible trade as toolmaking cannot be presented in a short chapter on the subject. Here only certain basic concepts can be discussed.

19.1 BASIC TOOLMAKING CONCEPTS

1. *Materials*. Almost all types of materials are used for tooling purposes, especially in the aerospace industry. This industry has even used concrete and wood for tooling. There are special formulations of urethane rubber, silicone rubber, and thermosetting epoxy plastics for tooling purposes. The author once used a stretchable cloth painted with silicone rubber for a special tooling device in forming plastics.

Fig. 234 An ingenious use of a material. Caterpillar Tractor Co. inspects the contour of internal gear teeth with the use of Dow Corning Silastic RTV Silicone Rubber. The silicone rubber, when cast in place, accurately reproduces the tooth contour. The rubber molding is removed and inspected (instead of the gear tooth) by optical methods. (Courtesy of Dow Corning Corp.)

However, most tooling must be made of steel. Most tooling must either be very rigid, or weldable, or heat-treatable, or have high hardness, wear resistance, or heat resistance, and the steels in their many alloys can provide all these service requirements for tooling.

The tool steels are the alloys usually associated with toolmaking: high-speed steels for cutters, low-alloy steels for cold-working operations such as shearing and punching, high-alloy steels for hot forging dies, and medium carbon chromium steels for the dies that shape plastics.

The toolmaker, therefore, must have extensive knowledge and experience of materials in all their characteristics: machinability, deformation, heat-treating, resistance to heat and scaling, grindability, hardness, and other pertinent information for his trade.

2. *Rigidity*. Again, rigidity must be mentioned. Tooling must be as rigid as possible. If the tooling deforms, then so does the part being produced by the tooling, and accuracy is lost. Very heavy sections are common for tooling, much heavier than would be acceptable in the product made with the tooling.

3. *Accuracy*. The tooling must be constructed to standards of accuracy exceeding those allowed in the part. Inspection gages must be ten times more accurate than the part to be gaged. If the part must be accurate to 0.001 in., then the gage must be accurate to 0.0001 in.

   Any inaccuracy in the tooling will be reflected in the part. Suppose a hole location must be accurate within 0.005 in. If the drill jig has an inaccuracy of 0.003 in. in locating the part to be drilled, then only 0.002 in. remains for all the other sources of inaccuracy, of which there can be very many.

4. *Foolproofing*. The tooling should be so designed that the part cannot be inserted into the tooling the wrong way, such as upside down, or rotated 90 deg, or burr side up, etc. An example of foolproofing is shown in Fig.

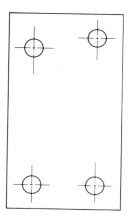

Fig. 235

235. Sometimes to ensure foolproofing of the part it may require a slight modification such as the provision of an extra drilled hole or a flat area.

5. *Safety*. All tooling must be designed with the operator's safety and comfort in mind. Sharp edges must be removed. Loading and unloading of the part must be made as easy as possible.

6. *Cost*. The most important consideration in tooling is its cost. Tooling for short production runs is often more difficult to design because it must be made at minimum cost, whereas a welding fixture for the manufacture of automobiles by the million may cost half a million dollars.

Suppose that a 1-in. hole must be punched in pieces of 11-gage ($\frac{1}{8}$ in. thick) mild steel. The cost of a simple punch and die for this purpose might be $200. Suppose the cost of steel sheet is 1¢, and labor and overhead are 2¢ per punched part. If there are, say, only 200 pieces to be punched, then the total cost becomes greatly inflated because the tooling cost must be written off against only 200 pieces:

Material	$0.01
Labor and overhead	0.02
Die charge	1.00
	$1.03

Generally, tooling can be designed and manufactured only if there is a large enough production run to justify these costs. In the circumstances of this example, clearly it is cheaper to drill and deburr 200 holes than to punch them, even though drilling is considered to be a very expensive manufacturing operation compared to punching. If, however, 2000 parts are to be punched, the die charge drops to $0.10, and punching becomes competitive with drilling. If 20,000 parts are to be punched, the die charge is only 1¢, and drilling becomes extremely expensive as compared to punching.

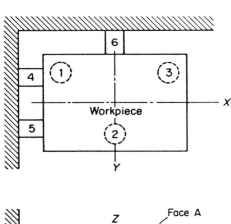

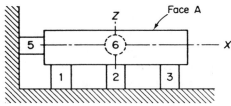

Fig. 236

19.2 BASIC FIXTURING CONCEPTS

To locate a body or part in three-dimensional space, six locating points are needed in a fixture.

Following Fig. 236, three pegs or rest buttons will locate the part in the horizontal plane. Two more are required in one vertical face of the fixture, and a final or sixth rest button is required in another vertical face at right angles to the first vertical face. These six locating points are the minimum number required; increasing the number contributes no further advantages to the design and increases the cost. The part lacks only a clamp to hold it in place. The clamping pressure should be applied to face *A*.

19.3 A HOLE-DRILLING PROBLEM

Occasionally, a seemingly innocent tooling problem can be difficult or even impossible. Suppose a designer calls for drilling the hole in the thin-walled tubing shown in Fig. 237, and some estimator decides that the job can be done on a jig borer for 50¢ a piece. In addition, some salesman guarantees the accuracy.

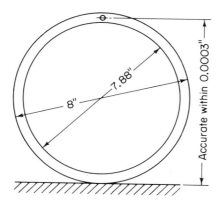

Fig. 237 A difficult fixturing problem for a drilling operation.

It is possible that this is an impossible job to do. No doubt an accurate jig borer can produce a drill jig to the accuracy required, or drill the hole itself to this accuracy. But if 0.0003 in. is to be satisfied, the deflection in the fixture, the deflection in the part, the deflection in the drill, the runout in the drill, and all other sources of error must not sum to more than 0.0003 in. If the tubing is clamped at opposite ends of a diameter, on release from the drilling jig the tube will relax and put the hole out of tolerance. Finger pressure alone could deform the tubing by more than 0.0003 in.

But let us suppose that all these machining problems are solved, and the hole location meets the allowable tolerance of 0.0003 in. After a few days, let us suppose that the hole location is checked again. It was within tolerance when inspected after drilling, but this second inspection is almost certain to show it out of tolerance. Why?

Because the presence of the hole will cause the thin-walled tube to stress-relieve and deform. The drilling operation has altered the state of residual stress in the tubing. If the tube has been cold-formed from flat sheet, it will certainly contain residual stresses. Since the tubing will almost certainly warp out of tolerance after it is delivered to the user, how can the accuracy specified be guaranteed?

By using a heavier wall for the tube, and turning the tube to size after drilling the hole?

By using a heavier wall for the tube and boring the tube to size after drilling?

By machining both I.D. and O.D. to size after drilling?

By centerless grinding a couple of thousandths off the tube diameter every week until the tube is dimensionally stable?

Is it possible that the tube will never be dimensionally stable due to the presence of a hole in a thin wall?

19.4 DRILLING JIGS

A drill jig is a tooling device to which a part may be clamped for a drilling operation, and which includes a means of guiding the drill to the correct location.

Figure 238 shows a sleeve that is fully machined except for the drilling and reaming of a 0.3125-in. hole. The drilling operation that precedes reaming must provide a drilled hole of $\frac{19}{64}$ in., the hole to be located with a tolerance

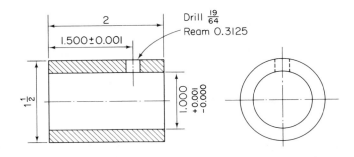

Fig. 238

range of 0.002 in. The sleeve is to be produced in lots of 300 four or five times each year.

The design of tooling such as a drill jig for this sleeve must provide the following components:

1. Locating stops, to locate the part correctly in position.
2. Clamping devices.
3. Work-supporting elements.
4. Devices to guide the cutter.
5. A frame to unite all these elements.

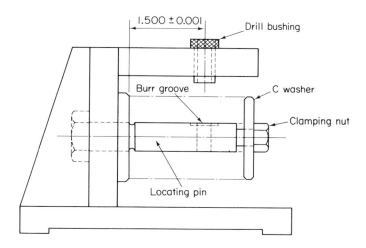

Fig. 239

A drilling jig for drilling and reaming this sleeve is illustrated in Fig. 239. The part is supported by its inside diameter by a pin ground to a suitable diameter. The rear end of the pin has a flange against which the sleeve is located. Clamping is arranged by a C washer and a nut on the end of the pin. To remove a sleeve and replace it with another for the operation, the nut is loosened sufficiently to allow the C washer to drop off. The nut is, of course, smaller than the bore of the sleeve.

The sleeve must be drilled, then reamed, and the drill jig must serve both operations. To guide both drill and reamer, a liner bushing is accurately located in the drilling jig plate. A slip bushing is inserted in the liner bushing for the drilling operation, this bushing having a bore of correct size to guide the drill. After all the holes are drilled, the drill bushing is removed and replaced with a slip bushing of the proper size to guide the reamer. Such bushings are further discussed in the following section.

The frame of this drill jig is welded. If the plates of the jig are too thin, welding will introduce distortion. The jig must not be made of material lighter than $\frac{3}{8}$-in. plate, and the minimum possible welding must be done, the arc being used rather than oxyacetylene.

When the drill completes the hole in the sleeve, a burr will be left at the bottom of the hole. To allow space for this burr, a flat should be milled or ground on the mounting pin at the region of the hole. A space must also be allowed between the sleeve and the drill bushing so that drilling chips can escape.

This drill jig has at least one deficiency: A certain degree of fumbling with the C washer and nut is necessary to load and unload the part. It is

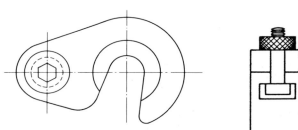

Fig. 240   **Fig. 241** Vee clamp drilling jig.

desirable to clamp and unclamp the part with a single quick movement of the clamping device.

A vee-clamp type of drill jig for drilling round rod is illustrated in Fig. 241. The jig plate can be equipped with both clamping screws and drill bushings.

Any drill jig or milling fixture should be identified with its tool number (say, T-3113) and the part number or part drawing number (say, 34709-D). The drill size should also be marked close to the drill bushing. Steel stamps or identifying plates may be used for such identification.

19.5 DRILL BUSHINGS

Drill bushings are hardened and precision-ground on both inside and outside diameter. The inside diameter of the drill bushing will be the nominal drill size plus a few tenths of a thousandth. The minimum inside diameter will be oversize about a half-thousandth per inch of drill diameter. A 1-in. drill bushing for a press fit has a minimum I.D. of 1.0004 in. and a maximum of 1.0007 in. Pressing the bushing into its hole will reduce the inside diameter slightly. Such bushings are made in several lengths, in a range roughly equal to drill diameter to twice drill diameter.

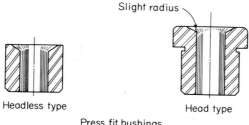

Slight radius

Headless type   Head type

Press fit bushings

Fig. 242

Press-fit bushings, Fig. 242, are available with or without a head. These bushings are pressed permanently into position. When worn, they must be pressed out again, which is an inconvenience. Therefore, this type is used only for low production volumes. The hole in the bushing is chamfered slightly to lead the drill easily into position.

Renewable bushings are made in two parts: the liner or outer sleeve, which is pressed into the jig plate, and the inner or slip bushing, which matches the drill diameter. Renewable bushings are especially useful if two operations requiring two diameters must be performed on the same hole, such as drilling and reaming. Two slip bushings of two different diameters are used for this purpose. This type of bushing must be clamped in place so that the drill will not rotate it or withdraw it (Fig. 243).

The spacing of jig plates from the workpiece requires consideration. See Fig. 244. If the jig plate is too close, chips will jam between the plate and the workpiece. Generally, the gap between jig plate and work should be approximately equal to the drill diameter. However, there are occasional

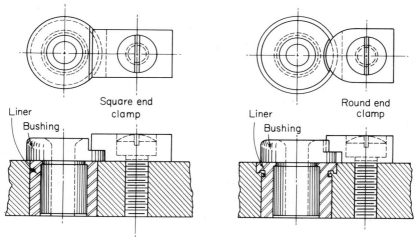

Liner   Square end   Liner   Round end
Bushing   clamp   Bushing   clamp

Fig. 243

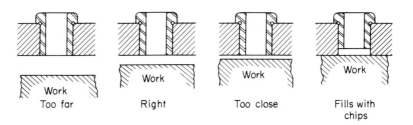

Too far   Right   Too close   Fills with chips

Fig. 244

materials which produce a continuous drill chip that does not break up. Such a chip will travel up the drill flutes, and for such a chip, chip clearance under the jig plate is not useful.

19.6 TOLERANCES

The system of interchangeable manufacture was invented by an American, Eli Whitney. Interchangeable manufacture means that the components of any assembly can be produced to so close a tolerance that they can be selected at random and assembled. Thus, if a bearing fails, you simply order another bearing of the same catalog number, knowing that it will fit its mating components as well as the bearing it replaced. Without interchangeable manufacture, you would have to hunt through a box of bearings to find one that would suit, or else manufacture the bearing, since every bearing would present a special case. Maintenance of modern equipment would be a nearly impossible undertaking without the invention of interchangeable manufacture.

Interchangeable manufacture is based on two principles: (1) a standard range of sizes; (2) standard tolerances. Thus standard sizes of pipe run 1, $1\frac{1}{4}$, $1\frac{1}{2}$, 2, 3, 4, and so on. These standard sizes are nominal sizes, and the produced parts approximate these sizes within limits of error. Thus a cold-rolled bar of steel $\frac{3}{4}$ in. nominal diameter will not be oversize, but may be as much as 0.002 in. undersize.

Suppose that 1000 hydraulic valve spools must be manufactured to fit interchangeably 1000 bored valve housings. Suppose also that for a close sliding fit between any spool mated with any housing, the clearance (on diameter) must be not less than 0.0005 in. This minimum difference in diameters between mating parts is termed *allowance*. A spool of 0.9995 in. in diameter will then mate properly with a housing bored to 1.0000 in.

However, neither part can be made to an exact dimension. There is no difficulty in centerless grinding the spools within a range of plus or minus 0.0005 in., and internal grinding of the housings can be done to this accuracy also without excessive cost. Suppose that a serviceable assembly could allow a maximum variation between the two diameters of 0.0015 in. The allowance or minimum was set at 0.0005 in.; therefore, the clearance between mating parts must always fall between 0.0005 and 0.0015 in. Both parts must be manufactured to some tolerance, that is, some maximum variation permitted in the dimension of a part. The sum of the two tolerances of the two parts must not exceed 0.001 in. Suppose a tolerance of 0.0005 in. is allowed on the two mating parts.

In order to tolerance the two components, we must settle on a basic dimension. Suppose this basic dimension to be a spool diameter of 1.0000 in. Then the basic dimension of the housing must be 1.0000+0.0005 or 1.0005 in., the sum of the spool diameter plus the allowance.

The spools must be ground to $1.0000 \begin{smallmatrix} +0.0000 \\ -0.0005 \end{smallmatrix}$, and the housings must be bored to $1.0005 \begin{smallmatrix} -0.0000 \\ +0.0005 \end{smallmatrix}$. See Fig. 245. The smallest clearance in 1000 parts produced to these tolerances will be given by a spool 1.0000+0.0000 mating with a bore 1.0005−0.0000, which is the allowance 0.0005 in. The largest clearance in 1000 parts produced to these tolerances will be given by a spool 1.0000−0.0005 mating with a bore 1.0005+0.0005, which is 0.0015 in.

In this example unilateral tolerancing was used; that is, the total tolerance was in one direction from the basic size. In a bilateral tolerance, the tolerance is specified in both directions, such as $1.500 \begin{smallmatrix} +0.001 \\ -0.002 \end{smallmatrix}$. The bilateral tolerance may be in equal or unequal amounts either way. Note that with unilateral tolerances, the tolerance is most conveniently given as plus for the hole and minus for the shaft.

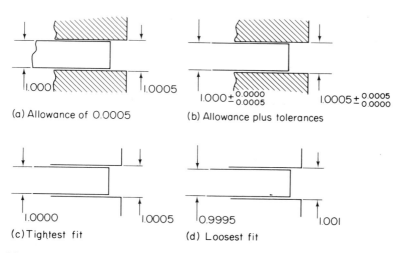

(a) Allowance of 0.0005

(b) Allowance plus tolerances

(c) Tightest fit

(d) Loosest fit

Fig. 245

19.7 CLASSES OF FITS

A designer can always play it safe by specifying very close tolerances, but this practice will often mean that components become too expensive to be used. It is clear that some components, such as fluid power valves, must have very close tolerances, but other components can safely use quite relaxed tolerances. Tolerances can be set based on the table of formulas for the standard fits given below. The results given by these formulas, however, are often modified by experience. For example, if the mating parts engage over a very considerable length, then the tolerances can be more generous. The following remarks explain the meaning of the classes of fits in the table.

Class 1.   *Loose fit.* Large allowance, where accuracy is not critical. Used in agricultural and mining machinery, and other machinery of similar grade.

Class 2.   *Free fit.* Liberal allowance, for running fits. Used with dynamos, engines, and a limited number of automotive parts.

Class 3.   *Medium fit.* Medium allowance. For running and sliding fits, accurate machine tool and automotive parts.

Class 4.   *Snug fit.* Zero allowance. This is the closest fit that can be assembled by hand. Used where no perceptible shake is permissible and where moving parts are not intended to move freely under load.

Class 5.   *Wringing fit.* Zero to negative allowance. The assembly is usually selective and not interchangeable.

Class 6.   *Tight fit.* Slight negative allowance. Light pressure is required for assembly and the parts are more or less permanently assembled. Used for drive fits and shrink fits on very light sections.

Class 7.   *Medium force fit.* Negative allowance. Pressure is required for assembly. Used for locomotive wheels on axles.

Class 8.   *Heavy force and shrink fit.* Considerable negative allowance. The fit causes heavy stress in the parts. The female part is heated, or the male part is cooled with dry ice, in order to make the assembly.

FORMULAS FOR FIT CLASSIFICATION

Class	Fit	Assembly	Allowance (Clearance)	Allowance (Interference)	Tolerance Hole	Tolerance Shaft
1	loose	interchangeable	$0.0025\sqrt[3]{D^2}$		$+.0025\sqrt[3]{D}$	$-.0025\sqrt[3]{D}$
2	free	interchangeable	$0.0014\sqrt[3]{D^2}$		$+.0013\sqrt[3]{D}$	$-.0013\sqrt[3]{D}$
3	medium	interchangeable	$0.0009\sqrt[3]{D^2}$		$+.0008\sqrt[3]{D}$	$-.0008\sqrt[3]{D}$
4	snug	interchangeable	0.0000		$+.0006\sqrt[3]{D}$	$-.0004\sqrt[3]{D}$
5	wringing	selective		0.0000	$+.0006\sqrt[3]{D}$	$+.0004\sqrt[3]{D}$
6	tight	selective		$0.0025D$	$+.0006\sqrt[3]{D}$	$+.0006\sqrt[3]{D}$
7	force	selective		$0.0005D$	$+.0006\sqrt[3]{D}$	$+.0006\sqrt[3]{D}$
8	shrink	selective		$0.001D$	$+.0006\sqrt[3]{D}$	$+.0006\sqrt[3]{D}$

19.8 A TOLERANCING EXAMPLE

The fit between the slots of a lathe chuck and the chuck jaws is critically important to the machinist. This makes a good example of tolerancing.

What are the conditions under which chuck jaws must perform? First, there must not be any slack or shake when the jaws are fitted; second, the jaws must be assembled into the chuck by hand without being pressed in; third, the jaws do not move except to grip or to release the part to be held. These conditions indicate a Class 4 fit. This fit has an allowance of zero.

Suppose the slots in the chuck are $\frac{3}{4}$ in. wide. Then the slot tolerance (hole tolerance) by formula is $+0.0006 \times 0.91$, or 0.0005 in. Jaw tolerance (shaft tolerance) is 0.0004×0.91, or 0.0004 in.

$$\text{Jaw} \quad 0.7500 \quad \begin{array}{l} +0.0000 \\ -0.0004 \end{array}$$

$$\text{Slot} \quad 0.7500 \quad \begin{array}{l} +0.0005 \\ -0.0000 \end{array}$$

The tightest fit gives a clearance of 0.0000. The poorest fit is 0.0009 in.

19.9 TOLERANCES AND SURFACE FINISH

Tolerances of tenths were required in the above example. A "tenth" is 100 millionths of an inch. It is clear that as tolerances become finer, the surface finish must be smoother, because surface irregularities then begin to approximate the size of the tolerance, and will influence the measurement. When tolerances go to "tenths," a ground finish will be required, since an ordinary machined surface can have irregularities as large as a "tenth."

The rule for surface roughness is that the surface roughness must be a tenth of the tolerance. The measurement of surface roughness is explained in the last chapter.

19.10 TOLERANCES FOR A DRILLING JIG

In Fig. 246 a part is shown, to be drilled at two locations with a #29 drill, with tolerances for the holes as indicated. The width of the part is ground to a variation of 0.001 in. Holes are to be jig-bored in a jig plate to hold drill bushings for the guidance of the #29 drill. The problem is to decide the tolerances allowed in drilling the jig plate.

The part is to be dropped into a nest or cavity that closely fits the part. The maximum width of the part is 1.1250 in. If the nest is given a width

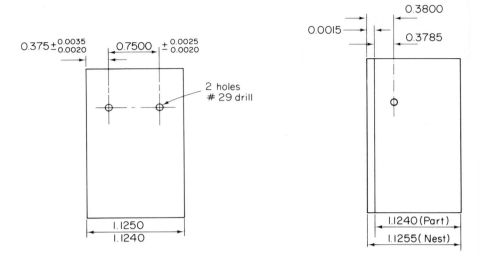

Fig. 246   **Fig. 247**

of 1.1250, the widest possible part will probably not seat in the nest. There-fore, a minimum nest width of 1.1255 is required to receive the part. This nest width must always be made as small as possible, because mismatch between the part and its receiving nest influences the error in drilling the holes.

Figure 247 shows the worst possible condition of the part in the nest. The narrowest possible part width is in the nest, against one side of the nest. The variation of 0.0015 in. between part and nest will be reflected in the location of the holes drilled in the part; that is, if the drilling of the jig plate is absolutely accurate, the hole locations could still be in error by the nest error of 0.0015 in.

Now suppose that the jig plate is bored with a bilateral tolerance of ±0.001 in. for the holes. The worst hole condition for the drilled part is given by the sum of maximum nest error (0.0015 in.) plus the maximum hole error (0.001 in.). These two errors total 0.0025 in. But one of the side toler-ances for the holes is only 0.0020 in. Therefore, a bilateral tolerance of 0.001 in. for jig-boring is not sufficiently accurate. The bilateral tolerance must be reduced to 0.0005 in., which is not difficult for a jig-boring operation. The maximum error in hole location is then

Maximum nest error + maximum hole error = 0.0015 + 0.0005 = 0.002 in.

This is the maximum error allowed.

There is no safety margin in this design, and this is not reassuring. If a thousand parts must be drilled, we can be sure that the nest will wear very slightly, though perhaps hardly noticeably, but certainly the drill bushing will wear by 0.0005 in. or more. When that happens, some hole will be drilled out of tolerance.

Probably there should be a relaxation of hole tolerance in the part to a bilateral ± 0.0025 in. if this is possible. If this is not possible, perhaps the width of the part could be ground to a variation of half or two-thirds of a thousandth.

19.11 THE JIG BORER

Many components of machines must be made to tolerance ranges of a few thousandths or less. To meet such tolerances, the tooling, such as drilling jigs, that is to produce the component must be produced to even closer tolerances, as in the example given above. A tolerance range of ± 0.0005 in.

Fig. 248 Pratt and Whitney numerically controlled jig boring machine in a boring operation.

or even finer is not unusual in tooling. The range of types of machine tools must, therefore, include machines capable of superior accuracy in drilling and milling; such machine tools are called jig borers.

The first manufacturer of jig borers is still famous in this field: The Societe Genevoise d'Instruments de Physique, of Geneva, Switzerland, more familiarly known as SIP. A large number of SIP jig borers are in use in North America, though excellent machines are, of course, manufactured on this continent by deVlieg, Pratt & Whitney, Moore, and others. Measuring accuracy of all these machines is in the range of 0.00005 to 0.0001 in.

It is not possible to make general remarks on the measuring systems of jig borers and their operation. Some machines use optical systems for accurate positioning. Those that position to ± 0.0001 in. generally use mechanical devices that may include dial indicators reading to 0.0001 or 0.00005 in., inside micrometers, end-measuring gages, and duplicating bars with lengths made to extreme accuracy. The use of leadscrews with micrometer graduations to move the worktable and to make the positioning measurement is usual on ordinary machine tools, but is unacceptable for a jig borer. For this machine tool the worktable is moved, and a separate measuring system must measure the movement.

19.12 JIG BORING METHODS

The ability of the jig borer and its operator to measure to 0.0001 in. does not guarantee such accuracy. Suppose that we first consider a mismanaged jig-boring operation. The jig plate of Fig. 249 is to be drilled with a 1-in. drill, starting with hole 1 and finishing with hole 4. An accuracy of 0.0001 in. in hole location is desired. The material is a steel of Rc 25, which is somewhat hard, and therefore some heat will be generated in the drilling operation.

The drill is accurately located over hole 1 with an accuracy of 0.00005 in. The hole is drilled and the spindle is next located over hole 2 with an accuracy of 0.00005 in.

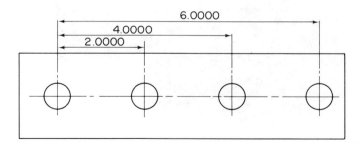

Fig. 249

However, the drilling operation on hole 1 has generated sufficient heat to raise the temperature of the workpiece an average of 10 deg, let us say. The coefficient of expansion of the steel workpiece is 0.0000065 in./in. length for every degree of temperature rise. Then the two-inch distance from hole 1 to hole 2 has grown in length by

$$2 \text{ in.} \times 10 \text{ deg} \times 0.0000065 = 0.00013 \text{ in.}$$

After the drilling operation, the jig plate will cool back to room temperature and in doing so, this accurately measured two-inch distance will shrink by 0.00013 in., reducing the measured 2.00000 ± 0.00005 by 0.00013, or 1.99987 ± 0.00005 in.

Similarly, if the drilling of hole 2 raises the temperature of the plate another 10 deg, for a total of 20 deg, the error introduced into the second two-inch measurement will be double the error of the first measurement, or 0.00026 in. Clearly, jig boring cannot be done without temperature control, both of the room in which the jig borer is located, and of the part being machined. The proper procedure is the following.

The four holes are first spot-drilled and drilled to the required accuracy, an undersize drill being used. The jig plate will then be allowed sufficient time to come back to room temperature. After cooling, the thermal errors mentioned will move the hole locations out of position. The four holes will then be bored to accurate size in multiple boring cuts. The boring operation removes the thermal errors. Sometimes the workpiece is spot-drilled on the jig-boring machine, drilled on an ordinary drilling machine, and then bored on the jig borer.

The tools used with a jig borer must be made to the same standards of precision as the jig borer itself. Standard shop tools such as drills and end mills cannot be interchanged between the jig borer and other machine tools. Such tools may not meet the standards required in jig boring, and in addition they meet with rougher usage and more damage in routine production operations than would be allowed for jig boring use. Drills for jig boring work must be short, and 0.015 to 0.020 in. below standard sizes to allow for the final boring operation.

For laying out work to be done on other machine tools, such as the scribing of center lines, a scribing punch can be inserted into the spindle of the jig borer.

Precision parallels, hardened and ground, are used between the machine table and the workpiece to provide clearance for drilling and boring through-holes.

Layout operations on a jig borer must, of course, start from a known point or a known edge. If the operator is to lay out from a given hole machined into the part in a previous operation, the hole must be carefully bored, with a smooth finish, and must not be out of round. Surfaces of the part used for layout must be flat, straight, square, and smooth. If layout work is to be done to ± 0.00005 in. (this is 50 millionths of an inch), then a ground surface will be necessary, since machining roughness can be 50 millionths or greater. Holes are picked up by precision center-finders equipped with precision dial indicators. Locating microscopes (Fig. 250) are inserted into the spindle to set the spindle axis over the edge of a part or the intersection of two datum lines. Proving bars are used to pick up a previously machined face, in conjunction with gage blocks or thickness gages where necessary.

The proving bar is simply a plain parallel cylinder of accurate diameter, usually 1.0000 in., ground in accurate alignment with its taper shank.

For accurate layout of holes around a pitch circle, accurate dividing tables are used to index the workpiece. Typically such tables are accurate to 5 seconds of arc.

Many, though not all, jig borers use sets of precision end-measuring rods for positioning. These end-measuring rods are made in different lengths

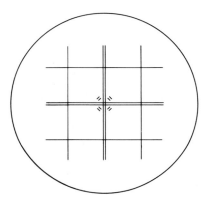

Fig. 250

with one-inch increments. An inside micrometer head with a vernier scale is used to complete the measurement. For the use of these end-measuring rods, there is a trough attached to the side of the machine table and parallel to the table. An adjustable stop is located at one end of each trough, and a precision dial indicator at the other end, fixed in position. A precise location is made by movement of the table until the stop pushes the end-measuring rod and micrometer head into the dial indicator until it reads zero. The micrometer head makes the fine measurement, not the dial indicator, which is used as a reference stop. Although it is the table which moves, it is convenient, as it is in numerical control programming, to think of the spindle as moving over the table. Measurements can be made direct or in a positive direction when the spindle moves toward the operator or to the right. For this reason, coordinate dimensions on drawings for jig-boring operations are laid out to read from left to right and from the top of the drawing to the bottom. If two reference surfaces of the workpiece are ground straight and perpendicular to each other, the intersecting point of these surfaces will be located toward the upper left-hand corner of the worktable or of the drawing as in Fig. 251.

Though tolerances are given with each coordinate on the drawing of the part to be jig bored, the operator always works to the limit of accuracy available to him.

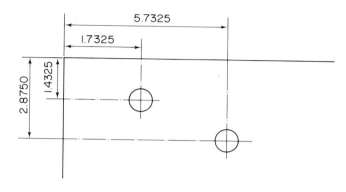

Fig. 251

Occasionally it is more economical to produce a batch of parts on the jig borer than to design and build an expensive drilling jig.

Since some jig plates must be accurately drilled and bored, and then hardened, the heat-treating operation can produce some distortion and consequent error in dimensions. The errors introduced by heat-treating distortion are removed by a jig grinder, the previous boring operation leaving sufficient material for the final jig-grinding operation.

19.13 MILLING FIXTURES

A milling fixture must locate and clamp the part, and present the part to the cutter free of obstructions. Since the depth of cut must be set up for a milling operation, the fixture should include a surface to establish this depth of cut. Cutter pressures can be high in a milling operation; therefore, the milling fixture should be substantially built and rigid.

The use of rest buttons and clamps for a milling fixture is illustrated in Fig. 252. The clamps are located directly over rest buttons to avoid

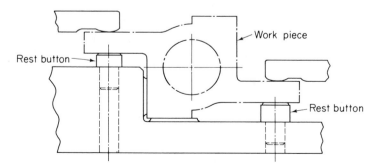

Fig. 252

springing the part. Cutter force is not resisted by clamping pressure, but by surfaces on the fixture itself against which the part bears.

Stops and locating pins of different design are illustrated in Fig. 253. The stops shown have rounded surfaces that can leave a mark in soft workpieces. This may require that a flat surface be ground on the stop. A dowel pin pressed into a plate makes a suitable stop pin, since it has an accurate and known diameter and is hardened against wear. An adjustable stop may be required when workpieces have some size variation.

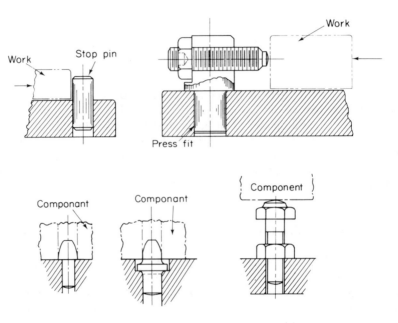

Fig. 253

Socket head cap screws are preferred for bolting together the frame of a fixture. If parts of the fixture must be closely aligned and located, then reamed dowel holes with dowels must be used for this purpose. Bolts are used to hold the parts together, but do not give accurate alignment.

The setting of the depth of cut for the cutter by the cut-and-try method is inconvenient and may spoil the first few pieces. The depth of cut is usually established by means of one or more *set blocks* (Fig. 254). These are hardened and ground blocks that are dowelled and bolted to the body of the fixture. The setting face of the set block, from which the cutter depth is gaged, is ground to final dimension after assembly. A feeler gage of flat stock is also ground, to be used with the set block. The feeler gage is needed so that the cutter will clear the set block when the part is milled. The feeler gage should be attached to the milling fixture by a wire to prevent loss.

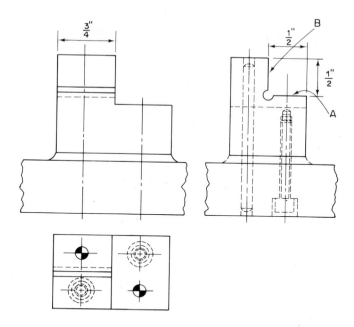

Fig. 254

    The set block of Fig. 254 has two ground surfaces for setting the cutter. Surface *A*, with its feeler gage, sets up the depth of cut. Surface *B*, with the same or a different feeler gage, is used to establish the correct position of the milling machine saddle for the milling cut across the part.

    Unless a fast clamping method is used, it is possible that as much time will be required to set up the workpiece in the fixture as to machine it. There are a great many types of clamps suitable to jig and fixture design. A sampling is shown in Fig. 255, some of them using a quick-clamping design. The quick-acting clamp assemblies can be bought much more cheaply from supply houses than they can be made.

QUESTIONS

1. Explain the meaning of foolproofing.
2. What advantages do rest buttons offer in jigs and fixtures?
3. Show or explain how six locating points will fix a part in three-dimensional space.
4. What circumstances call for the use of renewable drill bushings?
5. What is the meaning of "allowance" in tolerances?
6. Explain how a tolerance can be affected by surface finish.

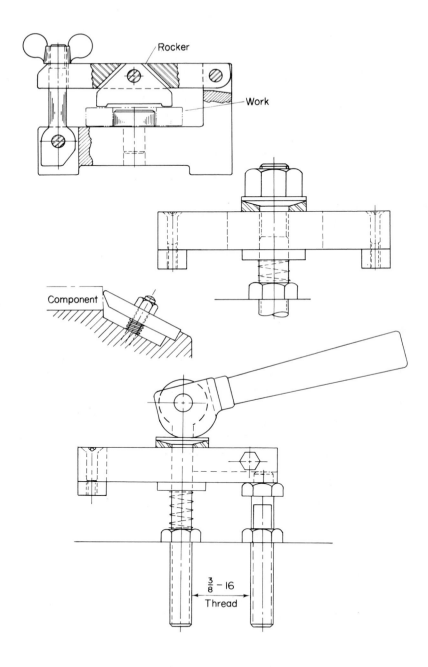

Fig. 255

7. Why is hole-boring necessary in an accurate layout of holes?

8. For the following cases, determine the allowance, the hole tolerance, the shaft tolerance, the allowable size range for the hole, and the allowable size range for the shaft:

   a. A rock crusher shaft rotating in bearings. Shaft nominal diameter 15.000 in. Note that precision fits are not used in heavy mining machinery.

   b. Seamless steel hydraulic tubing with essentially no tolerance variation on outside diameter. This tubing is to be shrunk into a steel manifold.

   c. A precision steel plunger pump. Plunger 0.732 in. diameter. Provide a reasonably tight sliding fit for axial movement. There is no rotation.

   d. Steel shaft, 1.000 in. nominal size, rotating in a sleeve bearing. Commercial quality only, no severe requirements.

9. Obtain two lengths of seamless hydraulic tubing 1 in. and 4 in. long in any inside diameter. Grind a plunger to fit inside this tubing:

   a. With zero allowance.

   b. With 0.0005-in. allowance.

   c. With 0.001-in. allowance.

   What is the largest plunger that you can fit to the 1-in. tube?

   What is the largest plunger that you can fit to the 4-in. tube?

10. The part shown in Fig. 256 requires to be milled as shown. Sketch an angle-plate type of milling fixture for the milling of this part. Include a cutter set block to gage depth of cut, using a feeler gage about 0.1 in. in thickness.

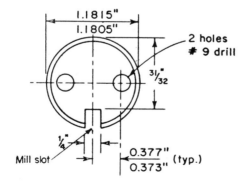

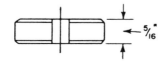

Fig. 256

11. Design a drilling jig for the drilling of the four holes in the part shown in Fig. 257. Will you hold the part in the jig in the position shown, or upside down?

12. Design a milling fixture to mill the slot in the hub of the part of Fig. 257. The milling operation follows drilling.

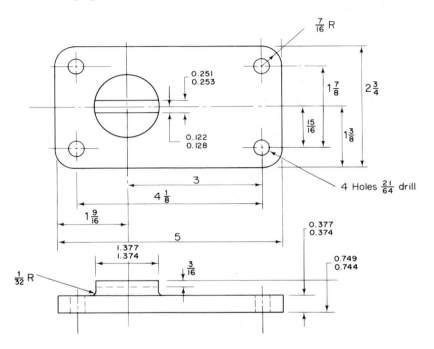

Fig. 257

Chapter 20

Power Transmission

Power must first be generated, then transmitted to the point of use by belts, or gears, or electric wires, or other means, then put to use by appropriate power-controlling and power-consuming devices such as electric motors or air cylinders. Power is generated in large quantities by central utilities in hydro, fuel-fired, and nuclear generating electric plants. Such power is distributed as high-voltage electrical power. Smaller amounts of power are produced by gasoline and diesel engines at the place where the power is consumed.

The cheapest and most efficient method of transmitting power is in the form of electrical power through transmission wiring. Consider that several decades ago coffee was made by boiling water on a wood-fired kitchen stove. Now we use an electric stove (or gas-fired stove). But if the electric utility supplying the stove and coffee pot generates electric power in a coal-burning electric-generating plant, note that the coffee is still produced by a fire, the difference being only that the fire is now located at the electric-generating plant instead of in the home.

Though electric power is conveniently and cheaply transmitted and controlled, perhaps most power is consumed as mechanical power in machinery such as machine tools. For the convenience of such machinery, mechanical methods of power transmission must be adopted. It is possible to couple the headstock spindle of a lathe directly to the shaft of an electric motor, but this is hardly desirable. Among many disadvantages, this direct connection prevents feeding of bar stock through the headstock spindle. The driving motor is, therefore, mounted off the spindle and its power is transmitted to the headstock spindle through a variety of mechanical power transmission devices, including gearing, belts, clutches, and brakes.

Every machinist must become involved in mechanical power transmission operations and the design and building of machines and components that consume and transmit power. This chapter is an introduction to the subject of mechanical power transmission. Some of the machining operations for certain of these power transmission components are also discussed.

20.1 FUNDAMENTAL POWER CONCEPTS

The following is a quick summary of the quantities used in power measurement.

1. *Force.* Force measures the interaction of any body on another body, the units of force being pounds. For example, an automobile may weigh 3500 lb. This is the vertical force exerted by the automobile against the pavement on which it rests. Similarly, the pavement exerts an upward force of 3500 lb against the automobile. A horizontal force of 100 lb pull may be required to tow the same car. This towing force is the force required to move the car on horizontal ground against all the friction forces in the automobile, including friction between the tires and the pavement.

2. *Pressure.* Pressure measures force in units of pounds per square inch of contact area. Thus if 60 sq in. of tire area come in contact with the pavement, then a 3500-lb car exerts a ground pressure of closely 60 lb per square inch (psi).

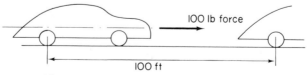

100 lb force

100 ft

(distance moved in the same direction as the force)

Fig. 258

3. *Work.* When a force moves a body a measured distance, work is done. Work is measured in foot-pounds (force times distance). Consider the automobile previously used as an example. It can be towed by a 100-lb force. If the car is towed 100 ft, then 10,000 ft-lb of work is done.

4. *Power.* Power measures the rate at which work is done. Clearly, it requires more power to move a vehicle at high speed than at low speed.

$$\text{Power} = \frac{\text{work}}{\text{time}} = \frac{\text{foot-pounds}}{\text{minutes}}$$

If the car previously referred to is moved 100 ft in 2 minutes, a towing force of 100 lb being used, then

$$\text{Power} = \frac{100 \text{ ft} \times 100 \text{ lb}}{2} = 5000 \text{ ft-lb per minute}$$

But if the engine of the same car propels it 100 feet in 1 second, then

$$\text{Power} = \frac{10,000}{1} = 10,000 \text{ ft-lb/sec} = 600,000 \text{ ft-lb per minute.}$$

Power is measured in many different (and confusing) units, including foot-pounds per minute or per second, in horsepower, in watts and kilowatts, and even Btu's (British thermal units). To convert from one power unit to another, the following conversion factors are needed:

$$
\begin{aligned}
1 \text{ horsepower} &= 33,000 \text{ ft-lb/min} \\
&= 550 \text{ ft-lb/sec} \\
&= 746 \text{ watts} \\
&= 0.746 \text{ kilowatts (KW)} \\
&= \tfrac{3}{4} \text{ KW closely} \\
1 \text{ HP-hour} &= 2544 \text{ Btu} \\
1 \text{ HP-minute} &= 42.4 \text{ Btu} \\
1 \text{ KW-hour} &= 3412 \text{ Btu} \\
1 \text{ KW-min} &= \text{about } 60 \text{ Btu} \\
1 \text{ Btu} &= 778 \text{ ft-lb of work}
\end{aligned}
$$

The Btu is defined as the energy or work required to heat 1 pound of water 1°F.

Referring again to the 3500-lb automobile, suppose its engine propels it at 100 feet per second. Then the power output

$$= \frac{10,000 \text{ ft-lb/sec}}{550} = 18 \text{ HP}$$

If this seems a surprisingly small horsepower compared to the engine horsepower installed in the car, consider that the engine needs horsepower additional to this to drive its auxiliary equipment such as the fan, fuel pump, air conditioner, etc., and also that additional horsepower is required to accelerate an automobile.

Power that is lost through friction and other inefficiencies is dissipated as heat. These losses are substantial, as disclosed in the two examples next.

Example 1. As an example of the great confusion in the use of power units, consider the case of a fractional horsepower electric motor. The power into the motor is measured in kilowatts; the power taken out of the motor through its shaft as mechanical power is measured in horsepower;

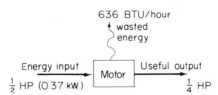

Fig. 259

the power wasted through inefficiencies is measured in Btu's of heat, which raises the temperature of the motor. If the motor is rated at ¼ HP, this is its mechanical output. If in an hour of continuous operation this motor develops 636 Btu's of heat, what is its electrical power input in kilowatts?

Select the hour as the most convenient unit of time.

Power into the motor = useful output power + wasted power

$$= \tfrac{1}{4} \text{ HP} + 636 \text{ Btu}$$

But 636 Btu = ¼ HP-hour, since 1 HP-hour is 2544 Btu. The total power into the motor is ½ HP, which is 0.37 KW.

The motor is 50 per cent efficient.

Example 2. The 3500-lb automobile previously discussed gives 18 miles to the gallon of gasoline. If each gallon of gasoline contains 150,000 Btu's of heat energy, what is the apparent efficiency of this automobile?

It requires a 100-lb force to move this car, and 100 ft-lb of work (energy) to move it 1 ft. But 1 Btu = 778 ft-lb. Then 1 Btu of energy will move this car 7.78 ft.

But 1 gallon of gasoline contains 150,000 Btu's. Therefore, 1 gallon will move the car $150{,}000 \times 7.78$ feet, which is 1,165,000 ft or 220 miles, if the car were an ideal car.

The actual mileage per gallon is 18; therefore, the apparent efficiency of the car as a vehicle is $\frac{18}{220}$, or 8.2 per cent. This is an unusually high efficiency for an automobile.

If only 8.2 per cent of the input energy to the motor appears as useful work in moving the automobile, then 91.8 per cent of the energy in the gasoline is wasted. The wasted energy due to friction and other causes is turned into heat. In the case of the fractional horsepower electric motor, 50 per cent of the input power was turned into heat in the windings. Very little of the input energy is consumed as frictional heat in bearings, etc. In the case of the automobile, too, friction effects account for only a small fraction of the energy losses. The automobile is a better heater than a vehicle; about three-quarters of the energy in the gasoline fuel is used to heat the water in the car radiator and the air taken into the engine by the carburetor and discharged to the exhaust. Clearly, there are good reasons why internal combustion engines are not used to drive machine tools.

Larger machines show better efficiencies. A multihorsepower electric motor may have an efficiency exceeding 80 per cent. Small lathes with a driving motor of about 1 HP show efficiencies of 50 per cent or less, which means that about $\frac{1}{2}$ HP is consumed in friction effects within the lathe mechanism.

If there is difficulty understanding that friction means a power loss

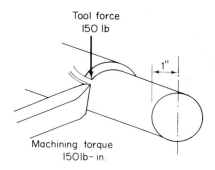

Tool force
150 lb

1"

Machining torque
150lb- in.

Fig. 260

through heat, consider a familiar example: the heating and softening of a dead center on a lathe. This accident can happen only when there is excessive friction at the dead center.

5. *Torque.* Torque is a twisting or turning effort around a shaft tending to cause rotation. Torque from a crescent wrench is an example. Torque is measured in pound-feet or pound-inches, the product of the applied force times the leverage distance of the force. See Fig. 260.

20.2 ELECTRIC MOTORS

The electric motor is the most popular of all prime movers in the power transmission field. Compared to internal combustion engines, electric motors are smaller, cheaper, and considerably more efficient.

Direct-current motors are readily adaptable for speed control, whereas the alternating-current motor is basically a constant-speed motor. Speed variation for machine tools is arranged through gearing or belt drives while the motor turns at a fixed rpm.

The basic rpm of an AC motor is determined by the frequency of the alternating current supplied to it. The standard frequency in North America is 60 Hertz (cycles) per second. The theoretical speed, or synchronous speed, of an AC motor is given by the relationship

$$\text{Synchronous rpm} = \frac{120 \times \text{frequency}}{\text{no. of poles}}$$

Motor poles are always in pairs: 2, 4, 6, 8, etc. Therefore, with 60-cycle electricity, a two-pole motor has the fastest possible synchronous speed, 3600 rpm. The four-pole motor is more common, because it has a more convenient synchronous speed of 1800 rpm.

Only synchronous motors rotate at these synchronous speeds. The motors that the machinist meets will almost always be AC squirrel cage induction motors, so-called because the rotor has the general appearance of a squirrel cage. Induction motors under their rated load or horsepower will "slip" or lose about 4 per cent of their synchronous speed. If the synchronous speed is 1800 rpm, then 4 per cent of 1800 rpm is 72 rpm, and the speed given on the motor nameplate will be 1725 rpm.

Poles	Synchronous speed	Induction motor speed
2	3600	3425
4	1800	1725
6	1200	1140

Slow-speed motors of many poles are less common, because they are larger and more expensive. Speed reduction by gears, chain, or belts is cheaper.

Any shaft must be rotated at some required rpm. In addition, the motor must supply sufficient torque to rotate the load.

$$HP = \frac{torque \times rpm}{63,000}$$

If the gearing between motor and load reduces the speed to, let us say, one-sixth, then the torque at the slower speed is increased by a factor of 6, if we ignore small inefficiencies in the power transmission that absorb a small fraction of the horsepower. The extra torque at the lower speed will require a heavier shaft.

Two torque requirements are imposed on the motor by its load: a starting torque and a running torque. Some loads have a high inertia and are difficult to accelerate up to speed, such as an air compressor. Other loads may be easy to start but may have a high running torque, such as an engine lathe. An engine lathe can be brought up to speed readily by the motor; the high running torque from the cutting tool is loaded on to the motor after the load is up to speed. Three different torque ratings are provided in the specifications for any electric motor:

1. Full load torque. The torque developed at rated horsepower and speed.
2. Breakdown torque. The maximum torque developed without stalling the motor. This is higher than full load torque.
3. Locked-rotor torque. The maximum torque developed with the motor stalled.

The type of motor enclosure must be specified when one is buying a motor. The type of enclosure influences the cost. Of the many types of enclosures, the following are the more usual ones:

Open enclosures	*Totally enclosed*
drip-proof	fan-cooled
splash-proof	nonventilated
semi-guarded	explosion-proof
externally vented	
weather-protected	

For clean ventilated locations the drip-proof motor is preferred, since it is less expensive. The totally enclosed fan-cooled (TEFC) motor is protected from the surrounding atmosphere. Explosion-proof motors are required by regulation in hazardous locations where sparking could ignite combustible gases or explosive dusts. The enclosed types of motors are usually equipped with ball bearings.

20.3 SHAFTS

Shafts are usually made of cold-finished or centerless ground bar: 1020 alloy for light-duty shafting, 8620 for carburized shafts, or 1040 for induction-hardened and ground shafting. Hollow bar is sometimes used.

Shafts must carry both bending loads and torque loads from gears, pulleys, sprockets, flywheels, and other power transmission devices. If the shaft is subject to heavy loadings of these kinds, shoulders cut into the shaft must be designed with care. Sharp corners such as that of Fig. 261 must not

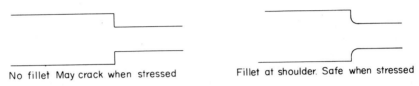

No fillet May crack when stressed   Fillet at shoulder. Safe when stressed

Fig. 261

be used; instead, a smooth fillet is necessary at the corner to prevent fracture of the shaft due to stress concentration arising from a sharp change of cross section.

Misalignment of bearings will cause bending stresses in the shaft and will reduce the life of the bearings. The surface of the shaft must be smooth in order to receive the bearings that support it. If the shaft must slide in and out, it must be wear-resistant. Wear resistance is obtained by giving the surface of the shaft a hardness of about Rc 55; for more severe conditions, the shaft is plated with hard chromium.

Gears, clutch plates, and other components are secured to shafts by a variety of methods, including keys and splines. Keys and keyways were discussed in an earlier chapter. Splines are machined into mating components for the same purpose as a keyway, but are superior to a keyway in that they are a less severe stress concentration and do not weaken the shaft or its mating part excessively.

Square splines are in use, but splines with an involute profile are superior. The involute spline transmits more torque for its size than any other type of spline, has a high strength at its root, is self-centering, and can be cut and inspected on the same types of machines that cut and measure involute gear teeth. The involute curve is described later in this chapter in connection with gears.

The common involute splines are shown in Fig. 262.

The 20-, 25-, and 30-deg pressure angles are usually selected, with a

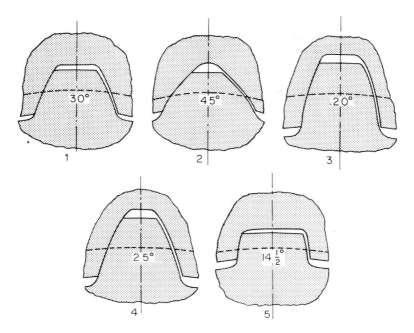

Fig. 262

depth of spline about 75 per cent of the full depth of a gear tooth of the same pitch. The 45-deg design is used for fine-pitch involute serrations up to about 10 pitch.

Internal splines are broached. The fit of mating splines is easiest to control if the mating is to the outside of the external spline. For press fits an interference of half a thousandth to two thousandths of an inch is used. An even number of spline teeth are cut.

Handbooks must be consulted for formulas for addendum, dedendum, and other dimensions for splines.

20.4 COUPLINGS

Couplings are used to connect shafts end to end. The typical case is the direct coupling of an electric motor shaft to the shaft of a pump or other device.

If there is no possibility of misalignment between the shafts to be coupled, a rigid coupling can be used. The usual rigid coupling consists of a flange on each shaft, with the flanges bolted together.

Flexible couplings are preferred to rigid couplings. It is usually impossible to obtain perfect alignment between two coupled shafts. It is

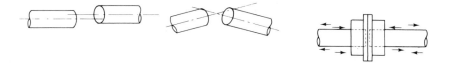

Fig. 263

possible to obtain good alignment when one is installing a shaft, but under operating conditions one shaft may go into misalignment because of bending or other loads from drive chains or other devices. There are three possible types of misalignment: shown in Fig. 263: parallel, angular, and end float. In the case of end float, the shafts tend to pull away from each other.

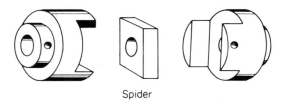

Spider

Fig. 264

The many types of flexible couplings cannot be discussed here. Hubs with projecting jaws may mate with an insert (Fig. 264). The chain and sprocket coupling of Fig. 265 is an economical choice. A sprocket is mounted on the end of each shaft, and the sprockets are coupled by a double-width strand of roller chain. The loose fit of sprocket and chain allows for misalignment. Still other types use a rubber connection between the shafts. The familiar universal joint must be used for severe misalignment.

Brakes are required for the rapid stopping of a rotating shaft. A clutch is a device for connecting and disconnecting one shaft from another, especially a prime mover such as a motor from its load. Both clutches and

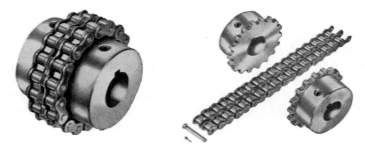

Fig. 265 Chain coupling.

brakes are made in a variety of designs, usually mechanical or electric, though some types use an air or oil system.

20.5 BEARINGS

The purpose of a bearing is the provision of support and freedom of rotation to a shaft. The selection of a suitable bearing requires knowledge of the load to be supported by the bearing, the rpm, operating conditions such as grit and temperature, and misalignment or flexibility in the shaft to be supported. There are two broad classes of bearings:

>   plain or sleeve bearings (journal bearings)
>   ball and roller bearings (antifriction bearings)

In a sleeve bearing, an oil film separates the bearing from the shaft. In the antifriction ball and roller bearings, balls or rollers separate the two components. Sliding is characteristic of the sleeve bearing, and rolling motion is characteristic of the antifriction bearing.

Sleeve Bearings. Sintered bronze, graphite-lubricated, and nylon bearings are self-lubricating.

Bearings mounted in housings of a shape suitable for bolting in place are called *pillow blocks* (Fig. 266).

Press-fit bearings are pressed into a reamed hole; for bronze press-fit bushings the amount of interference in the press fit should be from 0.001 in. to 0.002 in. per inch of outside diameter. For aluminum and bronze bushings, shaft clearance should be a minimum of 0.001 in. per inch of shaft diameter

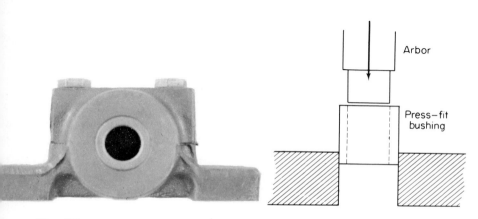

Fig. 266   **Fig. 267**

and a maximum of 0.003 in. per inch. The outside diameter of the bushing should be at least 25 per cent larger than shaft diameter, and the bearing length should be at least equal to shaft diameter.

Press-fit bushings should be pressed with a shouldered arbor, as illustrated in Fig. 267. The arbor diameter should allow for the one or two thousandths that the bearing will close in after pressing.

The heavier the load on the bearing, the harder must the bearing material be. Teflon and nylon can carry only light loads at speeds below 1000 rpm. Sintered bronze will sustain heavy loads at speeds up to 1500 rpm.

Ball and Roller Bearings. Ball bearings have one or two rows of hardened steel balls (Rc 62) positioned between raceways. The balls are usually supported in a separator between the outer and the inner ring. Roller bearings use the same general construction with cylindrical or conical rollers instead of spherical balls. Both ball and roller bearings have very low starting friction, and are self-aligning. Ball bearings are used for light or moderate loads and roller bearings for heavy or impact loads. The ball has a contact area not greatly larger than a point, while the roller makes contact along a line. The smaller contact area for a ball means that contact pressures must be exceedingly high; such pressures are considerably lower for rollers.

Once each revolution, each ball receives a high contact stress of the order of hundreds of thousands of psi. A million revolutions imposes this unusually high contact stress a million times. The bearing fails ultimately because of fatigue in the contact surface of the ball or roller. Harder materials have longer fatigue life—hence the necessity for a very hard ball or roller.

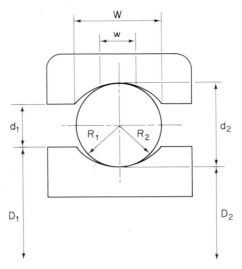

Fig. 268

The minimum life or "B-10" life of such a bearing is defined as the number of revolutions that will be reached or exceeded before fatigue failure by 90 per cent of a group of identical bearings operating under identical conditions. The average life to failure, that is, the life required for 50 per cent of a group to fail, is about five times the B-10 life.

Some type of seal is necessary to prevent entry of dirt into the bearing and to retain the lubricant. Antifriction bearings, like sleeve bearings, require a lubricant. Grease-lubricated bearings are pregreased during manufacture and are usually capable of being relubricated. Oil lubrication is used for high-speed and high-temperature bearings.

The bearing should have a snug fit on the shaft, and should be pressed up against a shaft shoulder. A smooth finish is required on the shaft. When one is pressing the bearing into the housing or onto the shaft, no force should be transmitted through the balls or rollers.

Most ball and roller bearing designs involve some sliding, and therefore are not fully rolling bearings. This is explained for a ball bearing by Fig. 268. The surface speed of a point near the outside diameter of the inner race is $\pi D_1 \times$ rpm. The speed at the bottom of the groove in this race is less, because the diameter D_2 is less. In the case of the ball, the maximum surface speed is the ball rpm $\times \pi d_2$, but at a point at d_1, the diameter is less and the surface speed is lower. Thus a slower part of the ball is in contact with the fastest moving part of the race, and therefore there must be sliding. The manufacturer makes the groove in the race with a radius slightly greater than the ball radius; this partially prevents slippage between them. Hence the roll path is a narrow path of width w instead of the full groove width W. Sliding friction and wear are slight if the bearing is lightly loaded, but become more severe under heavy loads. If there is end thrust on the ball bearing, there is a displacement of races and ball as shown in Fig. 269, because the grooves have a larger curvature than the balls. Under this condition of end thrust, sliding wear is more severe.

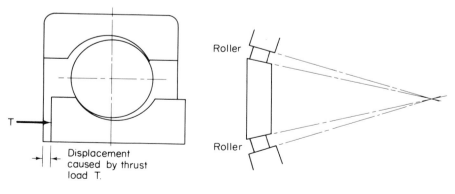

T →

Displacement
caused by thrust
load T.

Roller

Roller

Fig. 269   **Fig. 270**

Similar conditions of sliding will occur in some designs of roller bearings. One design of bearing that provides true rolling motion without sliding is the Timken bearing of Fig. 270. The surfaces are all conical surfaces, and each component rolls on the other. This bearing can carry considerable end thrust without harm.

20.6 V-BELT DRIVES

The V-belt drive is the least expensive type of power transmission between parallel shafts. It develops great pulling power because the shape of the V-belt causes it to wedge in the sheaves of the pulley, and it needs only moderate tension. The belt is made of a core of cords or a single cord to carry the tension force in the belt; the rest of the belt is made of fabric and rubber. A single-ply belt has a single layer of cords; multiple-ply belts use several layers of cords.

V-belt sizes are standardized for all manufacturers. Figure 271 shows the five standard sizes for industrial V-belt cross sections. The included angle of the belt is 40 deg for all cross sections. A C section belt will be $\frac{7}{8}$ in. wide and $\frac{9}{16}$ in. deep, regardless of the brand name. Each belt size requires its mating sheave; a C section belt will wedge properly only in a C section sheave.

A V-belt has three possible lengths: an outside length, an inside length, and a pitch length (length at the pitch line). The pitch length cannot be measured with a tape as can the others. Manufacturers' catalogs supply

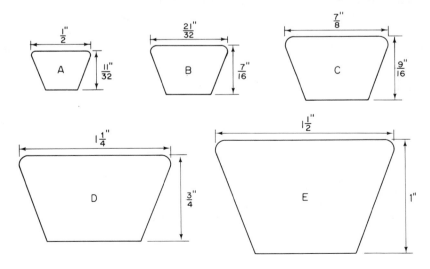

Fig. 271

tables giving inside, outside, and pitch lengths for V-belts. A C105 belt has a C section and is a nominal 105 in. long.

In addition to the industrial sizes of V belts, narrow V-belts are made in three sections: 3V, 5V, and 8V, shown in Fig. 272. The 3V size is $\frac{3}{8}$ in. wide, 5V is $\frac{5}{8}$ in. wide, and 8V is 1 in. wide. Such belts require matching sheaves, 3V, 5V, or 8V. A 5V1050 belt signifies a 5V narrow belt 105 in. long. Note that the length designation for narrow belts is in tenths of an inch.

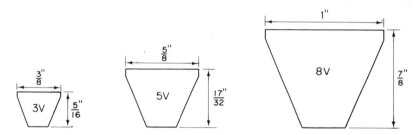

Fig. 272

Fractional horsepower V-belts, usually called FHP belts, are a third type. These are designated either 3L, 4L, or 5L, and are $\frac{3}{8}$ in., $\frac{4}{8}$ in., and $\frac{5}{8}$ in. wide, respectively. The "L" designates FHP or light duty. The length designation follows again in tenths of an inch; thus 4L380 is a 4L section 38 in. long.

20.7 CHAIN DRIVES

Power chains are produced in many types, especially for conveyors, but for chain drives only roller chain is employed, usually with offset sidebars (Fig. 273). The chain pin is press-fitted and riveted to one of the sidebars and connected by a fastener to the other sidebar.

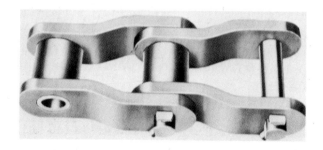

Fig. 273

Power chain must articulate over the sprocket wheels. Because of articulation, there is wear between pins and bushings, and as a result, the chain elongates with use. The chain elongation can be continued until the chain no longer matches the pitch of the sprockets. The sprockets are designed to accept from 3 to 6 per cent chain elongation. See Fig. 274. Elongation will be influenced by chain tension and by sprocket size. Larger sprockets will reduce wear, since the chain does not flex through a large angle when travelling over a large sprocket.

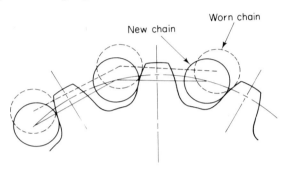

Fig. 274

When one is mounting drive chain on the sprockets, the narrow end of the offset links on the tight side (tension side) of the chain should face the smaller sprocket (Fig. 275). The reason for this arrangement is that it produces the least wear in the chain.

A minimum arc of contact with the sprocket of 135 deg is necessary, or a minimum of three sprocket teeth on the smaller sprocket must be in contact with the chain.

The chain length that is required for the drive must be determined as the number of pitches of chain, which is the number of links. The number of pitches can be calculated by formula if a table of correction factors is available. Such information is available from manufacturers' catalogs.

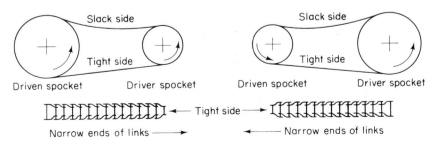

Fig. 275

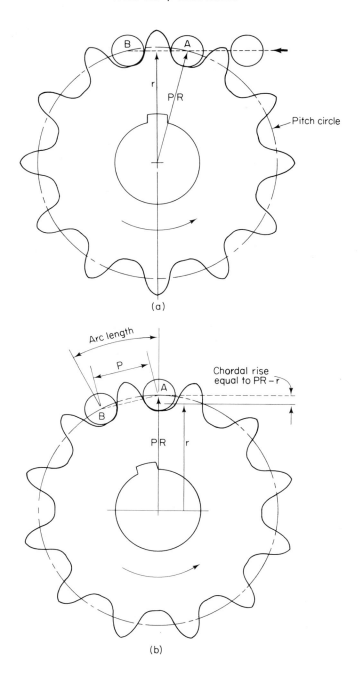

(a)

(b)

Fig. 276

The standard numbering system for drive chain is the following:

Number of chain	Pitch (in.)
25	$\frac{1}{4}$
35	$\frac{3}{8}$
40	$\frac{1}{2}$
50	$\frac{5}{8}$
60	$\frac{3}{4}$
80	1
100	$1\frac{1}{4}$
120	$1\frac{1}{2}$
etc.	

The pitch of the sprocket must match the pitch of the chain.

Chain drives have a special characteristic called *chordal action*. This is the radial motion of the chain on the sprocket that results when the straight segment of chain tries to follow the circular pitch line of the sprocket. In Fig. 276(a) the roller chain link with roller A entering the sprocket is not tangent to the pitch circle of the sprocket, but below it. As this link moves to the next position B, it will be lifted to the pitch line and then dropped below it again. The rise and fall due to chordal action is equal to PR-R, as shown in the figure. If the sprocket is a driven sprocket, the chain will drive it with a fluctuating speed, faster when the roller is elevated and more slowly in the dropped position. These speed variations will be quite pronounced for fewer than 10 teeth in the sprocket, but decrease as the number of teeth increase. For a 15-tooth sprocket the speed variation is only 2 per cent.

20.8 GEARING

Some aspects of gearing were presented in Chapter 12. This chapter must carry these concepts further.

Gears are wheels with cam-shaped teeth for transmitting rotary motion from one shaft to another. Four general types of gears are in use:

1. Spur gears.
2. Helical gears.
3. Bevel gears.
4. Worm gears.

Spur gears have teeth parallel to the axis of the shaft. The driving and the driven shaft must be parallel to each other. Helical gears, like spur gears, are cut from a cylindrical gear blank, but the teeth are at some helix angle to the shaft. Helical gears may substitute for spur gears in a parallel-shaft drive, but are equally suitable for shafts at 90 deg or any intermediate angle.

A rack, Fig. 277, which is a toothed straight bar, will have teeth of straight sides if it is to mesh with gears of the usual involute tooth profile. A rack and pinion will produce rotary motion from linear motion or linear motion from rotary motion.

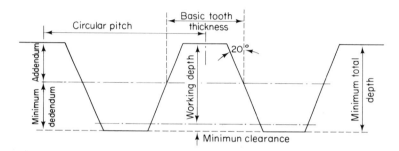

Fig. 277

The blank for a bevel gear (Fig. 278) is a truncated cone. Since the teeth must be cut into the conical surface, they must become narrower nearer the apex of the cone. Most bevel gear drives have shafts at angles of 90 deg to each other.

A worm is a kind of helical gear, but does not serve the same purpose. It has a worm or thread with a gear-tooth cross section for driving a mating gear at an angle of 90 deg.

If a pair of meshing spur gears were replaced by two cylindrical drums driving each other by friction and preserving the same speed ratio of the gears they replace, the drums would have diameters equal to the pitch

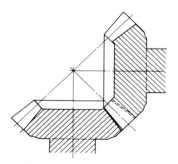

Fig. 278

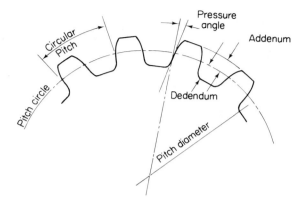

Fig. 279

diameters of the gears. The *pitch diameter* of a gear, worm, or rack, is, therefore, the effective diameter or base diameter of the gear. The *addendum* is the radial height of the gear tooth measured from the pitch circle to the end of the tooth. Similarly, the *dedendum* is the radial distance from the pitch circle to the bottom of the tooth space.

The helix angle of a helical gear was defined in Chapter 12.

When two gears mesh, they roll on each other at the pitch circle, but slide when contact between them is made elsewhere on the tooth face.

20.9 THE INVOLUTE TOOTH FORM

Although there are a few other tooth shapes in less frequent use such as the cycloidal tooth, almost all gear teeth conform to an involute curve. This is the curve traced by the end of a cord as it is unwound from the circumference of a circle. See Fig. 280. The size of the base circle off which the involute tooth curve is drawn is given by

Base circle diameter = pitch diameter × cosine of pressure angle

The pressure angle is usually 20 deg.

To draw an involute curve, divide the circumference of the base circle into equal divisions, marked *A*, *B*, *C*, etc., in the figure. At each point *A*, *B*, *C*, draw a tangent to the circle. Make the tangent *Bb* at *B* equal to the arc *AB*; make the tangent *Cc* at *C* equal to the arc *AC* or 2*AB*; make the tangent *Dd* at *D* equal to arc *AD* or 3*AB*, and so on. The ends of the tangents are points on the involute curve.

Figure 281 shows an involute gear tooth enlarged. The angle of engagement with the mating gear at the pitch diameter is indicated in the

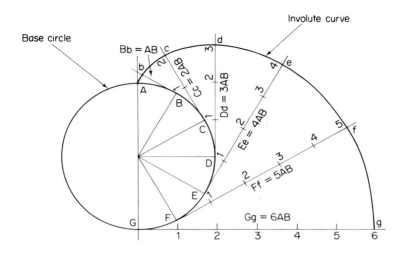

Fig. 280

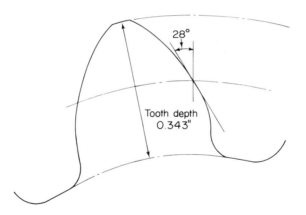

Fig. 281

figure as 28 deg. This is the *pressure angle* of the gear. Twenty degrees is the usual pressure angle for power transmission gearing, though $14\frac{1}{2}$ deg is also in use; 25 or 28 deg is often the choice for the gears in gear pumps. This larger pressure angle increases the volume of the tooth space and thus increases the pumping capacity of the gear. In the case of worms, a $14\frac{1}{2}$ deg pressure angle is recommended for single and double thread worms, and 20 deg for triple and quadruple.

The word "pitch" as applied to gearing refers to *diametral pitch*, the ratio of the number of teeth of the gear to the pitch diameter, expressed as a whole number. Thus if a gear has 44 teeth, with a pitch diameter of 11 in., the diametral pitch

$$DP = \frac{N}{D} = \frac{44}{11} = 4$$

Diametral pitch is also a measure of the size of the gear teeth. If the pitch diameter remains constant, but fewer and therefore larger teeth are used, the diametral pitch is a smaller number. Relative sizes of some diametral pitches are shown in Fig. 282.

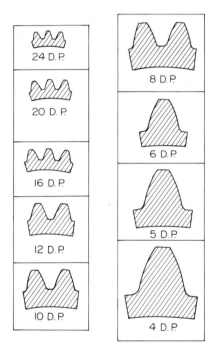

Fig. 282

Circular pitch is the distance in inches from a point on one tooth to the corresponding point on the next tooth, measured along the pitch circle. Circular pitch is a measurement in inches; diametral pitch is a number, not a measurement.

In the case of a bevel gear, the circular pitch would decrease from the large side to the small side of the gear. In this case circular pitch refers to the large end of the tapered tooth. Similarly, addendum and dedendum of a bevel gear are measured at the large end.

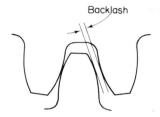

Backlash

Fig. 283

To prevent interference of mating gears, a certain amount of backlash must be allowed between them. This backlash, or clearance, is measured on the pitch circle, as shown in Fig. 283. Backlash is obtained by cutting the tooth spaces slightly deeper than standard to make the teeth thinner than the theoretical standard thickness.

For two spur gears to mesh, two conditions must be satisfied:

1. The two gears must have the same diametral pitch.
2. The two gears must have the same pressure angle.

The following table gives dimensions of standard full-depth teeth in diametral pitches from 3 to 20.

Diametral pitch	Circular pitch	Arc thickness of tooth (pitch line)	Addendum	Dedendum	Whole depth of tooth
3	1.0472	0.5236	0.3333	0.3857	0.7190
4	0.7854	0.3927	0.2500	0.2893	0.5393
5	0.6283	0.3142	0.2000	0.2314	0.4314
6	0.5236	0.2618	0.1666	0.1928	0.3595
8	0.3927	0.1963	0.1250	0.1446	0.2696
10	0.3142	0.1571	0.1000	0.1157	0.2157
12	0.2618	0.1309	0.0833	0.0964	0.1798
16	0.1963	0.0982	0.0625	0.0723	0.1348
20	0.1571	0.0785	0.0500	0.0579	0.1079

20.10 FORMULAS FOR FULL-DEPTH TEETH

1. Diametral pitch $= \dfrac{\text{number of teeth}}{\text{pitch diameter}}$

2. To obtain pitch diameter, given outside diameter and number of teeth:

$$\text{Pitch diameter} = \frac{N \times (\text{O.D.})}{N+2}$$

  where O.D. = outside diameter.
  N = number of teeth.

3. To determine outside diameter, given diametral pitch and number of teeth:

$$\text{O.D.} = \frac{N+2}{P}$$

  where P = diametral pitch.

4. Addendum = $1/P$ (reciprocal of diametral pitch)
5. Dedendum = $1.157/P$
6. Whole depth of tooth = $2.157/P$
7. Average backlash = $0.040/P$
8. Center-to-center distance of mating gears: Divide the total number of teeth in both gears by twice the diametral pitch.

$$\text{C-to-C distance} = \frac{N+n}{2P}$$

  Alternately, the center-to-center distance is half the sum of the pitch diameters.

9. Chordal thickness of tooth (see Fig. 169). This is the thickness of the gear tooth that must be checked during manufacture.

$$\text{Chordal thickness} = D \times \sin \frac{90°}{N}$$

  where D = pitch diameter.
  N = number of teeth.

10. Chordal addendum of tooth (see Fig. 169). When one is measuring the chordal thickness, the vertical scale of a gear tooth caliper is set to the chordal addendum to locate the jaws of the caliper at the pitch line.

$$\text{Chordal addendum} = \frac{P}{2}\left(1 - \cos \frac{90°}{N}\right) + \text{addendum}$$

  Tolerances for gears should be minus and as small as possible. Outside diameter of a gear blank should be $+0.0000$, -0.005 in. maximum, though fine-pitch gears require tighter tolerances. Center-to-center distance for mating gears should have a tolerance of about 0.005 in. Concentricity of the gear blank should be better than 0.001 in.

20.11 GEAR INSPECTION

The following gear characteristics require inspection:
1. Surface hardness.
2. Surface finish.
3. Outside diameter.
4. Bore diameter.
5. Parallelism.
6. Runout.
7. Tooth profile.
8. Tooth spacing (pitch variation).
9. Tooth thickness.

For surface hardness, surface finish, outside diameter, bore diameter, parallelism, and runout, the standard inspection techniques discussed earlier in this book or in Chapter 25 are used. In the determination of outside diameter, bore diameter, runout, profile, spacing, and tooth thickness, it is usual to inspect to tenths of thousandths.

Profile inspection may be done on an optical comparator (Chapter 25) to an accuracy of a few tenths of a thousandth in the case of smaller teeth, and a thousandth or so for larger teeth. The limitations on accuracy are determined by the magnification allowed by the gear tooth size. Most optical comparators have a 14-in. viewing screen. Consider displaying a 12-pitch tooth on such a screen. The tooth has a total depth of almost 0.2 in. If magnified 20 times, the tooth will measure 4 in. on the screen. The next magnification lens available is 50X, but this magnification produces an enlargement too great to be contained on the screen—there is some optical distortion at the edges of the viewing screen. At 20 magnifications, an error of 0.001 in. will be enlarged to 0.020 in., which is easily visible. An error of 0.0001 in. will not be visible at this magnification.

Tooth thickness can be determined by measurement over pins or wires. The method is simply to gage over two pins located in diametrically opposite tooth spaces, a micrometer or other device being used. This method needs a measuring fixture; otherwise, it becomes a juggler's act: The inspector must manipulate two pins or wires, a micrometer, and the gear itself. The formulas for such measurements are rather complex, but tables are available in gear handbooks.

The gear tooth caliper uses a simpler method. This instrument was discussed in Chapter 12.

20.12 HELICAL GEARS

Helical gears use the basic involute shape and the usual pressure angles.

In the case of a spur gear drive, the tooth force is taken instantaneously by the whole width of the tooth. If, instead, helical gears are substituted, the teeth mesh gradually and the meshing action is distributed over more than one tooth; shock effect is minimized. However, helical gears provide an axial thrust to the shaft that must be resisted by the bearings. Double helical or herringbone gears use teeth with opposite hands to neutralize this end thrust.

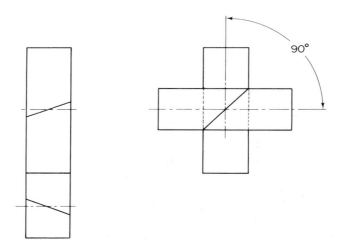

Fig. 284

The hand of the helix must be correctly selected. For two meshing helical gears on parallel shafts, one gear must have a left-hand helix and the other a right-hand (Fig. 284). The helix angles must be the same. If the shafts are at 90 deg, both gears must have the same hand.

The helix angle of a helical gear is measured on the pitch circle.

$$\text{Tangent of helix angle} = \frac{\pi \times \text{pitch dia.}}{\text{lead}}$$

$$\text{Lead} = \pi \times \text{pitch dia.} \times \text{cotangent of helix angle}$$

For a helical gear, the standard tooth dimensions are measured normal to the flank of the tooth, that is, at right angles to the helix. But with the teeth at the angle of the helix, the curvature at the pitch line is different from that of a spur gear of the same number of teeth and the same tooth size. Therefore, an imaginary spur gear must be calculated in order to select the proper milling cutter. This imaginary gear has a radius at the pitch line that corresponds as closely as possible to that of the helical gear, as seen at right angles to the helix angle. The formula for this imaginary gear is

$$N_s = \frac{N^h}{\cos^3 H}$$

where N_s = number of teeth in imaginary gear.
N^h = number of teeth in helical gear.
H = helix angle.

Alternately, the following table may be used. If the number of teeth in the helical gear is multiplied by the number in the table, the number of imaginary teeth is obtained.

Helix angle	10°	15°	20°	25°	30°	35°	40°	45°
Correction factor	1.05	1.12	1.23	1.35	1.54	1.85	2.23	2.86

As an example, a helical gear has 24 teeth, 5 DP, with a helix angle of 45 deg. Select the cutter.
The correction factor is 2.86.

$$24 \times 2.86 = 69 \text{ teeth}$$

From Sec. 12.2, a number 2 cutter is required.

20.13 BEVEL GEARS

Bevel gears resemble a friction cone drive (Fig. 285), and therefore the shafts are at an angle to each other, often 90 deg. The intersection point of the axes of the two shafts usually is the apex of the two pitch cones.

Since the tooth section becomes progressively smaller as the apex of the pitch cone is approached, only that length of the cone close to its base is used, actually not more than one-third of the length of the full pitch cone. All such dimensions as pitch diameter, diametral pitch, addendum, and dedendum are measured at the large diameter of the bevel gear. Like the helical gear, the bevel gear produces an end thrust in the shaft.

Besides the straight tooth bevel gear, other styles are in use, including helical, spiral, hypoid, skew, and zerol types.

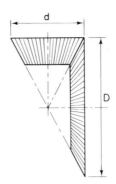

Fig. 285

When one is milling a bevel gear, the blank is carried on the dividing head with the larger end of the blank toward the dividing head. The blank is swung to the root angle of the gear, as shown in Fig. 286; that is, the bottom of the tooth space is in a horizontal plane. This angle is not the same angle as was machined on the gear blank in the lathe.

Small gears are shaped in two cuts, one on each side of the tooth. The angular rotation required to bring the opposite tooth flank into position for cutting is given by the angle $180°/N$, where N is the number of teeth. When the teeth are to be milled in three cuts, the first gashing cut down the center removes the bulk of the material. To bring the tooth flank into position

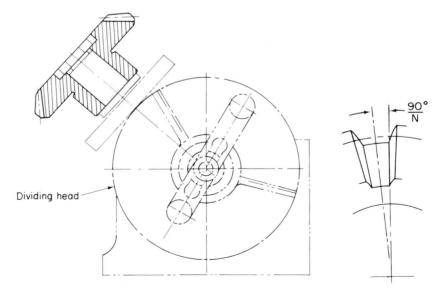

Fig. 286   **Fig. 287**

on a line passing through its center, the blank must be swung through an angle $90°/N$. This brings the pitch point over the center line of the blank. See Fig. 287.

The milling cutter is selected for the large diameter of the bevel gear; therefore, the teeth are out of shape at the small end. If the teeth do not mesh properly at the small end, the teeth may have to be filed above the pitch line. The filing must taper off to the large end.

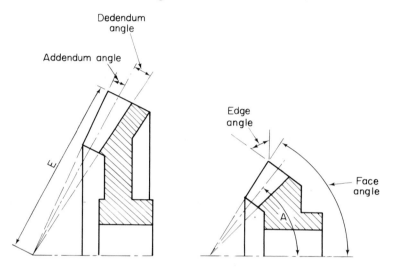

Fig. 288

The following formulas are required for bevel gear design and layout:

1. To find the pitch cone angle A of the bevel gear (Fig. 288): Divide the number of gear teeth by the number of pinion teeth to obtain the tangent of A.

$$\tan A = \frac{N}{n}$$

If the tooth ratio is 1 to 1 (miter gears), then the pitch cone angle must be 45 deg.

2. Cone distance E:

$$E = \frac{D}{2 \sin A}$$

3. To find the addendum angle:

$$\text{Tangent of addendum angle} = \frac{\text{addendum}}{\text{cone distance } E}$$

4. To find dedendum angle:

$$\text{Tangent of dedendum angle} = \frac{\text{dedendum}}{\text{cone distance } E}$$

5. To find face angle: Face angle is equal to the pitch cone angle A plus the addendum angle.
6. To find the root angle: Root angle is equal to the pitch cone angle A minus the dedendum angle.
7. To find the outside diameter of the bevel gear:

$$\text{O.D.} = \text{pitch diameter} + 2 \text{ (addendum)} \times \cos A$$

20.14 FLUID POWER SYSTEMS

Energy is most commonly transmitted down a wire as a stream of electrons under the pressure of a voltage. Energy may also be conveyed in the form of a liquid through a conduit under the pressure of a pump. The liquid for a fluid power system is usually a mineral oil similar to lubricating oils. The hydraulic system serves either cylinders, which act as linear motors, or fluid motors, which provide torque to rotate applied loads.

Fluid power systems are capable of developing small or extremely large forces. Variable speeds of operation are easily arranged. Fluid rotary motors are much smaller in size than electric motors of the same horsepower, with the additional advantage that if stalled they cannot burn out. Precise positioning is also possible with fluid power, as is evident from the number of numerically controlled machine tools using fluid power systems.

The complete fluid power system has five basic components:

1. Oil reservoir.
2. Oil pump.
3. Tubing or other conduit for distribution of the oil.
4. Valves for control of oil flow and oil pressure.
5. Cylinders and motors to supply force, torque, movement, and power.

In machine tool operations, fluid power systems are frequently employed in planers, surface grinders, and numerically controlled milling machines. Fluid pumps, motors, and valves offer extremely interesting problems in machining, grinding, and deburring, and some of these machining aspects of fluid power components merit mention. The spools of four-way hydraulic valves require sizing to a few tenths; spools for some servovalves may be sized to 0.0001 in.

20.15 FLUID POWER PLUMBING

The oil reservoir has two functions:

1. Storage of the hydraulic oil.
2. Cooling of the oil.

The cooling function is an important one, since considerable heat can be generated in the oil as it passes through valves and cylinders. To provide sufficient residence time in the reservoir for cooling, and also to ensure an adequate oil supply for the pump to draw upon, the tank is sized usually for a number of gallons equal to three times the pump capacity in gallons per minute. Thus, if the pump can deliver 10 gpm, then the reservoir will probably have a capacity of 30 gallons, unless special circumstances dictate a larger or smaller tank.

The oil conduits conducting the oil from one component to another may be either flexible hose or rigid steel tubing or pipe. Such tubing must have a pressure rating large enough to sustain the operating pressures in the system. The pressures used in the fluid power systems of machine tools are not higher than 1000 psi; hydraulic presses may have pressures as high as 10,000 psi.

The use of screwed joints in hydraulic tubing is not recommended, though such joints have been used on less critical fluid power systems. Metal particles from the threading operations can break off and enter the oil. These

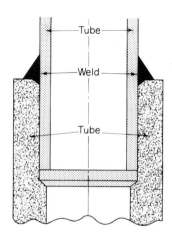

Fig. 289

particles are damaging to O-rings, seals, and wipers of valves and cylinders and can score the spools of valves.

Welded joints are used for high-pressure systems. A socket joint (Fig. 289) is used to prevent welding particles and slag from entering the oil. Such a joint also provides alignment for the welding operation and is vibration-resistant.

The more usual joint is a flared joint (Fig. 290). The end of the tube is flared with a flaring tool and is held against the body of the fitting, which has either a 45- or 37-deg flare. The 45-deg flare is suited to softer nonferrous tubing, while the 37-deg flare is used for carbon steel and stainless steel tubing, which may split if flared to 45 deg. The flared fitting may be a two-piece or a three-piece connection; Fig. 290 shows two types of three-piece flared connections. The flareless type of connection must be used with thick-

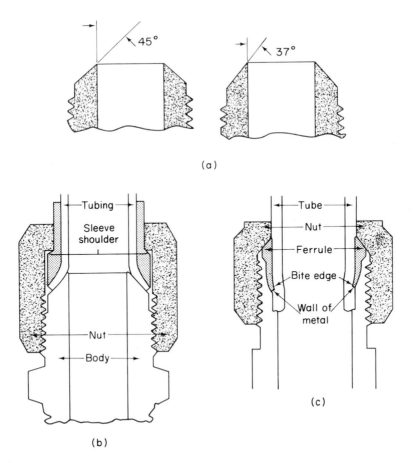

(a)

(b)

(c)

Fig. 290

walled tubing; it uses a bite-type ferrule to grip the tubing. The bite-type fitting should not be used on thin-wall tubing, as it may collapse the tube.

20.16 FLUID POWER PUMPS

Three types of pumps are in use in fluid power systems:

1. Gear pumps.
2. Vane pumps.
3. Piston pumps.

Gear pumps are used wherever possible, since this type is the cheapest to manufacture. This type, however, is less efficient, is noisy, and its life expectancy is limited. It is restricted to pressures below 1500 psi generally.

A gear pump rated at 10 gpm is shown in Fig. 291. One of the gears

Fig. 291 Drive shaft, gears, and part of the housing of gear pump. The gears are 5-pitch, and the tooth profile is shown in Fig. 281.

is driven by an electric motor; it in turn drives its mating gear. Both gears deliver oil. The casing is a close fit to the gears. Oil is trapped in each space enclosed by two gear teeth and the casing and is delivered around the periphery of the gear from the suction inlet to the discharge outlet at the opposite side of the pump. There is some leakage back to the suction side along the sides of the gears and in the region where the two gears mesh. The oil delivered by the gear pump is equal to the number of tooth spaces on both gears that deliver oil to the discharge outlet in a given time.

The gear pump is usually driven at a fixed speed by an electric motor. Since a fixed volume of oil is delivered for each revolution of the pump, a constant volume is delivered per minute at a fixed speed. This volume will be delivered whether the hydraulic system has space to receive it or not. Therefore, the fluid power circuit requires a pressure-relief valve to protect it from excessive pressure. This valve opens at a set pressure to discharge excess oil back to the tank.

The larger the pressure angle of the gear tooth, the larger the volume of the tooth space will be. Pressure angles of 25 or 28 deg are often used in these gears.

The vane pump of Fig. 292 has a rotor that is eccentric to the casing, with sliding vanes in slots in the rotor. When the rotor rotates, these vanes move outward to thrust against the casing, trapping oil and transporting it from suction to discharge in a similar manner to the gear pump. Since the volume between vanes is much larger than the volume between gear teeth, this pump is suited to moving large volumes of oil at low or medium pressures.

The vanes must be made of heat-resistant, wear-resistant, and high-strength steel. The oil pressure produces a high bending stress in the vanes, and the rubbing against the casing results in both wear and heat.

Piston pumps are found in high-quality hydraulic systems such as

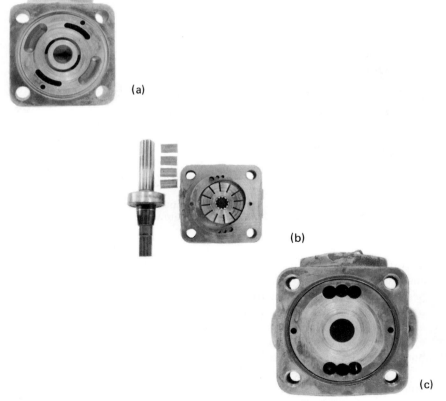

(a)

(b)

(c)

Fig. 292 Vane pump (a) and (b) the housing (c) splined drive shaft and rotor. Four of the vanes are also shown.

those that are used in numerically controlled machine tools. Two types are used: axial piston and radial piston pumps. This is a superior pump, highly efficient with a long life unless damaged by contaminants in the oil. Close clearances and smooth surface finishes between pistons and cylinders, and the more complex design, make this a more expensive pump than the other types.

The piston pump has a pulsating oil flow. Pulsations are minimized by using an odd number of pistons, such as seven or nine.

The two basic system characteristics of a hydraulic pump are its capacity in gallons per minute at its operating speed and its rated maximum pressure. The pump capacity must be sufficient to supply the cylinders of the

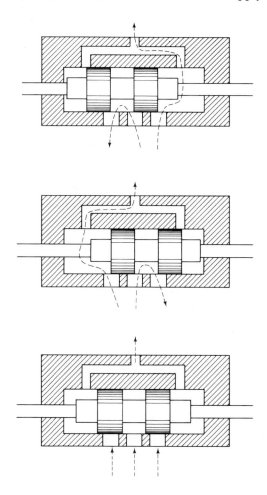

Fig. 293

circuit at their required speed of stroke. The pump pressure must be sufficient to move the loads on the fluid power system.

The trend in fluid power systems is toward higher system pressures, with the advantages of improved efficiency, smaller system components, and smaller pump capacity.

20.17 VALVES

Only the basic types of fluid power valves are discussed here.

A *relief valve* is a normally closed, two-way valve that opens against spring pressure when system pressure exceeds the pressure setting on the spring. When the relief valve opens, oil is released from pump to reservoir. This valve must be located close to the pump discharge.

A *check valve* permits oil flow in one direction only. This valve contains a ball that seats against a conical seat. If the check valve is to be leakproof when closed, the ball seat must be carefully ground.

To cycle a hydraulic cylinder forward and back, oil must be supplied to one end of the cylinder to advance the piston and rod, then to the other end to retract the piston and rod. This double action requires a valve that can reverse the oil flow to the two ends of the cylinder. Such a valve is a *four-way valve*, with four oil connections. The internal flow for such a valve is indicated in Fig. 293, and a photograph of such a valve, rated for 3000 psi, is given in Fig. 294. A connection must be provided to both ends of the cylinder, with also a connection to the oil supply and to the oil exhaust to tank. The drafting symbol for this valve, Fig. 295, shows the two flow configurations of the valve. Some four-way valves have a third or neutral position.

The spool of the four-way valve, shown in Fig. 294, is ground to a high surface finish, and the difference in diameter between the spool diameter and bore diameter is a few tenths only.

Fig. 294 A dismantled Vickers 3000 psi four-way valve.

A four-way valve must reverse the stroke of a hydraulic shaper or grinder at the end of the stroke. Stops or dogs must be positioned to give the length of stroke required, and a lever pushes the valve spool to its opposite position for oil flow reversal. The hydraulic system for such a machine tool is shown in Fig. 296.

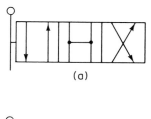

(a)

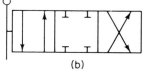

(b)

Fig. 295 Drafting symbols for three-position four-way valves. (a) Valve open-center in neutral position. (b) Closed center (blocked ports).

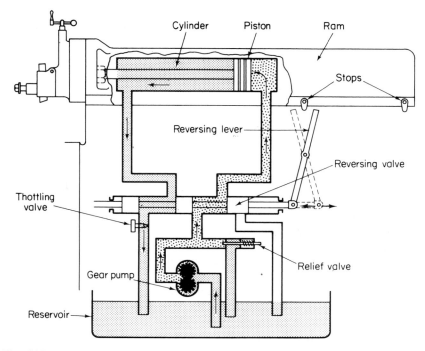

Fig. 296

Because of pressure surges and other unknown factors, suppose that a design pressure of twice the rated 80 psi is used. $2 \times 80 = 160$ psi, or say 200 psi. This is design pressure.

Next we require the inside diameter. To obtain 1000 lb force from 80 psi air, a cylinder area of 12.5 sq in. is required ($\frac{1000}{80}$). This area is given by a diameter of 4 in.

$$\text{Wall thickness} = \frac{P \times D}{40,000}$$

$$= 200 \times \frac{4}{40,000}$$

$$= 0.020 \text{ in.}$$

Do not use a cylinder wall thinner than 16-gage, which is approximately $\frac{1}{16}$ in. Find a piece of seamless tubing approximating what is required; perhaps $4\frac{1}{4}$ in. O.D. by $\frac{1}{8}$ in. wall is available.

A factor of safety of 3 is used in the wall thickness formula given above. A larger factor of safety would be used for high-pressure cylinders.

The piston rod must be of sufficiently large diameter to prevent its buckling under the compression load to which it is exposed.

As shown in Fig. 299, the piston requires an O-ring or O-rings, and the rod requires a packing.

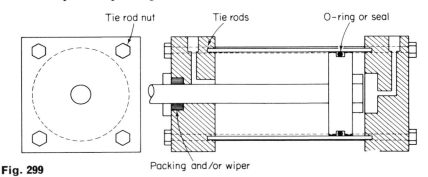

Fig. 299   Packing and/or wiper

20.21 DESIGN AND MACHINING OF A GEAR PUMP

It is not difficult for the machinist to make his own gear pump, though it is doubtful whether he can obtain a pressure exceeding 1000 psi from a pump of his own manufacture.

1. Design

The gear pump rpm and delivery in gallons per minute must first be decided. The pump speed should be in the range of 800 to 1000 rpm. Induction motors with speeds of 1140 and 1725 rpm are available.

To determine the motor horsepower, use the formula

$$\text{Horsepower} = 0.000583GP$$

where G = gallons per minute.

P = pressure.

As an example, suppose 10 gpm are to be delivered against a pressure of 1000 psi. Then

$$\begin{aligned} \text{HP} &= 0.000583 \times 10 \times 1000 \\ &= 5.8 \end{aligned}$$

To allow for inefficiencies, a 7.5-HP motor would be selected.

Gears can usually be bought more cheaply than they can be made. Purchased gears will have a 20-deg pressure angle; a $14\frac{1}{2}$-deg pressure angle will reduce the capacity of the pump.

Designing the pump for a specific delivery in gallons per minute is best explained by an example. Suppose that the above 10 gpm is required. Not knowing what gears to select to give this capacity, try a pair of 24-teeth 20-deg-angle 8-pitch gears, 1 in. wide.

Obtain a full-size profile of these gears from a catalog. With a 6-in. rule estimate the area of the tooth space. For 8-pitch gears the tooth space approximates $\frac{1}{4}$ in. $\times \frac{1}{4}$ in., which is 0.06 sq in., or 0.06 cu in. if the gear is 1 in. long. Two such gears contain 24 tooth spaces. In each revolution two gears will deliver

$$24 \times 0.06 = 1.44 \text{ cu in. of oil}$$

If the pump is to rotate at 1000 rpm, the delivery will be

$$1000 \times 1.44 = 1440 \text{ cu in.}$$

There are 231 cu in. in 1 gallon. Converting to gallons gives about 6 gallons per minute. However, leakage in a handmade pump should be at least 10 per cent, so that this selection of gears should not provide more than $5\frac{1}{2}$ gpm.

This gear is not acceptable. A longer gear or a 6-pitch gear should suffice.

2. Machining Details

Gear pump housings are always gray iron castings. For a home-made gear pump select pieces of heavy plate. Narrow gears will reduce the size of plate required. The housings must be bored for a very close fit to the gear diameter, and must allow a clearance at the sides of the gears of only a few thousandths of an inch. The parts of the housing must be accurately aligned with each other by means of dowels and bolted together with four cap screws.

The design and layout of the O-ring grooves in the housings may present some problems. Use press-fit sintered bronze bearings for the shafts. For other details, consult an available gear pump.

QUESTIONS (GENERAL)

1. An average man is capable of a sustained effort of 0.1 HP each hour. What work can he achieve each hour in foot-pounds?

2. A work horse is capable of a sustained effort of $\frac{2}{3}$ HP. What is its output in foot-pounds per minute? (A horsepower is actually the output of $1\frac{1}{2}$ horses.)

3. Approximately how many kilowatts are represented by the following horsepower: (a) 20 HP; (b) $1\frac{1}{2}$ HP?

4. An electric motor of 10-HP output has an 80 per cent efficiency. What is its kilowatt output? What is its kilowatt input?

5. An induction motor in an aircraft has 8 poles and is supplied with 400-cycle power. What is its synchronous speed?

6. What is the synchronous speed of a 10-pole electric motor supplied with 60-cycle power?

7. A gear pump draws 10 HP at 1000 rpm. What is the torque in the shaft in foot-pounds?

8. A $\frac{1}{4}$-HP electric motor rotates at 1725 rpm. What torque does it deliver?

9. If this $\frac{1}{4}$-HP motor delivers power to another shaft through a V-belt drive that reduces the speed to 862 rpm, what is the torque in the driven shaft?

10. What is the advantage of splines over a keyway?

11. What three types of misalignment of coaxial shafts are possible?

12. If bearing balls were made of soft steel, would there be more or less friction in the bearing as compared to hard balls?

13. Why must a ball or roller for a bearing be hard?

14. Why does a drive chain elongate with use?

15. When does a drive chain require to be replaced due to elongation?

16. For what reasons might a drive chain disengage from its sprocket?

17. Explain chordal action of a drive chain.

18. Should chordal action have an effect on the life of a drive chain?

19. Explain addendum and dedendum of a gear.

20. Make a simple sketch showing the pressure angle of a gear.

21. Which gives a larger volume to the space between two gear teeth, a small or a large pressure angle?

22. What is the difference between pitch diameter and diametral pitch?

23. Where is gear backlash measured?
24. Why will a gear of 20-deg pressure angle not mesh with a gear of $14\frac{1}{2}$-deg angle?
25. What instrument would you use to inspect the following characteristics of a gear?
    a. surface hardness.
    b. outside diameter.
    c. bore diameter.
    d. parallelism.
    e. runout.
26. Where is the pitch diameter of a bevel gear measured?
27. How is a hydraulic reservoir usually sized?
28. Why are screwed joints not recommended for fluid power connections?
29. State when you would use (a) 45-deg (b) 37-deg flared connectors for hydraulic joints.
30. Why do all hydraulic pumps require relief valves for the protection of the hydraulic system?
31. What is the difference between a meter-in and a meter-out flow control circuit?
32. Size a cylinder internal diameter to deliver a force of 15,000 lb with the following system pressures:
    a. Air at 100 psi.
    b. Oil at 3000 psi.

QUESTIONS (GEARS)

33. A spur gear has an O.D. of 3.250 in. and 24 teeth. Find
    a. Pitch diameter.
    b. Diametral pitch.
    c. Whole depth of tooth (addendum plus dedendum).
    d. The number of the milling cutter required (from the table in Sec. 12.2).
34. For the gear of Question 33, find the chordal addendum.
35. From full-size profiles of gear teeth, estimate the volume of the following tooth spaces. The gear is 1 in. wide.
    a. 12-pitch
    b. 10-pitch.
    c. 8-pitch.
36. Estimate the delivery in cubic inches per minute and in gallons per minute of a gear pump equipped with two 6-pitch 15-tooth gears 1 in. long. Speed is 1000 rpm.

37. Disassemble any available gear pump. From measurements on the gear teeth only, estimate the pump delivery at 1000 rpm. Compare your estimate with the specified delivery of the pump. If there is a difference, attempt to account for it.

38. A spur gear is 8 DP, 11 teeth. Determine:
    a. The pitch diameter.
    b. The outside diameter.
    c. The whole depth of tooth.
    d. Center-to-center distance of two such mating gears.

39. What is the circular pitch of a spur gear of 11 teeth, 8 DP?

40. For a spur gear of 12 DP, 11 teeth, find the following dimensions:
    a. Pitch diameter.
    b. Outside diameter.
    c. Whole depth of tooth.
    d. Circular pitch.
    e. Chordal addendum.
    f. Chordal thickness of tooth.

41. For a spur gear of $\frac{1}{2}$ DP and 180 teeth, find the following dimensions:
    a. Pitch diameter.
    b. Outside diameter.
    c. Whole depth of tooth.
    d. The number of the milling cutter required.

42. A pair of bevel gears 8 DP of equal size transmits power between shafts at 90 deg.
    a. What is the pitch cone angle of the gears?
    b. Find cone distance E.
    c. Find the tangent of the dedendum angle and the dedendum angle.
    d. To what angle should the dividing head be swung for machining the bevel gear teeth?
    e. Obtain all required dimensions for the bevel gear blank. Sketch and dimension the blank.

43. For a 90-deg bevel gear drive with a 2:1 speed ratio, 8 DP, find the following:
    a. Pitch cone angle of gear and of pinion.
    b. Cone distance E of gear and pinion.
    c. Dedendum angle of gear and pinion.
    d. Angle to which the dividing head must be swung for machining the gear and the pinion.
    e. All dimensions for both pinion blank and gear blank. Sketch and dimension both blanks.

44. Obtain any sample gear. Measure the O.D. Calculate diametral pitch, pitch diameter, and whole depth of tooth. Check your calculations against the actual gear.

Chapter 21

The Turret Lathe and the Automatic Lathe

The turret lathe and the automatic lathe are used when dozens to thousands of the same part must be produced. The turret lathe requires an operator; the automatic lathe requires only minimal attention from an operator.

21.1 GENERAL CHARACTERISTICS

The tool turret on a turret lathe is moved toward and from the headstock by a handwheel; in an automatic lathe these movements are automatically controlled. The turret has four, five, six, or eight tool faces, on each of which one or more cutting tools may be mounted. When the turret is retracted from the workpiece by the operator, the turret automatically indexes the next tool face into position for cutting. The advance distance to be travelled by the tools in each turret position is controlled by stops or cams that must be preset.

In addition to the turret, both turret and automatic lathes have cross-feed toolholders. No compound rest is used. The cross slide can carry a front toolholder and a rear toolholder. Often the rear toolholder carries the cutoff tool. Those cutters mounted on the rear toolpost must cut upside down.

There are two basic types of turret lathe construction, the ram type and the saddle type. The turret of the ram type of lathe is mounted on a ram slide. The ram itself is mounted on a saddle that can be locked to the lathe bed at a suitable distance from the headstock. The saddle type of turret lathe is a heavier machine than the ram type. In this machine the turret is mounted

Fig. 300 Turret lathe equipped with indexing chuck. (Courtesy of the Warner and Swasey Co.)

directly on the saddle, which is moved longitudinally by the handwheel or a power traverse. Lacking the overhanding ram with its deflections, the saddle type is suited to heavy cuts and large tool forces.

Both turret lathes and automatic lathes are available as either bar or chucking machines. Chuckers are used to machine castings, pipe fittings, and other irregular shapes that cannot be made from bar stock and therefore require to be held in a chuck. The chuck may be two-, three-, or four-jaw, and often is air-operated. The turret lathe of Fig. 300 is equipped with an indexing chuck, which can present any of the four arms of the pipe fitting to the turret tools for machining.

The bar machine operates on bars passed through the spindle and held with a collet. The outboard end of the bar is carried in a bar feeder. When the collet chuck is opened, the bar feed drives the bar forward against a stop located in a face of the turret. The collet chuck then closes on the bar and the next machining cycle begins. The final operation when one is bar feeding is a cutoff operation.

The automatic lathe, after being set up and checked out, will repeat the complete sequence of machining operations to make the part without any attention from the operator, except to insert new bar stock into the bar feeder and spindle and to replace dull cutting tools. The automatic lathe

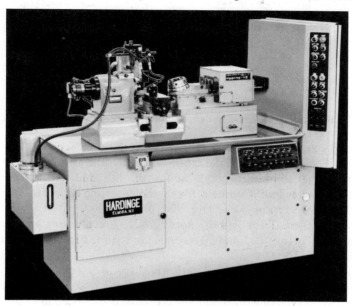

Fig. 301 Hardinge Super-Precision DSM-A Second Operation Automatic Lathe.

automatically changes its spindle speed if the next turret position requires a faster or a slower speed. Complete automation would include chip removal by a conveyor, automatic insertion of the next part into the chuck if the machine is a chucker, automatic closing of the chuck, and automatic removal of the finished part. The automatic lathe, therefore, does not require the large turret handwheel or capstan that is the distinguishing feature of the turret lathe.

During completion of the workpiece the turret must cycle through all its faces so that when the next piece is ready for machining the first turret position is presented to the part. Every job, however, may not require cutting tools in every turret position. Suppose that a lathe has a six-position turret, but that only three turret tools are required for the machining cycle. This situation can be handled in two ways. If the turret can be double-indexed, the tooling is inserted into the first, third, and fifth turret position, and the turret indexes two positions each time. If double-indexing is not available,

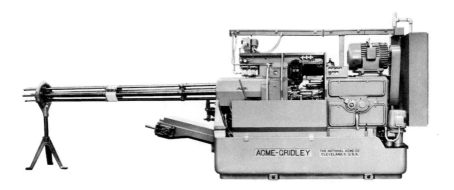

Fig. 302 Acme-Gridley six-spindle bar machine. (Courtesy of National Acme)

then probably the tooling will be inserted into the first, second, and third turret faces. The cutoff cycle, if the cross slide is used, is always long enough to allow the turret to index through the fourth, fifth, and sixth positions in time for the next bar feed. Consider, for example, cutting off a 1-in. steel bar. The spindle may be turning at perhaps 900 rpm, a carbide cutoff tool feeding 0.002 ipr being used. Then slightly more than 250 revolutions are required to sever the bar. Between 15 and 20 seconds are required for cutoff. A turret can be indexed in about 1 second.

The numerically controlled lathe is also an automatic lathe, but operates on entirely different principles from turret and automatic lathes, and on a different type of workpiece. The NC lathe is discussed in Chapter 23.

21.2 THE MULTIPLE-SPINDLE AUTOMATIC LATHE

This machine has four, five, six, or eight spindles, and is available in both bar and chucking types.

The several spindles are carried on a rotating spindle carrier that regularly indexes each spindle clockwise (as viewed from the motor end of the machine) into the next position. This is illustrated in Fig. 304, which shows the method of numbering the spindles. Since the spindle and bar material are indexed into position, it is not necessary to index the tools; therefore, there is no tool turret. Tools are mounted on the end slide, shown in Fig. 303; this end slide must, of course, have as many faces as there are spindles. For each spindle there is also a cross slide for such tools as cutoff tools. All end-slide and all cross-slide tools on all spindles operate simultaneously; then all tools are withdrawn and the spindles rotate to the next spindle position. Bar feeding is performed in the lower spindle position on

Fig. 303 Spindles and end slide of an Acme-Gridley multiple-spindle automatic lathe. (Courtesy of National Acme)

the rear side—the fourth, fifth, sixth, or eighth position if the machine has 4, 5, 6, or 8 spindles. The cutoff operation must then be performed at the third, fourth, fifth, or seventh position.

All end-slide tools, since they are all mounted on the same carrier, are fed together into the workpiece, withdrawn together, and have the same length of travel. The time per piece is, therefore, the time required for the longest cutting operation. If some cut, such as a deep drilling operation, requires excessive time, the drilling operation is half-completed at one position and finished at the next position in order to reduce cycle time.

For chucking operations the multispindle machine is usually equipped with a parts conveyor and a mechanism to feed the part into the chuck or collet. Chip conveyors are also required on large machines because of the large volume of chips that can be generated.

There is a significant difference in operation between the single-spindle and the multispindle automatic. In the case of the single-spindle machine, each tool cuts only once during the complete sequence of turret indexing. In a multiple-spindle machine, each tool is cutting continuously except for the short idle times during indexing. For satisfactory tool life, cutting speeds must often be lower for multispindle automatics. Stoppages for tool changes

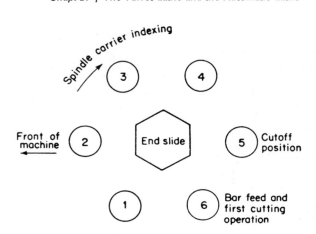

Fig. 304

can be expensive in terms of lost production on a multispindle automatic; such a machine can make a complex steel part every few seconds.

21.3 A PRODUCTION PLANNING EXAMPLE FOR AUTOMATIC MACHINING

In this section a simple case of production planning for a single-spindle automatic lathe is analyzed. The lathe is assumed to be a small machine, similar to the Hardinge of Fig. 301, with a half horsepower motor; therefore, high-speed steel cutters are used.

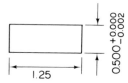

Fig. 305

The part to be produced in lots of 3000 is shown in Fig. 305. The pin is not to be chamfered, and the only machining operations are the cutting-off of the pin to length and facing the end of the bar after cutoff. The diameter tolerance of -0.002 in. can be met with the use of cold-drawn bar stock.

1. Costs

The customer will accept pins of 1015 plain carbon steel, 12L14 free-machining steel, or 360 leaded brass, whichever is cheapest. Prices per pound:

1015: 13.0 cents

12L14: 14.7

360: 60.0

One lineal foot of bar in any of these materials weighs 0.67 lb.

For the moment it is not possible to decide which material will be cheapest, since the final cost of the pins is the cost of the bar stock plus the cost of the machining operation. The leaded brass, for example, is expensive as raw material, but will be the cheapest to machine.

For operating costs, suppose that the depreciation rate for the lathe is $2.50 per hour. Other overhead charges and a small profit (if any—automatic lathe work is hardly to be described as profitable) will be taken at $3.00 per hour, and the operator will be paid $4.50 per hour. Total hourly charges are, therefore, $10.00.

If we allow 30 minutes to prepare tooling and set up the machine, the setup charge will be taken at $5.00.

2. Setup

Machining bars are 12 feet long. The operator must check the ends of the bars for burrs, since these may score the collet or interfere with the bar feeding operation. Assume that the last 8 in. of the bar cannot be fed by the bar feed mechanism and must be wasted.

The cutoff tool is set up on the cross slide. It is 0.10 in. wide, and ground to a side angle of 10 deg, as shown in Fig. 306. This is done so that

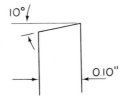

Fig. 306

the face of the piece cut off will be cut clean through. Material left on the bar face will be removed with a wide facing tool, which will clean up the bar almost instantaneously.

The turret has four faces. A short length of round bar is inserted in the first turret position to act as a stop for the bar feed. The facing tool is placed in the second turret position. The operator sets up the stops for the correct advance of these two turret positions by trial and error.

If the bars are 144 in. long, with 8 in. of bar as scrap, only 136 in. of bar can be converted into pins. The total length of pin plus cutoff tool width is 1.35 in. Then 100 pins can be obtained from each bar. A total of 30 bars is required if no scrap is produced in 3000 pieces. This, of course, is not possible.

3. Machining Rates

The following machining speeds are decided upon for the three competitive materials when one is using a cutoff tool:

$$1015: \ 120 \text{ sfpm, } 0.002 \text{ ipr}$$
$$12L14: \ 150 \text{ sfpm, } 0.002 \text{ ipr}$$
$$360: \ 300 \text{ sfpm, } 0.004 \text{ ipr}$$

These speeds must be converted to rpm's. The lathe has the following spindle speeds (rpm): 400, 725, 800, 975, 1450, 1750, 1950, 3500. The periphery of a half-inch round bar measures $\frac{1}{8}$ foot; therefore,

$$\text{rpm} = 8 \text{ sfpm}$$

Material	Calculated rpm	Machine rpm
1015	960	975
12L14	1200	975
360	2400	1950

The nearest lower machine rpm to the calculated rpm is selected, except for 1015, where a difference of 15 rpm is not significant. Notice that the range of speeds available in the machine is a major influence on machining times and machining costs. Because of the restricted range of speeds, in this case the more machinable 12L14 cannot be machined any faster than the cheaper 1015. Therefore, the only competitive materials are 1015 and 360. For a different bar diameter, or a different lathe, the competitive positions of the three materials would be entirely different, on this or any other automatic lathe.

The cutoff tool will make a rapid traverse toward the bar and begin feeding at 0.002 ipr when 0.010 in. from the bar. Because it has a side angle, it must be fed 0.010 in. past the center of the bar. Total feed will be 0.270 in., requiring 135 revolutions, or 68 revolutions in the case of 360 brass.

The facing operation is almost instantaneous and is not calculated. Assume 1 second to traverse the turret rapidly to the work and 1 second to retract it. The turret will be indexed back to position 1 during the cutoff operation.

4. Times and Costs

Cutoff times per pin:

> 1015   135 revolutions at 975 rpm, 0.14 min
> 360   68 revolutions at 1950 rpm, 0.036 min

Add 1 second each for rapid advance and rapid retract.

Total Machining Times (minutes)

Cross slide	1015	360	
in and out	0.035	0.035	(2 sec)
cutoff	0.14	0.036	
End slide			
in and out	0.035	0.035	(2 sec)
bar feed	0.035	0.035	(2 sec)
Total	0.245	0.141	

The superior machinability of 360 is of little advantage in this operation, simply because so little machining is done—only 2 seconds of machining with 360 alloy. Free-machining metals are not advantageous unless at least 10 per cent of the volume of the bar is reduced to chips. The free-machining characteristic should not be paid for unless it can be used.

Time and Cost per 100 Pins (no setup)

1015	24.5 min	$4.08
360	14.1 min	$2.35

Cost per 100 Pins or per 12-foot Bar (no setup)

Material	Machining cost	Material cost	Total cost
1015	$4.08	$1.04	$5.12
360	2.35	4.80	7.15

21.4 TOOLING FOR SINGLE-SPINDLE AUTOMATICS

In Fig. 307 may be seen an example of the cluster tooling possible in automatic lathe operations. The end-slide tooling comprises a boring bar, a counterbore cutter, and a chamfering cutter, all mounted on the same turret face by means of a combination tool holder. The front cross slide carries two facing

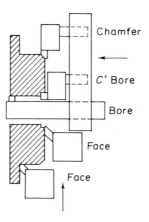

Fig. 307 Cluster tooling.

cutters. In setting up such tooling, the setup man must sequence end- and cross-slide movements so that the tools do not interfere with each other.

Usually the larger tools are used first, such as the balance turning tool, box tool, and die head. Smaller tools are held for later operations in the sequence. Drilling may be the last operation because it is slow, and can sometimes be performed at the same time as cutoff from the cross slide, which is also slow. Form tools are held for later stages in the machining sequence if the forming operation weakens the cross section of the workpiece.

Each turret position may require a different spindle speed from that for the previous position. The required speeds are preselected during the setup operation.

If several production runs of the same part are to be made during the year, at the end of each run all cutter bits are sharpened, and all tools are set up and stored in the toolroom ready for the next run and held for the one production job only. Sometimes a separate turret complete with tooling is segregated for each such production job.

21.5 TURRET TURNING TOOLS

The *box turning tool* of Fig. 308(a) is a turret tool for turning longer lengths of stock. It uses one or more cutter bits with backup support for the work, either a vee or rollers. If two cutters are used, usually the second cutter is a finishing cutter. If the bar length to be turned is relatively long, then the bar must pass through the holder, its shank, or even the hole in the turret. This is not possible on smaller automatics with tool shanks of small diameter. If the box tool is used for rough turning with considerable depth of cut, a

Fig. 308 Turret tools. (a) Box turning tool. (b) Adjustable hollow mill. (c) Combination tool holder mounting three knee tools and a boring bar. (d) Balance turning tool. (e) Swing tool.

preceding tool should bevel the end of the work so that the box tool can be led on to the bar with a lighter cut until the backrest is engaged.

The *balance turning tool* of Fig. 308(d) is excellent for heavy roughing cuts because two opposed cutters are at work on the bar opposite to each other.

The *hollow mill* of Fig. 308(b) may be plain or adjustable for the diameter to be turned. The turned bar passes into the hole in the mill. The adjustable mill cannot make heavy cuts, and cannot be set to diameter with great accuracy.

The *swing tool* of Fig. 308(e) has a cutter that swings on a pivot in the toolholder. This turret tool is pushed into the workpiece by a guide mounted on the front cross slide. It can produce a taper, a recess, turning behind a shoulder, a contour, or even straight turning (if the cross slide does not move). The shape produced is determined by the movement of the cross slide. The *slide tool*, also pushed by the cross slide, has a slideway instead of a pivot.

The *knee tool* is frequently used for turning, especially in chucking work. It can turn up to a sharp shoulder. This tool sometimes includes a drill, a boring bar, centering tool, or other tool for simultaneous internal cutting. Knee tools are shown in the combination toolholder of Fig. 308(c).

The *centering and facing tool* faces and at the same time centers the bar for drilling. The bar feed mechanism cannot feed out an exact length of bar but will be in error by a few thousandths because the bar bounces against the stop. Accurate lengths are obtained by feeding about 0.010 in. extra bar and facing off with the centering and facing tool.

The multiple turning head or *combination tool holder* of Fig. 308(c) can carry a drill or boring bar for inside work, with several knee tools to work on a range of diameters or multiple cuts.

21.6 CROSS-SLIDE TOOLS

Forming, chamfering, facing, cutting off, plunge cuts, and cross-drilling of holes such as the one in the planetary pin of Fig. 4 are all possible from the cross slide. The cross slide can also operate the swing or slide tools.

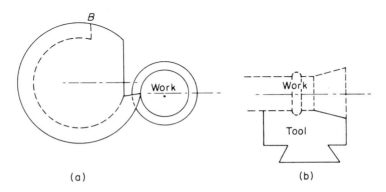

Fig. 309 Cross-slide form tools. (a) Circular form tool. This tool may be re-sharpened until position *B* is reached, at which point the cutter must be replaced. (b) Vertical dovetail form tool.

Form tools are plunged into the workpiece, a typical example being the grooves in pulley sheaves or O-ring grooves. A convenient form tool is the *circular form tool* of Fig. 309. This will maintain its cross section through repeated sharpenings. The dovetail tool is shaped to the desired contour and is fitted to its holder by a vertical dovetail joint. Form tools should not cut a form longer than $2\frac{1}{2}$ diameters of the bar; otherwise, the bar will undergo excessive deflection from tool pressure.

21.7 HOLE TOOLS

Before a hole is drilled from the turret, the preceding turret position may require a spot drill or starter drill to locate the hole accurately.

There are two methods of drilling deep holes. One method uses several drills in several turret positions. The other is a woodpecker sequence with turret retractions and advances. The woodpecker method is slower, but the other method may occupy too many turret faces and require extra drills and sleeves.

Sometimes a drilling operation from the turret requires a high spindle speed, while at the same time the cutoff tool in the cross slide requires a slow spindle speed. This conflict in speed requirements between two tools operating simultaneously is resolved with the use of the *high-speed drilling attachment*. This rotates the drill in the opposite direction to the spindle in order to speed up the drilling operation.

Drills, counterbores, and reamers frequently require *floating holders* to allow the cutter to find the axis of the hole.

When a tap is threaded into the workpiece, it must be threaded out again. The spindle can be reversed, but during reverse rotation no tools can cut. *Tapping attachments* are used which rotate the tap as it cuts at a higher speed than the spindle speed and in the same direction. For tap withdrawal,

Fig. 310 Self-opening die head and collapsible tap.

the tap rotation is stopped. In all but small sizes, *collapsible taps* (Fig. 310) are also used. The cutters of this tool collapse into the body of the tap when the thread is completed.

Self-opening die heads (Fig. 310) complete the thread and then release the thread chasers for withdrawal of the head.

Tap drill size for automatic lathe work is often selected for as little as 60 per cent of full thread, particularly when one is tapping strong and tough metals such as most steels. The tapping of difficult metals such as some of the austenitic stainless steels may not be performed on automatics because of the possibility of tap breakage.

21.8 CAM CONTROL OF TOOL MOTIONS

Control of the tool slide motions is frequently managed by means of cams, though other methods are also used. Disk or flat cams are used with single-spindle machines, and drum cams with multispindle machines. Both the length of the tool stroke and the feed rate are controlled by the cam. The principle of cam control is illustrated by Fig. 311.

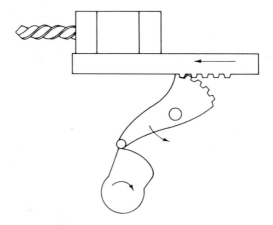

Fig. 311 End-slide mechanism showing a drilling operation controlled by a cam.

Because length of stroke and feed rate must vary from job to job, standard or off-the-shelf cams cannot be used, though sometimes a cam made for a previous job approximates the requirements of a new job to be set up and will be used for it. But cams normally are produced in the toolroom as required.

The principle used in designing the cam is that one complete revolution of the cam occurs for each complete machining cycle, that is, between one bar feed and the next. Generally three cams are required:

An end slide cam, sometimes called a lead cam
A front slide cam
A rear cross-slide cam

The circumference of each cam blank is marked in hundredths of a circle instead of degrees. The total number of revolutions of the spindle required to produce the part must first be known, including the revolutions for idle time for bar feed, indexing, and any others. The total revolutions are divided by 100, and the cam is designed from the revolutions per hundredth.

The simple cutoff operation of Sec. 21.3 can be used to illustrate the basic methods of cam design. For this operation, 135 revolutions were required for cutoff, but the total number of revolutions per machining cycle was not determined. The complete sequence is the following:

Operation	Time	Revolutions
Bar feed	1 sec	16.25
End slide approach	1 sec	16.25
End slide retract and cross slide approach	1 sec	16.25
Cutoff		135
Cross slide retract	1 sec	16.25
		200 revs

Note that any supposed accuracy of hundredth parts of a revolution is a myth, since the spindle speed of 975 is nominal only, and the actual speed of the lathe is certainly either slightly more or slightly less than 975 rpm.

Each cam hundredth comprises two revolutions of the spindle. Here is the operation sequence tabulated as hundredths:

Operation	Revs	Hundredths
Bar feed	16	8
End slide approach	16	8
End retract and cross advance	16	8
Cutoff	136	68
Cross retract	16	8
	200	100

The number of revolutions are adjusted for convenience. Figure 312 shows the significant hundredths laid out on the cams.

To design the lead and cross-slide cams for an automatic lathe, the layout man must know the amounts of slide movement required, the characteristics

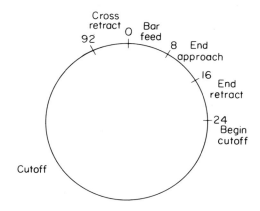

Fig. 312

of the machine, its indexing, speed changing, bar feed, and other idle times, its range of spindle speeds, and the characteristics of the tooling to be used (the cam design will not be the same for a compression tap holder as for a tension tap holder). A proper exposition of cam design for automatics, therefore, requires that a specific lathe of specific characteristics should be selected. The following explanation will avoid reference to specific lathes.

Turning first to the end slide in the present example, we will suppose that this slide must make a rapid advance and retract of 1.600 in., with a machining dwell of 4 revolutions or 2 hundredths. The rapid advance must begin at the 8th hundredth and be completed at the 16th hundredth. The 2 hundredths dwell begins at the 16th and is completed at the 18th hundredth. Rapid retract begins at the 18th and is completed at the 26th hundredth. For the remaining hundredths, the slide is retracted.

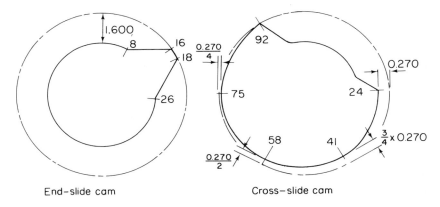

End-slide cam   Cross-slide cam

Fig. 313

We will assume also that the cam blanks for this machine are 5 in. in diameter, or $2\frac{1}{2}$ in. in radius. When the cam follower is riding on the full 5-in. diameter of the cam, the tool is fully advanced. When the tool is fully retracted, the cam follower must fall 1.600 in. toward the center of the cam. See Fig. 313.

To move from full retract to full advance, the cam follower must move outward on the cam shape 1.600 in. in 8 hundredths, which is a rate of 0.200 in. in each hundredth. To lay out this part of the cam contour, step out each hundredth by another 0.200 in., as shown in Fig. 314. Draw a smooth curve through these points. This contour gives a constant speed of rapid advance, or what is called a constant-rise cam.

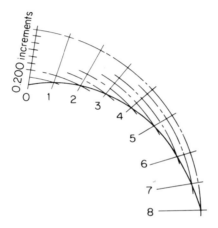

Fig. 314

The dwell holds the facing tool in contact with the work for 2 hundredths. For this interval of time the cam follower dwells at the full 5-in. cam radius. The follower must be retracted in the same way as it was advanced. The front cross-slide cam design is given in Fig. 313. The cams rotate clockwise.

The cams can be made by band-sawing and filing, by drilling and filing, or by end milling with a dividing head. The milling cutter must have the same diameter as the cam follower.

21.9 SPINDLE SPEED CHANGES

The design of these cams is based on the number of spindle revolutions per hundredth. Often, however, the spindle speed is changed during the machining cycle. A change in spindle speed is managed in the following way.

Suppose that the basic spindle speed for the machining cycle is 600 rpm, but that this speed must be reduced to 200 rpm for tapping a hole $\frac{1}{2}$–20 NF to a depth of 0.5 in. (10 threads).

Here 10 revolutions at 200 rpm are required for tapping and 10 revolutions in reverse to withdraw the tap. It is usual to add at least three revolutions to allow the tap to approach at the start of the cut and also to clear after withdrawal. This means a total of 13 revolutions to tap in and 13 revolutions to tap out, both at 200 rpm. The time of the threading operation must, however, be based on 600 rpm. The equivalent revolutions at 600 rpm are 39 to tap in and 39 to tap out. The length of the threading lobe of the cam is laid out from 39 revolutions.

The threading lobe of the cam must move the tap 0.05 in. (the thread lead) for each revolution at 200 rpm. Actually, it might be desirable to force the tap somewhat for the first 4 or 5 revolutions to ensure that the tap will bite (recall that the first 3 revolutions are tapping air). On the basis of 600 rpm, the cam must lift the cam follower 0.05 in. for every 3 revolutions. If it is assumed that the design is based on $2\frac{1}{2}$ revolutions per hundredth, then in every hundredth the tap must be fed $2\frac{1}{2}/3 \times 0.05$ or 0.4166 in.

The production planning and cam design for a single-spindle automatic follows this sequence:

1. Determine the part diameters for the cuts and the spindle speeds, selecting the nearest available speed offered by the machine, usually the nearest lower speed.
2. Determine the sequence of operations, including idle times, and the tooling.
3. Determine the travel and the feed per revolution of each tool.
4. Determine the number of revolutions for each operation, including all idle times.
5. Decide which operations can be overlapped and the amount of overlapping. Check for interference between tools.
6. Calculate the revolutions for each of the idle movements.
7. Determine the hundredths for dwells and clearance.
8. Determine the total revolutions per piece and the revolutions per hundredth.
9. Calculate the hundredths for each operation.
10. Design the cams.

This type of work is sufficiently complex and detailed that a second example probably is required. The following section explains the procedures for producing the crank pulley center pin of Fig. 2 on a single-spindle automatic lathe.

21.10 PRODUCTION OF A CRANK PULLEY CENTER PIN

The pin of Fig. 2 is to be produced in runs of 1500 from leaded 12L14 steel 1⅜ ∅. The automatic lathe has a six-position turret and spindle speeds of 1200, 1052, 891, 753, 643, 548, 457, 390, 332, 283, etc. Time to feed bar stock: ⅔ sec; to change spindle speed: ⅓ sec; to index the turret and clear tools: 1 sec. High-speed steel tooling will be used in this example only because of its familiarity; actually, carbides would be used. The milled flat will not be produced on the lathe.

The calculated cutting speeds are these:

Cutoff tool, part diameter 1⅜	330 rpm	
Turning, part diameter 1⅜	415	
Facing, part diameter 1	415	
Threading, part diameter 1	310	

Spindle speeds of 390 and 332 are available. The speed of 332 is a little high for threading, but the threads are fine and the bar is free-machining.

These turret positions are selected:

1. Turret stop.
2. Combination knee tool, one cutter turning the head, the other the shank.
3. Combination knee tool for finishing cuts, two cutters as before, and a facing tool.
4. Chamfer tool.
5. Self-opening die head.
6. Not used.

The two cross slides will chamfer and cut off. A cutoff tool width of 0.15 in. is assumed, with a side angle of 10 deg. These are not necessarily the best tooling arrangements.

Tool Travel. For the chamfering tool that chamfers the head of the pin, the tool travel is decided as 0.134 plus 0.010 approach for a total of 0.145 in.

Part of the work of the cutoff tool will have been performed by the chamfering tool. To simplify the example, assume that the cutoff tool must traverse the full radius of the bar, but the 0.010 in. usual approach distance will be dropped because of the chamfer cut. The side angle ground into the cutoff tool requires this tool to travel 0.030 in. past the center of the bar. Total cutoff travel is 0.656 + 0.030, or 0.686 in.

The two knee tools must travel 2.844 in., including 0.010 in. for approach. The turret chamfer tool has a total travel of 0.072 in. The die head travels 1 in., allowing approximately three threads for approach, or 14 revolutions (14 threads).

Feeds:

Cutoff and chamfer	0.002 ipr
Roughing	0.015
Finishing	0.010
Threading	0.0714

Revolutions per Tool

1. Cross-slide chamfer: 0.145/0.002 or 72 revolutions at 415 rpm.
2. Cutoff: 0.686/0.002 or 343 revolutions at 330 rpm, which is 431 revolutions at 415 rpm.
3. Roughing: 2.844/0.015 or 190 revolutions at 415 rpm.
4. Finishing: 2.844/0.010 or 285 revolutions at 415 rpm.
5. Turret chamfer: 0.072/0.002 or 36 revolutions at 415 rpm.
6. Threading: 14 revolutions at 330 rpm, which is $17\frac{1}{2}$ revolutions at 415 rpm.

The cross-slide chamfer tool and the cutoff tool can begin cutting at the same time.

Idle movements:

1. Feed bar stock: $\frac{2}{3}$ sec, or 5 revolutions.
2. Change spindle speed to 330 rpm for threading and cutoff: $\frac{1}{3}$ sec, or 4 revolutions.
3. Index turret: 1 sec, or 7 revolutions.

The Machining Sequence

1. Bar feed	5 revs
2. Index turret	7
3. Roughing	190
4. Index turret	7
5. Finishing	285
6. Index	7
7. Chamfer	36
8. Index (with speed change)	7
9. Cutoff, chamfer, and thread	431
10. Index and change speed	7
	————
	982 revolutions

There are 9.8 revolutions per cam hundredth. The time per piece is

$\frac{982}{415}$ or 2.124 min, giving 28 pieces per hour. If we allow a factor of 20 per cent for delays and spoilage, the expected production would be 23 pieces per hour. Actually, with carbide tooling and more attention to details, a production rate considerably better than this is possible.

21.11 TOOLING FOR MULTIPLE-SPINDLE AUTOMATICS

Tooling for multiple-spindle automatic lathes is of the same general types as used on single-spindle machines. End-slide tools are not attached to turret holes and faces but to tee-slots on the end slide. The end-slide tools for the rear spindle positions cut upside down. This condition, therefore, requires two types of toolholders for some tools—one cutting from below work center and one from above.

Since spindles cannot be reversed, taps cannot be threaded out of tapped holes. The threading attachment is driven from the main drive shaft at a higher speed than the spindle and in the same direction, the difference in speeds giving the required threading speed. A tap is retracted by a trip that opens the chasers. If a solid tap is used, it is withdrawn by tripping the threading spindle to a lower speed than the work spindle.

The high-speed drilling attachment that rotates drills in the opposite direction to the spindle is also used on the multispindle machine. Cross-drilling and milling attachments permit drilling and milling at right angles to the axis of the bar while the spindle is stopped. Eccentric drills drill holes parallel to the axis of the workpiece. The two lower spindles, where bar feed and cutoff are executed, cannot be stopped.

The pickoff attachment, which functions somewhat like a collet, holds and rotates the outboard end of the piece after it is cut off. This tool permits operations to be done on the back of the piece from the cross slide, such as chamfering, milling, and slotting.

The swing tool and slide tool are not used on a multispindle machine. End slide recessing tools are fully operated from the end slide.

A wide range of other tooling may be used, including internal and external broaching attachments, stencilling toolholders to impress characters into the periphery of the work, and cross-tapping attachments. Eccentric turning tools oscillate to turn an eccentric section of the piece. Thread rolling attachments roll threads instead of cutting them. The thread roller must be preceded by a shaving tool to size the diameter to the half-thousandth for accurate size of blank.

The multispindle lathe can execute a remarkable range of operations in a few seconds. Figure 315 shows an interesting example of this type of operation on an Acme-Gridley bar automatic. It was made from B1113 cold-drawn steel $\frac{9}{32}$ ∅ on a $\frac{7}{16}$-in. six-spindle machine in 6 seconds, the following tooling being used:

Fig. 315 A small component made on an Acme-Gridley six-spindle machine from $\frac{9}{32}$ in. cold-drawn B-113 steel in 6 seconds.

Position	Cross slide	End slide
6	form outboard end	spot drill
1	form inboard end	drill
2	cross-drill, c'sink	high-speed ream
3	cross-tap	mill end
4	shave O.D.	deburr drilled hole
5	cutoff	pickoff and c'sink back end

The crank pulley center pin may serve for a comparison of single- and multiple-spindle operation. In single-spindle operation, a production time of 2.124 minutes was determined if HSS tooling is used. If we used a six-spindle machine under the same conditions, the piece time would be 0.47 min, or a reduction in time of over 75 per cent. However, the production quantities would have to be impressively large to warrant six-spindle operations.

QUESTIONS

1. Explain how the cutoff cam of Fig. 313 was designed.
2. How many cubic inches of chips are produced in making the 3000 pins discussed in Sec. 21.3?
3. In the case of the above pins, what percentage is the volume of chips to the volume of the bar stock?
4. Repeat the analysis of Sec. 21.3, changing only the pin diameter to $\frac{3}{4}$ in. Which of the three competitive bar materials is cheapest? How do the relative costs compare with those for the $\frac{1}{2}$-in. bar?
5. Free-machining alloys are advantageous in automatic lathe work, but harder to justify on standard engine lathes. Why?
6. For the unchamfered pin discussed in Secs. 21.3 and 21.8, change the pin diameter to $\frac{3}{4}$ in. Design the end-slide and cross-slide cams, following the procedure of Sec. 21.8. Idle times remain the same. Because of the larger diameter, the spindle must be reduced. See Sec. 21.3 for the list of available spindle speeds.
7. Over a short period of time at least, a machinist should be able to match the production of a single-spindle automatic lathe as he operates a turret

lathe. What reasons do you see for installing automatics rather than turret lathes? Does the length of the production run influence the choice?

8. Does a numerically controlled lathe compete with an automatic lathe?

9. Sketch and dimension throws for form, cutoff, and lead cams for a $\frac{3}{8}$–16 NC nut:

| | | | *Hundredths* | |
Operation	Throw	from	to
1. center drill	0.113	4	12
2. index turret		12	14.5
3. drill	0.529	14.5	40.5
4. index		40.5	43
5. tap in	0.481	43	57
6. tap out		57	60
7. form	0.066	60	81
8. dwell		81	82
9. cutoff	0.226	60	98
10. clear		98	100

10. The bogie pin of Fig. 316 is to be machined from 4-in. 12L14 bar on a single-spindle automatic. This will require a first and a second chucking operation because both ends of the pin must be turned. Select tooling

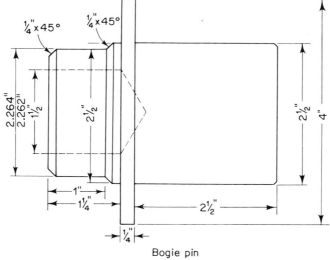

Bogie pin
Material: 12L14

Fig. 316

for cross slides and turret positions and decide the number of turret positions required.

11. For the pin of Question 10, determine the time per part for both first and second operations. Use the following data:

    a. Chucking and indexing time: 0.6 min (total time for all idle times).

    b. Turning 4-in. diameter to $2\frac{1}{2}$ in., depth of cut $\frac{3}{4}$ in.: Use carbides at 600 rpm and 0.015 ipr. No finish turning.

    c. Turning $2\frac{1}{2}$-in. diameter to $2\frac{1}{4}$ in.: Use carbides at 850 rpm and 0.015 ipr.

    d. Cutoff, 4-in. diameter: Use carbides at 600 rpm and 0.005 ipr.

    e. Finish turning to tolerance in second operation: Use carbides at 1200 rpm, 0.010 ipr.

    f. Drilling $1\frac{1}{2}$-in. hole: HSS drill at 220 rpm and 0.015 ipr.

12. For the bogie pin above, estimate the lathe horsepower, if 1 HP is required to remove 1 cu in. of material per minute.

Chapter 22

The Basic Techniques of Numerical Control

Numerical control is a method of organizing the data for a machining operation and putting this data into a code of punched holes in continuous tape which the machine tool reads and executes. Numerical control is not a different method of machining. It is a different method of organizing a machining operation.

The standard numerical control systems are discussed in this chapter. Numerically controlled machining operations are discussed in Chapter 23.

22.1 AN ASSESSMENT OF NUMERICAL CONTROL

A machinist at work appears to be wholly preoccupied with tool and material-processing skills. In introducing a discussion of numerically controlled machining, the first observation that must be made is this: The machinist processes both *materials* and *information*. The following is only a selection of information-processing that is an integral part of the machining process:

1. Selection of tool angles.
2. Speeds, feeds, depths of cut.
3. Solution of a chatter problem.
4. Sequence of cuts.
5. Selection of cutting tool material.
6. Determination of the amount of grinding allowance.
7. Decisions on when to change cutters.
8. Dimensions of hole locations.
9. Tolerances.

A study of the applications of numerical control reveals that the machinist processes more information, and processes information at a faster rate, than any other skilled trade.

Numerical control techniques do not introduce any basic changes to machining techniques. Numerical control is not a machining method; it is a different method of organizing machining information and a different method of putting this information into the machining process. The basic machining skills are built into the numerically controlled machine tool. The machinist, therefore, does not use his material-processing skills, but still requires his mental or information-processing skills. It is simply not true that no machining experience is needed in numerical control operations; tools can burn out and surface finish can be as bad in an NC operation as on a standard machine tool, and an NC lathe can produce tool chatter as easily as a standard lathe.

Even though the methods of numerical control make it possible to machine shapes that are beyond the capacity of manual skills, it is still easier to machine even simple shapes by numerical control methods. The programming methods for numerically controlled machines are usually easy to learn, with the exception perhaps of NC lathes.

Although any type of machining or grinding can be executed by numerical-control methods, only those workpieces that require a high degree of information processing are machined by numerical control, that is, workpieces that are complex in shape or which require considerable layout work. Examples of such work would include helicopter blades, cams, screw threads with a variable pitch, or tube sheets of boilers or heat exchangers that require the drilling (and therefore the locating) of dozens or hundreds of holes.

In numerically controlled machining, the sequence of tool movements required to produce the part is programmed in holes punched into a continuous tape. The machine reads the code of holes and executes the movements commanded by this code. The tape-punched instructions may include tool movements in X, Y, and Z directions in three-dimensional space, rotation of an indexing table, control of coolant, control of spindle speed and of tool feed, automatic changing of tools in the spindle, or any other operation that may be required.

22.2 POSITIONING AXES

Although punched tape instructions for numerical control can be prepared by means of a computer, most tapes are prepared by manual methods without the assistance of a computer. Computer methods are not discussed in this book. But the machinist should not suppose that the computer methods are difficult, or that they are formidably mathematical. They are not difficult, nor are they mathematical—the mathematics is done by the computer, not the programmer—but use elementary geometry and trigonometry of the kind that the machinist is accustomed to in bench layout methods.

The NC programmer writes out his machine instructions in numerical blocks of information on suitable program manuscript paper. These blocks of information vary somewhat from one machine to another, though all follow certain standard methods to be discussed in this chapter. Since numerical control codes are standardized, the machinist should learn those standard practices that will give him familiarity with all NC machines, and not restrict himself to the coding and programming of any single machine. The latter method has obvious handicaps.

The numerical instructions are then punched into the control tape on some type of tape punch or tape-punching typewriter. The tape is inserted into the tape reader of the numerically controlled machine. The machine reads the information blocks one block at a time and executes the commands given in the block, after which the next block is read. If the operation is the drilling of holes, the simplest kind of numerical control, the location of each hole to be drilled is given in a separate block of information. The machine reads the location of the next hole, positions the workpiece for the drill, drills, then reads the next information block.

If the workpiece contains dozens or hundreds of holes, the programmer would have to calculate and program hole positions for several hours. To avoid this kind of wearisome and costly arithmetic, and the liberal possibility of error in the calculations, he would program a computer to carry out such calculations. This is done by describing the pattern of holes to the computer in a brief PATERN/ statement. The computer word PATERN/ (not PATTERN/, because computers are not programmed to read words longer than six characters) is actually a command to the computer to calculate and print out all the hole locations in the hole pattern.

The punched tape instructions control worktable and tool movements, which is exactly what a machinist does. Indeed, any numerically controlled machine can be switched to manual operation for control by the machinist instead of the tape, because occasionally tapes are wrong, and always a new tape is under suspicion until proved out.

Each movement that involves positioning of the tool or workpiece is called an *axis*. Many training institutes and colleges are equipped with the two-axis Cintimatic vertical-spindle mill. These Cintimatics can control movements in both the X direction (parallel to the machine bed) and the Y direction (across the machine bed). They cannot read Z dimensions punched into the tape. Other institutes have a Bridgeport vertical-spindle mill equipped with Slo-Syn controls or a Compudyne Contoura, usually with three-axis control in X, Y, and Z. A few have a fourth axis, which is a rotating worktable that can be programmed for angular movement. Most NC lathes are of the two-axis type, with Z movements parallel to the ways and X movements across the ways.

The Z axis of motion is the basic axis. This is the axis through the spindle of the machine. Whether the spindle axis is vertical, as on a Bridgeport mill, or horizontal, as on a lathe, the Z axis is the spindle axis.

An axis must have a positive and a negative direction of movement. There is an industry standard for these directions, which for the moment will not be discussed. Some machines do not follow this standard, and others, such as the Cintimatic, do not use negative directions. In any case, the operator can always consult the operating manual of his machine for such information. Some typical axis systems are given in Fig. 317. All of these are standard. The X axis is the long axis of the worktable, and the Y axis is the remaining axis after Z and X are settled. In the case of vertical spindle mills, the operator standing in front of his machine is looking in the $+Y$ direction, while $+X$ is to his right.

Most NC machines use five-digit dimensions with three decimal digits. The decimal point is omitted, and *must* be omitted. If a decimal point is punched into the tape coding, the tape reader would stop reading and the operation would, therefore, be interrupted. Thus $X = 11.625$ in. is punched into the tape as X11625, $Y = 3$ as Y03000. Sometimes trailing zeros may be omitted, and if so, Y03000 could be punched as Y03. A few machines allow the omission of leading zeros. The operating manual for your machine must be followed in these matters; you cannot assume that trailing zeros may be omitted. The NC machine, of course, will provide an accuracy at least equal to the number of decimal places that can be programmed.

Lathes require six-digit accuracy with four decimal positions for reasons to be discussed later. A few milling machines use four-decimal accuracy. Most NC machines position only to thousandths of an inch.

Numerically controlled machines are positioned to this degree of precision by means of hydraulic or electric servomotors. A servomotor is a positioning motor. The circuitry and computer logic devices that translate the tape code into machine movements are of the electronic type. Some limit switches are also used to control simple operations such as drilling to

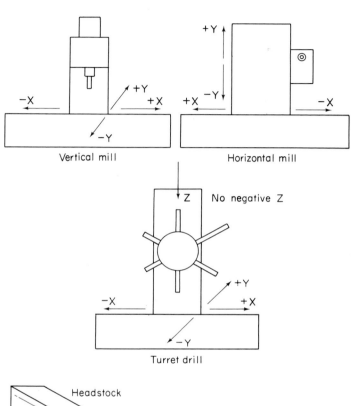

Vertical mill   Horizontal mill

No negative Z

Turret drill

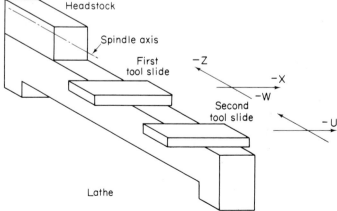

Lathe

Fig. 317

preset depths. However, a knowledge of electronics is not necessary to the programming or operation of numerically controlled machines.

22.3 POSITIONING AND CONTOURING CONTROL

The machinist is accustomed to controlling two types of tool movement: positioning and contouring.

If the machinist must position a radial drill for drilling a hole in a workpiece, he is indifferent to the path followed by the drill head in reaching its hole location—it is sufficient only that it arrive at the correct location. In such an operation, there is no machining until the positioning is completed. This is *positioning control* in an NC operation.

In the case of tool movements when one is turning on a lathe, the tool begins the cut as it moves, and must continue cutting until it arrives at a terminal location down the bar. Here the cutter must follow a controlled path in positioning to its destination. This is *contouring control*, where the tool cuts as it positions.

Positioning control is simpler and less expensive than contouring control, since the machine control unit does not control the path of the tool but only the terminal point of the tool movement. Contouring control systems must be more complex, because the position of the tool and its velocity must be controlled throughout the tool path, whether the tool cuts a straight line, an arc, or a complex curve. The punched control tape is also longer and the information more complex for contouring control. Often the contouring program may be sufficiently difficult that it must be produced by a computer.

Neither positioning in numerical control nor dimensioning of a part print can be done unless there is an origin or a base line to dimension from. In numerical control, positioning is done from an origin or zero point. This zero point is a point on the worktable of the machine, or, in the rare case, it is a point off the worktable. This zero point is the location of $X = 00.000$ $Y = 00.000$. In the case of the well-known Kearney & Trecker Milwaukee-Matic horizontal spindle mills, $Z = 00.0000$ is not located at the point $X = 00.0000$ $Y = 00.0000$, for reasons of convenience, though this unusual case does not make these machines harder to program.

For convenience in setting up the workpiece within the XY coordinate system, most machine control units have control knobs for shifting this zero point to any other location on the worktable.

When one is programming a series of drilled holes on a machine equipped with positioning controls, such as the series of holes of Fig. 318, two methods of dimensioning are possible: *absolute* and *incremental*. Absolute dimensioning is usual for positioning controls, while contouring machines such as lathes almost always use incremental dimensioning.

In absolute dimensioning, all dimensions are with reference to the

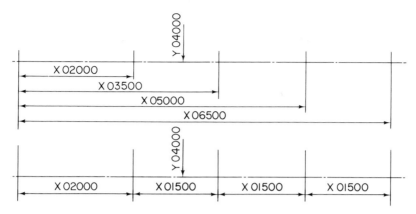

Fig. 318

zero point. Thus the position of the holes in Fig. 318 would be punched into tape thus in absolute dimensioning:

X02000 Y04000,   X03500 Y04000,   X05000 Y04000,   X06500 Y04000

If, instead, incremental dimensioning is used, then the previous position becomes the origin for the next position. In incremental positioning, these same holes would be punched

X02000 Y04000,   X01500 Y00000,   X01500 Y00000,   X01500 Y00000

Since the Y positions are all at 4.000 in., there are no Y increments.

In incremental positioning, incremental movements in X, Y, or Z may be plus or minus. Plus and minus movements for a vertical mill are indicated in Fig. 319 and for a lathe in Fig. 320. A minus movement requires a minus sign before the X, Y, or Z dimension, but a plus sign may be either

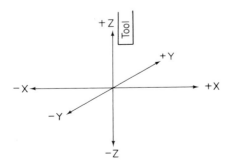

Fig. 319

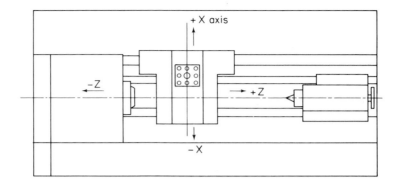

Fig. 320

omitted or included. Note from both Figs. 319 and 320 that an incremental movement in Z toward the spindle is a negative movement.

Positioning mills are equipped with a milling spindle and feed rate control for straight-cut milling operations parallel to either X or Y axis, as well as providing the standard positioning operations such as drilling, reaming, and tapping. This type of machine is commonly found in training schools and colleges. Fortunately, there are techniques for programming complex contouring operations on such a machine. It can mill an arc of a circle by making a very small movement of a few thousandths in X, then in Y, X, Y, alternately and thus move around the circle to any desired tolerance from the exact curve of the circle. The programmer may have to program a very long punched tape for such an operation, because the number of such small movements is very large if the tolerance is very small. By comparison, a machine with the more complex type of controls required for true contouring can program an arc in a couple of inches of tape. The techniques for contouring with a positioning mill are explained in the following chapter.

22.4 THE CONTROL TAPE

The usual medium for inserting information into a numerically controlled operation is punched tape, either of paper, mylar plastic, aluminum, or laminated aluminum-plastic. Dimensional specifications for numerical control tape are given in Fig. 321.

Each row of holes across the one-inch width of the tape is called a *track*. Punched tape for information processing may have 5, 6, 7, or 8 tracks. Numerical control uses 8 tracks. In addition, there is a row of smaller sprocket holes between the third and fourth tracks. The tape is driven through the tape reader of the machine control unit by a drive sprocket with teeth spaced to match the holes in the tape.

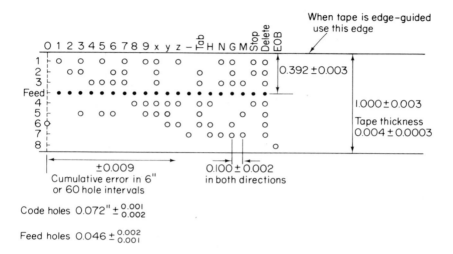

Fig. 321

Since holes are punched every 0.100 in. along the length of the tape, one inch of tape records 10 characters, each character being coded by a unique pattern of holes or no-holes in each of the eight tracks. A length of tape at the start and finish of the program, called a leader and a trailer, both at least 18 in. long, are needed for winding the tape on the reels.

Tapes are punched on teletype machines or special electric typewriters such as the Flexowriter of Fig. 322. Such a typewriter punches the tape in the punch mechanism on the left-hand side of the typewriter and at the same time produces a written record on a sheet of paper in the carriage of the typewriter. After the tape is punched, a second copy of it must be punched, since the original tape could be damaged or misplaced. To reproduce the tape, the original tape is inserted into the tape reader, also on the left side of the typewriter, and a blank tape is inserted into the tape punch. As the second tape is copied from the first, the typewriter can at the same time retype the manuscript information. This second copy of the manuscript information should be compared with the original sheet to check for errors. A Flexowriter out of adjustment can punch erroneous characters into the second tape, though ordinarily this is a thoroughly reliable machine.

Managing the typewriter is much less difficult than operating a machine tool, but the beginner at tape punching will make errors by striking the wrong key. Usually such an error is recognized as soon as it is made, and if so, it can be corrected by a special DELETE key. Suppose that the numerically controlled position X13232 is typed X13322, and that this error is immediately noted before any more characters are punched. The tape is backed up in the tape punch so that the first character in error is under the punch, in this case the third digit after X. The DELETE key is punched three times. This key

Fig. 322

punches three rows of holes across the tape, obliterating the erroneous
characters 322. The tape reader of the numerically controlled machine ignores
a DELETE code. The correct characters are next punched. The typed sheet
will read

$$X13322232$$

but the tape reader of the NC machine will ignore the three deleted characters
and read X13232. However, the punching of a row of DELETE holes across
the tape weakens the tape so that it is more easily torn.

22.5 THE TAPE CODE

Two character codes are now in use for punching letters, numbers, and other
characters into tape. These are compared in Fig. 323. Originally the EIA
code (Electronics Institute of America) was standard. Recently the ASCII
was introduced (American Standard Code for Information Interchange). In
time the ASCII code should replace the EIA code with which most existing
machines are equipped. Some recent models of NC machine tools have a
manual switch that selects the code to be read.

Both EIA and ASCII tape codes use the binary coded decimal number
system, a variant of the binary number system. The binary number system

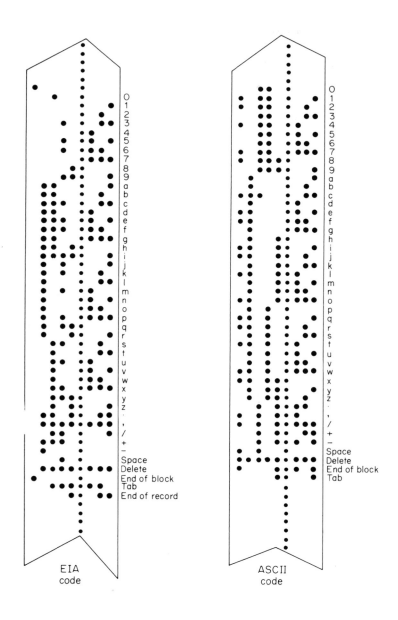

Fig. 323

uses only the digits 0 and 1. On tape, zero is represented by no-hole, 1 by a hole. Since there are only two digits, counting in this number system goes as follows:

Decimal number	Binary number
0	0
1	1
2	10
3	11
4	100
5	101
6	110
7	111
8	1000
9	1001
10	1010
11	1011
12	1100
13	1101
14	1110
15	1111
16	10000
17	10001
18	10010
20	10100
32	100000
64	1000000

The binary system is a much easier one to use than the decimal system, even though it requires more digits. Try multiplying 6×2 in the binary system:

$$
\begin{array}{rr}
6 & 110 \\
\times 2 & \times 10 \\
\hline
12 & 1100
\end{array}
$$

There is no multiplication table to memorize.

In the binary-coded decimal system, used in numerical control, each decimal digit is coded in binary instead of the whole number. Thus in binary arithmetic 32 is coded 100000. In binary-coded decimal (BCD) 32 is coded binary 3 binary 2, or 00110010 (using four digits for each number).

Most training shops have an NC machine that uses the EIA code for punched tape. The eight tracks of the EIA tape are organized as shown in

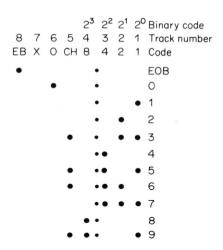

Fig. 324

Fig. 324. The binary levels 1, 2, 4 are on one side of the drive sprocket holes.

The coding of the digits 0 to 9 in the EIA code is also shown in Fig. 324. It will be noticed that the digits 3, 5, 6, and 9 have an additional hole in the fifth or CH track. When these numbers are punched (without the CH track) there is an even number of holes, all other numbers having an odd number of holes. Similarly, for the letters of the alphabet, if the number of holes is even, an extra hole is punched in the CH track. Thus every character punched into the tape must have an odd number of holes in the EIA code (or an even number in ASCII NC code, the eighth track being used for the extra hole). This is a method of checking the tape punch for malfunction, and is known as odd parity check (even parity check for ASCII). The tape reader on the NC machine will stop reading if a character has an even number of holes.

Track 6 in the EIA code is the zero track, and zero is represented by a hole in this track. Track 7 is called the X track. The 8th track is the EOB or end of block track. The EOB character must be punched at the end of each block of information, and for many machines must also be punched at the start of a tape program. Thus suppose a complete block of NC information comprised an X, a Y, and a Z dimension. This block of information would be punched

X01000 Y07500 Z03375 (EOB)

where EOB means the end of block or carriage return key on the typewriter. This carriage return key, as on any typewriter, returns the carriage of the typewriter to begin a new line. The machine control unit of the numerically controlled machine tool reads and stores the information from the punched tape, but takes no action on this information until it has read the EOB (carriage return) hole.

The coding of both numbers and letters is given in Fig. 323. In the EIA code, the letters A to I form a first group, with X and O tracks punched in addition to a number character: 1 for A, 2 for B, up to 9 for I. The odd parity also applies. Letters J to R form a second group of letters, using an X punch and number coding. The letters S to Z are coded with a hole in the O track.

The special symbols plus, minus, delete, end of block, end of record, and tab are also shown. The TAB key is used as in ordinary typing, to leave a space between columns of data, that is, to tabulate. With the use of this key, on the typed manuscript in the typewriter carriage, all the X dimensions of all the successive blocks of information are arrayed in a vertical column, and the Y's and other words likewise.

Programmers and NC machine operators must be able to read a punched tape, either to find a certain operation, to find an error in the tape that stops the tape reader from operating, or for other reasons. To read the tape, hold it vertically with the 1, 2, and 4 tracks to the right, with, of course, the beginning of the program at the top of the tape. It is not really necessary to memorize the hole patterns for the letters. Memorize only the number characters and look up the letters as you need to read them. Your own NC machine uses only a few letter characters. For practice, read a string of characters in any available tape, or read the samples given at the end of this chapter.

To understand the language of information processing, including numerical control, the following definitions must be understood.

A *bit* is the basic unit of information, either a hole or no-hole. "Bit" is an abbreviation of binary digit.

A *word* is a unit of information, such as a dimension (X00000 or Y12750) or delete, EOB, etc.

A *block* of information is a complete group of information words. For example, a block of information for a Cintimatic positioning mill contains five words (or six, if EOB is included):

H010 G81 X10000 Y09350 M00 (EOB).

Other machines may use different groups of words in the block.

22.6 TAPE FORMATS

The programming of NC data into suitable blocks of information for action by the NC machine control unit follows either of two standard formats: *word address* or *tab sequential*. A third type, the fixed block format, is used only with the Moog Hydrapoint positioning mills, and will not be discussed here. Word address is the format most commonly used.

Whether the format is word address or tab sequential, some machines allow the omission of trailing zeros (punching X10000 as X1) or of leading zeros (punching X00100 as X100). If so, this will be stated in the programming manual for the machine. When there is doubt, all zeros may be included for any machine using any tape format. Omission of zeros, however, reduces the length of tape and may, therefore, reduce the possibility of errors.

Omission of leading or trailing zeros is allowable for the dimension words X, Y, and Z only. M and G words, to be discussed presently, must include all zeros. If, for example, M06 is punched as M6 or G80 as G8, the tape reader will cease reading until the error is cleared through the tape reader.

A word read from the tape into the storage register of the machine control unit remains in the storage register until replaced by another word, or until the end of the program. For example, suppose a row of holes must be drilled on the line X = 6.000 in. thus

$$X06000 \quad Y06000$$
$$X06000 \quad Y07000$$
$$X06000 \quad Y08000$$
$$X06000 \quad Y09000$$

with a final hole at X07000 Y09000. This sequence of holes may be punched

$$X06000 \quad Y06000$$
$$Y07000$$
$$Y08000$$
$$Y09000$$
$$X07000$$

The only exceptions to this principle of not repeating words already in storage are rather obvious ones. For example, M00 is an instruction to the machine to stop at the end of the information block, and this instruction cannot be retained in storage, for if so the machine would stop at the end of each block of information.

Most NC machines use a five-digit dimension word for X, Y, and Z, with three decimal places assumed. The Gorton Tapemaster uses four digits with a method of shifting the decimal place. Lathes and Kearney & Trecker Milwaukee-Matic mills use six digits with four decimal places.

22.7 WORD ADDRESS FORMAT

A typical word address format is that for the Cintimatic positioning vertical-spindle mill found in many training colleges. A block of information for the Cintimatic mill might read

H016 G81 X12075 Y04375 M06 (EOB)

There are five words in this block, if EOB is neglected, each preceded by its letter address. The H word is identified or addressed by the letter H, and, when read by the tape reader on the NC machine control unit, is switched into the H information register. Similarly, the preparatory or G word is switched into the G register, and so for X, Y, and M words. The EOB word is a signal to the machine control unit to release the information read into the storage register and to operate with it on the workpiece. The letter addresses, therefore, are used as switching signals to switch each word to the proper electronic information storage.

The TAB key may be used between words in word address format to space out the information on the typed manuscript. The TAB character in the tape will be ignored by the machine control unit, just as the DELETE word is ignored.

22.8 TAB SEQUENTIAL FORMAT

To illustrate the tab sequential format, recall the previous example of a Cintimatic block of word address format, which was

H016 G81 X12075 Y04375 M06 (EOB)

If the machine control unit is designed to receive the tab sequential format, each word would not be letter-addressed, but instead would be preceded by a TAB punch. In tab sequential format the previous information block would read

016 T81 T12075 T04375 T06 (EOB)

The H016 word simply indicates to the machine operator that this is the 16th block of information. The NC machine does not do anything with this sequence number except to display it on a readout. It does not go into any information storage, and is not preceded by a TAB signal for this reason.

Imagine the words of a tab sequential format to be switched into information storage by means of a rotary stepping switch (Fig. 325). The first TAB moves this switch from OFF to the first rotary position, and 81 goes into this storage position. The second TAB moves the switch to the second switch position; thus all X dimensions go into the second storage location. This switching continues to the end of the block.

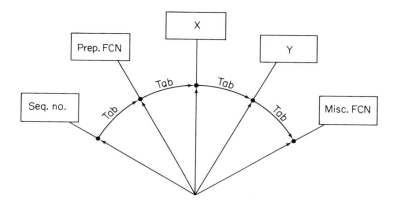

Fig. 325

As usual, words already in storage do not need to be repeated. Suppose the program reads

015 T81 T07875 T04375 T06 (EOB)
016 T81 T07875 T05625 T09 (EOB)

These two blocks of information may be punched

015 T81 T07875 T04375 T06
016 T   T   T05625 T09

Each block of information must have the required number of TAB's punched; otherwise, words would go into the wrong storage location. If the second block is punched

016 T05625 T09

then the machine control unit would attempt to put 05625 into the first or G storage position and 09 into the second or X storage position. But 05625 would not be a recognizable G word, and the tape reader would stop reading.

22.9 MISCELLANEOUS FUNCTIONS

Whatever the tape format used, almost all NC machines use certain standard miscellaneous or M functions. These must be familiar to programmers.

M00. Program stop. This is programmed if the operation is to stop at the end of a certain block for an inspection or any other reason. The operator presses the CYCLE START button when he is ready to continue the tape-controlled operation.

M01. Optional stop. The machine operator can override this stop command if he decides a stop is not necessary.

M02. End of program. The spindle is retracted and the coolant is shut off. The registers are cleared of all words. In some machines the tape may be rewound also.

M03. Start spindle, clockwise rotation.

M04. Start spindle, counterclockwise rotation.

M05. Spindle off.

M06. Stop for a tool change. Spindle stops rotating.

M07. Mist coolant on.

M08. Flood coolant on.

M09. Coolant off.

Not all machines use all these M codes. The Slo-Syn NC system uses in addition a few nonstandard miscellaneous functions 53, 54, 55, 56. The Compudyne Contoura uses M01 to command an indexing table to rotate one angular increment.

22.10 PREPARATORY FUNCTIONS

There are a considerable number of preparatory or G functions in use. Some are used only in lathe work, such as G33, which is the command for thread cutting. Some are applicable only to positioning operations, such as G84, which is a tapping command. Two G functions are in common use in positioning work:

G80. Retracted spindle; no Z motion during the block.
G81. Drill cycle. Drill the hole and retract the drill.

22.11 SEQUENCE NUMBER

The sequence numbers give the sequence of the blocks of information. That is, the first information block is designated 001, the next 002, and so on. However, if there is a possibility that additional blocks of information may be needed in the tape due to later modifications of the part, a series of numbers may be left out, or the blocks may be numbered 005, 010, 015, etc. Sometimes it is necessary for the tape reader to read the tape very rapidly, as when approximating a circle with a series of small straight lines, and in order to speed up the tape reading, sequence numbers may be omitted.

The sequence number is displayed on a sequence number readout on the machine control unit. With this display, the machine operator knows at all times where in the program the machine is working. Unless he knows this, he has no control over the machine and becomes a helpless onlooker.

Numerical control is not completely automatic under all circumstances. Indeed, a totally automatic machine has never yet been built. All systems, numerically controlled or otherwise, are only as automatic as circumstances and economics allow. If a cutter breaks or fails, certainly the NC machine does not automatically replace the failed tool with a new one. If tool chatter develops, the NC machine will not correct the condition. The operator must maintain control, slowing down or speeding up the feed rate, switching from tape to manual control in an emergency, stopping the operation to replace a tool or to adjust a workpiece, and so on. In order to have control over this "automatic" machine, he must refer to the sequence number readout and the program sheet.

22.12 SETTING UP THE WORKPIECE

In numerical control you are, of course, machining in some system of dimensional coordinates. Somewhere in space there is an origin or zero point, with coordinates X = 00.000, Y = 00.000. The spindle or the NC machine can be programmed by tape to any position in this coordinate system, to an accuracy usually of 0.001 in. Accurate positioning in a coordinate system, however, is not the objective of numerical control, rather, what is wanted is accurate positioning on a workpiece. For this to be possible, there must be some way of locating the workpiece in the coordinate system of the machine.

A common method of locating the workpiece in the XY coordinate

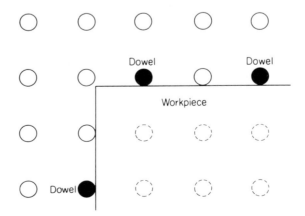

Fig. 326

system is shown in Fig. 326. The worktable of the machine, or a subplate clamped to the table, is accurately drilled with locating dowel holes in a pattern of XY locations. If the workpiece or fixture is located and clamped against locating dowels as shown in the figure, then its location is accurately known.

To obtain a locating accuracy of 0.001 in. by the three-dowel method, the two reference edges of the workpiece must fulfill all the following requirements:

1. Each edge must be straight.
2. Each edge must be flat.
3. Each edge must have a reasonably smooth machine surface.
4. The two reference edges of the workpiece must be exactly at 90 deg to one another.

Careful shapering or planing will produce these four conditions. A fifth condition is, of course, a clean worktable, with no chips or dirt to interfere with positioning of the workpiece.

Note that only three dowels must be used, two on one side and one dowel on the second side of the workpiece. If, for instance, three dowels instead of two were used for one side, there would be uncertainty as to which dowels the workpiece will bear against. Two dowels give only one locating possibility; three dowels offer three possibilities.

Sometimes a hole in the workpiece must be located at a certain XY point on the table. The spindle is moved by manual controls to this XY point, and the workpiece is clamped approximately in the required position. A center-finder device is then placed in the spindle, and the position of the workpiece is adjusted until the center-finder indicates that the hole is accurately centered.

Frequently a milling vise is used to hold workpieces for NC machining. Such a vise must be of good quality, without slack in the movable jaw, and with straight and parallel jaws. When a workpiece is clamped in the vise, its location in XY must be known, preferably the location of one corner. The best device for finding the location of a corner is an optical device that can be inserted into the spindle. The operator moves the spindle to a convenient location near the reference corner of the workpiece, such as X10000 Y03000. He then uses the *zero offset* controls to move the worktable until the reference corner comes under the spindle as he observes through the eyepiece. The spindle location and the reference corner remain at X10000 Y03000. This method thus moves the whole dimensional reference system to suit the location of the workpiece.

When one is clamping a vise to the machine table, the fixed jaw of the vise must be parallel to the X axis (or Y axis). Parallelism is determined by inserting a dial indicator in the spindle and passing the indicator along the length of the fixed jaw.

22.13 CHECKING OUT THE TAPE

When beginning a tape-controlled machining job, the operator never assumes that the tape is error-free. Occasionally serious damage results from such an assumption. For example, a clamp or other obstruction may be located between two hole positions for drilling. The programmer may absent-mindedly have forgotten the clamp and programmed the tool across it. If the tool strikes the clamp, tool breakage may represent only several dollars damage, but damage to the machine spindle will be a disaster.

On inserting a new tape in the machine, the operator checks out the program one block of information at a time, without any workpiece on the machine table. So that he can prevent any unforeseen trouble, he overrides the tool feed commands in the tape, allowing the machine to make only slow movements. He watches the Z depths on mills and drills to see that they appear to be realistic. If there is an apparent mistake, he marks the block of information on the tape with a pencil mark and notes the sequence number. When the tape is corrected, he makes another test run, again without a workpiece, or perhaps with a block of Styrofoam or polyurethane instead of a workpiece.

QUESTIONS

1. Why does the character DELETE have 7 holes in EIA and 8 in ASCII code?
2. Why is zero not coded as no holes in any of the tracks of punched tape?
3. Summarize the system of coding the 26 letters in both EIA and ASCII codes.
4. The miscellaneous functions M00, M02, and M06 are all stop commands. What are the differences between them?
5. What is the difference between a track and a row of holes in punched tape?
6. Sketch the numerically controlled axis systems that would be set up for the principal standard machine tools of your shop.
7. How many characters are punched in every 10 feet of tape?
8. Write the following numbers in the binary system:

$$3, 7, 9, 10, 13, 19, 25, 29, 31, 33, 40$$

9. Write the following numbers in the binary-coded decimal system, using four characters for each decimal number:

$$3, \ 7, \ 10, \ 13, \ 29, \ 232, \ 719$$

10. Make the following multiplications in the binary system:

$$3 \times 3, \qquad 3 \times 4, \qquad 4 \times 4, \qquad 5 \times 5$$

11. Suppose the holes punched into the EIA tape, including the parity holes, represent binary numbers (not binary-coded decimal). What number would be given by the hole pattern for the following characters?
   a. EOB   b. TAB   c. DELETE   d. 9   e. 5

12. You have punched an EOB in the wrong place in the tape. Can you use the DELETE punch to cancel it?

13. When one is feeding punched tape through a tape reader, cumulative error allowed in the tape is ± 0.009 in. in 6 in. of tape. Hole spacing is 0.100 ± 0.002 in. in both directions. A sprocket drum with 24 sprocket points is to be designed for driving punched tape. Determine drum diameter, its diameter tolerance, and the angular tolerance between sprocket positions.

14. Consult the EIA character code and read the following tapes.

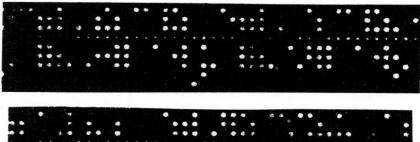

Fig. 327

Chapter 23

Numerically Controlled Machining

Most training institutes with a numerically controlled machine tool appear to be equipped with either the Cintimatic vertical-spindle mill or Slo-Syn controls fitted to standard vertical-spindle mills such as the Bridgeport, or the Compudyne Contoura. A few other types of machines are sometimes found in these institutions, such as the Pratt & Whitney Tape-O-Matic or the Gorton Tapemaster. The numerically controlled lathe is rarely found in schools and colleges.

Numerically controlled lathes likewise are somewhat less common in industry. Most industrial shops are equipped with drills or positioning mills of the type that can mill parallel to X and Y axes only.

In this chapter specific methods of operating numerically controlled machine tools will not be discussed, since the student machinist in his course must learn to operate the particular machine installed for his training. He has the operating manual of his machine to follow; this must take precedence over any remarks made in this chapter. Here only numerical-control techniques of general usefulness for all drills and positioning mills will be discussed, with special emphasis on contouring methods that may be applied to positioning mills. The principles that govern the programming of numerically controlled lathes will be explained, but the student machinist should be advised that the NC lathe can be somewhat difficult to program without computer assistance, unless the part is rather simple in shape, and requires him to process a considerable amount of trigonometric calculations.

23.1 A SIMPLE HOLE-DRILLING PROGRAM

We begin with a simple hole-drilling program using the workpiece of Fig. 328, as shown set up on the machine table. The holes are numbered— numbering of holes is always a helpful procedure in programming. A parking position for the tool at X18000 Y16000 is selected. This position is off the workpiece, so that the workpiece can be set up and removed from the machine

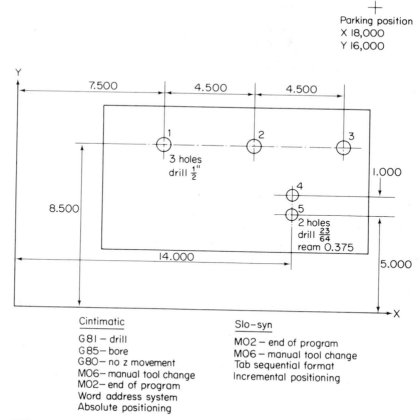

Fig. 328

without interference by the spindle or tool. Tools will be changed at this parking position.

This drilling and reaming operation will be programmed for both a Cintimatic vertical-spindle positioning mill and a Slo-Syn installation on a drilling machine. These two machines are selected first because they are in common use, and second because the first uses word address, and the second machine tab sequential tape format.

A. The Cintimatic. This machine uses word address format and absolute positioning. It is a two-axis machine; therefore, the depth settings for each tool must be set up on depth cams before the tape-controlled operation begins. We shall suppose that the following depth cams are used:

$\frac{1}{2}$-in. drill   —cam M53
$\frac{23}{64}$-in. drill   —cam M54
0.375-in. reamer—cam M55

These depth cams are called up as M or miscellaneous functions.

The information block for this machine is the following:

$$\text{H}xxx\ \text{G}xx\ \text{X}xxxxx\ \text{Y}xxxxx\ \text{M}xx$$

where   H = sequence number.
G81 = drill cycle.
G85 = bore cycle (for the reaming tool).
The drill cycle drills the hole and retracts the tool rapidly. The bore cycle feeds the tool in, then feeds it out of the hole at the same rate. Hence, G85 will produce a hole with a better surface finish than the G81 cycle.

$$\text{G84} = \text{tap cycle}$$

In the G84 tap cycle, the spindle is reversed at the bottom of the hole in order to retract the tap, then reversed again after the tap is retracted.

G80 = cancel cycle. No Z motion. The spindle remains retracted.
M02 = end of program.
M06 = stop for a tool change. The tool must be changed manually.

The program should begin with an EOB character. Dimension words do not have to be repeated if used in the previous block of information, nor do G and M words.

This is a very brief summary of the method of programming a Cintimatic vertical-spindle mill, but it is meant only to be sufficient for the reader to understand the program.

We assume that a starter drill is not needed in the following program. Remember that an XY position tells the machine the terminal position that it must move to; the G81, G84, G85, and M06 actions occur after the XY move in the information block has been made.

        EOB
        H001 G81 X07500 Y08500 M53   Drill Hole 1

The tool moves from parking position to hole 1. G81 drills the hole. Note that the spindle goes to the XY position in the block first, and the G81 drill cycle is applied at this destination.

        H002 G81 X12000 Y08500 M53   Drill Hole 2
        H003 G81 X16500 Y08500 M06   Drill Hole 3

After drilling hole 3 to depth as set up on cam M53, M06 stops the rotation of the spindle, which is also retracted. The spindle could be returned to the parking position for a tool change, but suppose we make the tool change over hole 3. Note that if the spindle is returned to parking position for a tool change, a G80 must be programmed; otherwise, G81 is still in the storage register, and a hole will be drilled at the parking position.

        H004 G81 X14000 Y06000 M54   Hole 4
        H005 G81 X14000 Y05000 M06   Hole 5

The tool change is made while the spindle is located over hole 5.

        H006 G85 X14000 Y05000 M55   Ream Hole 5
        H007 G85 X14000 Y06000 M55   Ream Hole 4
        H008 G80 X18000 Y16000 M02   Parking Position

G80 prevents any Z movement at the parking position X18000 Y16000.

    The program may be reduced by eliminating the repeated words, which are retained in the storage registers until changed by the receipt of other words:

        EOB
        H001 G81 X07500 Y08500 M53
        H002   X12000
        H003   X16500   M06
        H004   X14000 Y06000 M54
        H005   Y05000 M06
        H006 G85   M55
        H007   Y06000
        H008 G80 X18000 Y16000 M02

If it is desired, M06 may be separated as an independent block of information, H004 M06. If there is no change in X or Y, then the spindle does not move in such a block.

B. Slo-Syn. This numerical control system uses tab sequential format and incremental dimensioning. Incremental dimensioning requires a few words of explanation if confusion is to be avoided.

In the case of either the Cintimatic, the Slo-Syn, or most other two- and three-axis mills and drills, the spindle is described as moving to a given XY point. Now, of course, in these machines it is not the spindle, but the worktable that is moved by the positioning motors. Nevertheless, the programmer must think of the spindle as moving and the worktable as fixed in any and all NC programming. It is not intended here to explain at length why this should even matter. But one reason is that it is not possible to program with computer assistance except with the assumption that it is the spindle that moves. So, regardless of what happens in reality, it is the spindle that positions, not the table.

For the motions in incrementing, see the drawing of the part, Fig. 328. A spindle movement to the left, from parking position toward the zero point, is a −X movement (though the Slo-Syn motor actually moves the table to the right). A spindle movement to the right is a +X movement, say, from hole 1 to hole 2.

A spindle movement toward the operator, from parking position down the page to hole 5, say, is a −Y movement. A spindle movement away from the operator, or up the page, is a +Y movement. These motions are summarized in Fig. 319.

In the following program, the machine controls are set up so that a hole is drilled at each location programmed. Hence, there is no G word. The Slo-Syn information block does not include G words, but has M words. The complete block of information is the following, T being used to represent the TAB key:

(seq. no.) T (X increment) T (Y increment) T (M word)

There must not be a TAB character before the sequence number.

The Slo-Syn program must begin with an EOB, then a Rewind Stop Code.

	EOB ½-in. drill in spindle
0 RWS	EOB
1 T −10500 T −07500	EOB hole 1

The tool must move 10½ in. to the left and 7½ in. forward to hole 1.

There is no M word in sequence 1, so the last TAB may be omitted.

    2 T   04500   EOB hole 2

A movement of 4½ in. in the +X direction locates hole 2. The Y dimension remains the same, and is not repeated. The remaining TAB's may be omitted.

    3 T   04500   EOB
    4 T   01500 T   07500 T 06 EOB change to $\frac{23}{64}$ drill

The tool returns to the parking position for a tool change. The tool change is made manually. Note that if the miscellaneous function 06 were not included in this block, a hole would be drilled at the parking position.

    5 T −04000 T −10000   EOB hole 4
    6 T   T −01000   EOB hole 5
    7 T   04000 T   11000 T 06 EOB change to reamer

In sequence 7 the spindle is returned to parking position for a tool change.

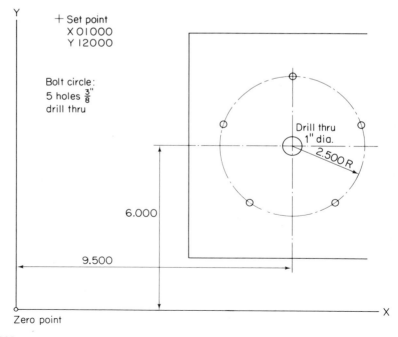

Fig. 329

The reader should next program the center hole and bolt circle holes of Fig. 329 for the Cintimatic, the Slo-Syn, and his own NC machine. The parking position of the spindle is designated SET POINT.

23.2 A SIMPLE SLOT-MILLING PROGRAM

The slot of Fig. 330 is to be milled with a $\frac{5}{8}$-in. two-lipped end mill. The parking position of the tool is designated SETPT.

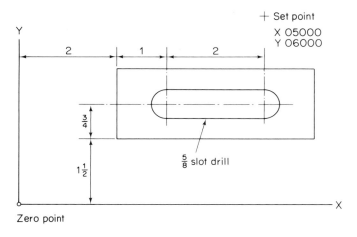

Fig. 330

A. Cintimatic. The operator must locate the workpiece on the machine table and set up the depth cams for the milling depth. Actually, two cams are required for Z motion of any tool: a rapid approach cam to bring the cutter rapidly to a position just above the workpiece, and a slow feed cam to stop the downfeed when the tool has reached the final depth. Controlled feed rate prevails between the rapid approach position and the final depth.

For this milling operation another G function must be introduced. This is G78, called *mill cycle stop*, which has the following motion sequence. The worktable moves at rapid traverse to the programmed XY position in the information block. The quill then moves down at rapid advance and slow feed rate to the final depth setting at the bottom of the slot. The tape reader stops reading, the spindle stops rotating, and a QUILL-CLAMP lamp comes on. The operator clamps the quill at this point so that there will be no variation in Z movement when milling. He then pushes a START button to continue the tape-controlled operation.

This G78 cycle is used to drill into the part at the beginning of a slot-milling operation. At the end of the slot, the spindle must be stopped again so that the operator can unclamp it before withdrawing it from the slot. A G78 can be coded in order to unclamp the quill. If G78 should be thus used at the end of slot-milling, the quill is already at final depth and, therefore, does not move in the Z direction; the G78 in this case is simply being used as a STOP code for the purpose of unclamping. To retract the quill, any suitable command may be used, such as G81 (drill cycle).

G79, Mill Cycle. In all the previously discussed "canned" or G cycles, the quill is retracted as it moves rapidly to the XY destination, and then on arrival at the destination makes movements in Z. The G79 mill cycle command allows for movement in milling at a given Z depth and at a controlled milling feed rate, which is set up manually. In the present example, the slot must be milled out with a G79 function.

We can now program Fig. 330 for a Cintimatic vertical spindle mill.

H001 G79 X03000 Y02250 M52

The slot drill depth settings are made on cam M52. The slot drill goes to the start of the slot, drills down to depth, stops, and the QUILL CLAMP light comes on. The operator clamps the quill, then presses the CYCLE START button. The tape reader then starts reading again

H002 G78 X05000

The slot drill mills to the end of the slot.

H003 G79

The G79 is programmed so that the QUILL CLAMP light will go on, reminding the operator that the quill is clamped and must be unclamped.

H004 G81

A G81 is used to retract the quill.

H005 G80 X05000 Y06000 M02

The spindle goes to SETPT with the quill retracted. The G80 prevents the previous G81 stored in memory from executing a drilling sequence at SETPT.

Note that there are other acceptable methods of programming this operation.

B. Slo-Syn. In programming this slot for a Cintimatic mill, a new operation had to be explained: a controlled milling feed rate at a given depth of cut. Previously, all tool operations simply required a rapid movement to an XY destination with a retracted tool, followed by a drilling or other operation at the XY position given. This new operation was programmed by a G78 milling operation to the XY destination given in the same block as the G78 function. The Slo-Syn operation provides the same function, but with M or miscellaneous functions.

The Slo-Syn uses a Tool Advance and a Tool Retract command, with a milling operation programmed between the two commands:

$$M52 = \text{tool advance in Z direction}$$
$$M53 = \text{tool retract in Z direction}$$

When the tool must position in XY rapidly, instead of at the milling feed rate set up for the operation, use

$$M55 = \text{high feed rate}$$

Here is the slot-milling operation as programmed for the Slo-Syn. T being used for TAB key:

```
                                    EOB
    0 RWS                           EOB
    1 T  −02000 T  −03750 T  55 EOB
```

The spindle moves rapidly (55) 2 in. to the right in X and $3\frac{3}{4}$ in. forward in Y to the start of the slot. The tool is still retracted. Leading zeros may be omitted, so that X and Y could be programmed −2000 and −3750.

```
    2 T 2000 T T 52                 EOB
```

The spindle moves an additional 2 in. in X, but in a milling operation with the tool at the bottom of the slot (52).

The slot is now milled. The tool must be withdrawn, and must then move to SETPT. M53 retracts the tool, M55 calls for a rapid movement to SETPT, and M02 must terminate the program. The Slo-Syn can handle more than one miscellaneous function in one information block. We can return the tool to SETPT and end the program with a composite M function 025355 (02 = end of program, 53 = tool retract, 55 = high feed rate). However, this composite M function need not include the second 5 in the two 50 codes; program it as 02535.

```
    3 T T 3750 T 02535              EOB
```

23.3 A POCKET MILLING OPERATION

The base pad of Fig. 331 has two pockets to be milled $\frac{3}{8}$ in. deep. Here we shall consider pocket milling of the bottom pocket 2 in. wide. Since the pocket corners have a radius of $\frac{1}{2}$ in., a 1-in. two-lipped end mill is required. Such an end mill is exactly one-half the width of the pocket; therefore, a milling pass around the pocket will likely leave a narrow strip of material in the middle of the pocket. To make the program simple, the convenient assumption will be made that the pocket will be completely cleaned out in two passes.

The workpiece is fixtured so that the bottom left-hand corner of the plate is located at X10000 Y03000. The parking position of the tool is at X05000 Y10000.

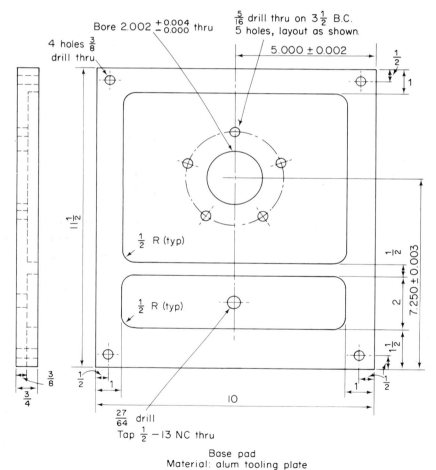

Base pad
Material: alum tooling plate
Number required: 3

Fig. 331

A. Cintimatic Mill. Suppose the pocket to be milled starting at the lower left-hand corner. Actually, if the end mill drills into a corner of the pocket, it will give an oversize hole at this point. The pocket will be drilled, therefore, at an interior point, and the end mill then will mill out to the periphery of the pocket.

```
        EOB
        H001 G78 X15000 Y05500 M54
```

Depth is set on cam 54. The axis of the mill goes rapidly to the center of the pocket, drills in to depth, and the quill clamp light goes on.

```
        H002 G79          Y05000
```

The cutter mills forward in Y to the edge of the pocket.

```
        H003      X11500
```

Mill to the lower left-hand corner of the pocket.

```
        H004               Y06000
        H005      X18500
        H006               Y05000
        H007      X14995
        H008 G79
        H009 G81
        H010 G80 X05000 Y10000 M02
```

B. Slo-Syn. The same sequence of movements will be used for a Slo-Syn operation. Recall that the tool starting position is X05000 Y10000.

```
        0 RWS
        1 T    10000 T  −04500 T 55
```

The tool goes to the pocket center at rapid speed.

```
        2 T          T  −00500 T 52
```

The tool moves forward 0.500 in. in Y. Leading zeros may be omitted from dimensions.

```
        3 T  −3500
        4 T          T    1000
        5 T    7000
        6 T          T  −1000
        7 T  −3500  T         T 53
        8 T  −10000 T    5000 T0255
```

The program concludes with M02 and M55.

23.4 ANGLE CUTS

A positioning mill such as the Cintimatic can mill parallel to either the X or Y axis, but not at an angle to these axes. The Slo-Syn positioning system can mill also at an angle of 45 deg to these axes. Now suppose that such a positioning mill must mill a slot at an angle of 60 deg to the X axis.

To mill such a slot on a positioning mill, it must be approximated by small movements first in X (or Y), then Y, and so on alternately in each axis, as indicated in Fig. 332. How large these small movements can be

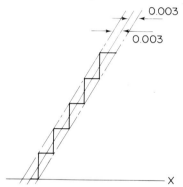

Fig. 332

depends on the allowable tolerance. Suppose this allowable tolerance to be ± 0.003, that is, 0.003 either side of the cut. This tolerance is shown in the figure in the X direction for convenience, rather than normal to the slot. To produce the slot, the cutter must mill in the movements shown in the figure. The X movements will be 0.006, the full range of the tolerance. The Y movements will be 0.0104, as determined by trigonometry.

A bilateral tolerance of 0.003 does not give an especially good finish. To improve the finish, program an X movement and a Y movement in the same block so that the tool moves simultaneously in both axes more closely to approximate the desired line.

Positioning machines employ relatively slow tape readers. The Cintimatic, for example, reads the tape at 60 characters per second. Since each block of information provides a cut of only a few thousandths of an inch, the tape reading time could approximately equal the cutting time and thus slow the operation. To speed the tape reading operation, only the first X and Y increment should include a sequence number, and the following blocks of information should contain only an X and a Y word.

23.5 CUTTING CIRCULAR ARCS ON A POSITIONING MILL

Two-dimensional contour milling is possible without the assistance of a

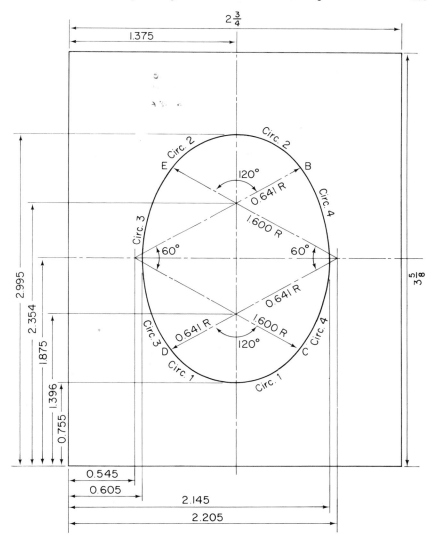

Fig. 333

computer if curves no more complex than a circular arc are used. Calculations for more complex curves become impossible without a computer.

The following discussion concerns the milling of a circular arc with a positioning mill limited to milling movements in X and Y only. The example used is an elliptical groove for an O-ring (Fig. 333). This groove, however, is made up of parts of four circles to approximate an ellipse. There is a considerable amount of repetitive calculation even for the case of a circular arc, and this can be handled in any of three ways:

1. Obtain a desk calculator and make the calculations manually. Without such a calculator, there will be too many mistakes and too much time checking calculations. For an NC mill positioning to thousandths of an inch, calculate to "tenths" and round off to thousandths.
2. Find a friendly computer programmer who will put your calculations through his computer in Fortran or other computer language.
3. You could, of course, learn the computer methods yourself. This is not an excessively tall order. You can become a sufficiently competent computer programmer in one computer language in one-tenth the time needed to become a competent machinist.

For the milling of circular arcs, three possible cases arise.

1. The cutter must cut on the outside of the circle to produce a convex curve.
2. The cutter must cut on the inside of the circle to produce a concave shape.
3. The axis of the cutter must lie on the circle, as when one is cutting a groove. In this case, the circle is the path of the axis of the end mill. In the first two cases, the edge of the cutter just touches the circle, or, rather must be within tolerance of the circle from which it is offset.

Hand programming for the third case only is discussed here. However, the method can be adapted to serve the other two cases by altering the radius of the circle to that required to be traversed by the axis of the cutter. This requires that the radius of the circle be adjusted by the amount of the cutter offset.

We assume here that we must contour, using circular arcs, on a positioning mill such as the Cintimatic. The NC machine can mill parallel to X and Y axes only. We must approximate a circle by short movements alternately in X and Y, the length of these movements being determined entirely by the allowable tolerance. As in the case of the slot just discussed, a smoother finish is obtained by including an X and a Y movement together in each information block.

When one is milling a circular groove, the radius is known and so is the allowable tolerance. The tolerance must be expressed bilaterally, for convenience of computation. Thus, if the radius and tolerance on the drawing are given as $3.200 + 0.100, - 0.000$, this must be converted to

$$3.205 \pm 0.005$$

Consult Fig. 334. This shows a circular arc of radius R and bilateral tolerance of n. The end mill commences cutting with the axis of the end mill on the radius at A_0, B_0, where A_0 is presumably an X dimension and B_0 a

Y dimension. The origin of coordinates for A and B dimensions is the center of the circle, so that B_0 is actually zero.

The end mill cuts in the Y direction (up the page) for a distance B_1. At this increment in Y it has reached the tolerance limit. The cutter must then move in the X direction until it reaches the inner limit of tolerance. This X increment is $(A_0 - A_1)$. The next movement is a Y increment back to the outer tolerance limit. X and Y alternate as the arc is approximated, with constantly changing increments in both dimensions.

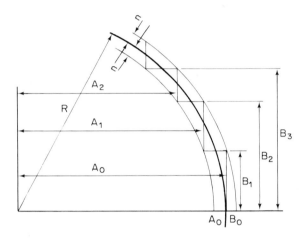

Fig. 334

The formulas for calculating these increments are derived from the geometry of the circle.

$$R = \text{radius}$$
$$n = \text{tolerance in one direction}$$
$$= 0.003 \text{ in this example, } not \ 0.006$$

$A_0 = R \cdot$	$B_0 = 0$
$A_1 = \sqrt{R^2 - 4Rn}$	$B_1 = \sqrt{2Rn + n^2}$
$A_2 = \sqrt{R^2 - 8Rn}$	$B_2 = \sqrt{6Rn + n^2}$
$A_3 = \sqrt{R^2 - 12Rn}$	$B_3 = \sqrt{10Rn + n^2}$
$A_4 = \sqrt{R^2 - 16Rn}$	$B_4 = \sqrt{14Rn + n^2}$
$A_j = \sqrt{R^2 - 4_jRn}$	$B_j = \sqrt{(4_j - 2)Rn + n^2}$

Frequently, n^2 is infinitesimal compared to the Rn component in the

B function and can be ignored. To repeat, the assumed origin of coordinates is the center of the circle.

What are the implications of errors and inaccuracies? Rounding-off errors must be assessed first. Numerical control programming is usually done to thousandths of an inch, which means that "tenths" could be significant when one is rounding off. The fourth decimal place must be watched carefully, but can sometimes be ignored. These calculations, therefore, virtually require the use of a desk calculator or a Fortran program put through a small computer.

Next consider the significance of calculating errors. Suppose an error is made in the calculation of A_2, and then A_3 is calculated by adding in $4Rn$ more. By this means a single error is promoted into a continuous error.

23.6 PROGRAMMING THE O-RING GROOVE

The formulas for incrementing around a circle in X and Y are simple enough. But the O-ring groove is composed of four circular arcs, and before programming a shape such as this, the programmer must be quite clear at all times as to the relation between *A* and *B* increments and the X and Y directions. There is an orientation problem here.

It does not matter where the calculations begin, but it ought to be obvious that you must start at one of the axes of symmetry of the O-ring ellipse. There are then four possible places to begin incrementing, and from any of these points the programmer increments out of the points of tangency where two arcs meet.

Suppose you were to begin incrementing at the upper end of the vertical axis of the ellipse, that is, the top point of the ellipse, and incremented clockwise (to the right). The vertical direction is Y and the horizontal direction is X. Then A_0 is a Y dimension and B_0 an X dimension. The *B*'s become larger in X and the *A*'s smaller in Y.

You would increment along the top small-radius arc until the point of tangency is reached for the larger-radius arc. The last increment in X and Y must give the point of tangency. Actually, the last two increments are unlikely to give this point exactly. Instead, the actual X and Y positions of the point of tangency are calculated from sine or cosine 30 or 60 deg.

The large-radius arc to the right of the ellipse comes next. The programmer is at the point of tangency, not on the intersection of the arc with the ellipse axis. You cannot increment from the point of tangency. On this large-radius arc, A_0 is an X dimension and B_0 is a Y dimension, just the opposite of the case for the small-radius arc.

Since the ellipse is symmetrical, the calculations for any quarter of the ellipse can be adapted to any other quarter.

23.7 PREPARING AND CHECKING THE TAPE

The punched tape for producing the O-ring groove on a typical positioning mill is about 50 ft long, or 6000 characters. A tape of this length offers plenty of scope for making errors. If your experience with the Friden Flexowriter or other tape-punching equipment is limited, you will probably require virtually a full day to punch a correct tape of this length. The commonest errors of inexperience are the following:

1. In glancing from the typewriter back to the written program, the wrong line may be read.
2. The wrong key may be struck.
3. O may be substituted for zero or lowercase *L* for unity.

It is preferable to have someone call the data from the program manuscript while you operate the typewriter. If you make mistakes, do not become emotional; emotions make for further mistakes. If your mistakes become too frequent, stop for a cup of coffee. Never prepare an NC tape under the pressure of a deadline.

When a punched tape is believed to be correct, it must be run through the tape reader of the machine, without operation of the machine tool. Any unusual characters in unusual places in the information block will cause the parity check light to go on.

The final check on the tape program is to make a test run on a piece of aluminum plate or a block of foamed polyurethane.

This O-ring groove is milled with a $\frac{3}{32}$ ball end mill. This is a small and fragile cutter. If checking out a tape for such a groove, use a somewhat larger cutter.

In the tape program for incrementing around such a groove do not punch sequence numbers into the tape, as this adds significantly to the tape reading time. The information block should include only an X and a Y dimension. The standard positioning mills will read the tape and cut this groove with a $\frac{3}{32}$ ball end mill in about $3\frac{1}{2}$ minutes in mild steel.

23.8 NUMERICALLY CONTROLLED MACHINING AND PROGRAMMING

A competent programmer in numerically controlled machining operations must progress much farther into these techniques than these two chapters go. What is presented here is only the basic approaches to programming any NC machine.

Expertise in numerical control requires first that you be a competent and reliable machinist, particularly in precision work. You must be constantly concerned to prevent errors; most of the workpieces machined by numerical control represent very expensive scrap.

Basic knowledge of the subject might be summarized as the following:

1. Ability to read and correct a tape.
2. Ability to program in either tab sequential or word address formats.
3. Ability to set up the workpiece and tooling for NC programs.
4. Experience with at least one NC milling machine.
5. Ability to contour lines and arcs as explained in this chapter.
6. Experience in presetting tools to length.

More advanced work would preferably include the following:

7. Programming an indexing table.
8. Programming automatic tool changes.
9. Programming of three-axis machines, such as the Kearney & Trecker Milwaukee-Matics or others.
10. Programming of contouring machines such as lathes.

At a still more advanced level are the computer techniques for the production of complex shapes using three, four, or five axes. This requires the study of some of the computer languages used for machining, such as ADAPT, APT, and AUTOSPOT. Fortunately, these are not difficult languages to learn, and are interesting in their techniques. Many of the computer languages used in business and engineering are more difficult.

23.9 PROGRAMMING OF NC LATHES

Of all the NC machine tools, the lathe is the most difficult to program by manual methods. Only those who have mastered the tangle of computations required for lathe programming can appreciate what the machinist can do on a standard lathe with only his hand, eye, and brain. It is possible here only to discuss the basic approaches to lathe programming.

Numerically controlled lathes are contouring machines, and hence are more complex in their programming than the positioning mills just discussed. Dimensioning is incremental. Dimension words for lathes require four decimal places; thus Z05200 means a Z movement from the previous Z position of 0.52 in., not 5.2 in. The reason for the fourth decimal place is that threads cannot be cut with sufficient accuracy in three decimal places; the thread lead must be given to four decimal places.

The axes of a two-axis lathe are shown in Fig. 320. A tool movement toward the headstock is a $-Z$ movement, and a tool movement away from the operator is a $-X$ movement. Plus signs are usually omitted.

Almost all lathes use word address format. An information block usually contains the following words:

Address	Word	Digits
N	sequence number	3
G	preparatory function	2
X	cross dimension	5 or 6
Z	longitudinal dimension	5 or 6
I	arc center offset in X	5 or 6
K	arc center offset in Z	5 or 6
F	feed rate	3 or 4
S	spindle speed	3
T	tool number	2
M	miscellaneous function	2

As usual, a word read into the storage registers remains in storage until erased by a new word read into the same address, with the usual exceptions of M00, M02.

23.10 THE TOOL PATH IN A LATHE PROGRAM

With the exception of a few special cutters such as threading cutters, lathe tools have a nose radius. This nose radius is the cause of irksome but necessary trigonometric calculations in determining the tool path for the cutter. Consider the tool contour of Fig. 335, where the cutter has a nose radius r. If it were a pointed tool, the path of the tool would be the dashed lines, and the path of

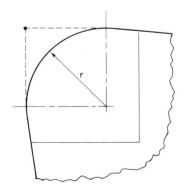

Fig. 335

the tool point would be the actual shape of the part. Now consider Fig. 336, which shows an external radius to be turned. Only a sharp-pointed tool could be programmed to follow the actual curve of the part, but such a tool would have a very limited life and would provide an unacceptable surface finish. The tool must be radiused. If, however, the radiused tool is programmed as a sharp-pointed tool, it cuts the curve shown as a dashed line, cutting first on one side of the tool, then at the end of the cut on the trailing side of the tool. As a result, there is a deviation between the desired curve and the actual curve produced, the maximum error being half the tool radius. Where accuracy is not critical, this deviation can sometimes be ignored. However, if accuracy is of secondary importance, the work is not likely to be done on an NC lathe. Therefore, tool radius must be allowed for.

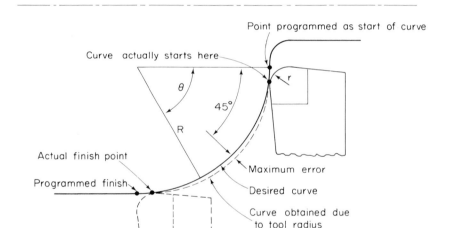

Fig. 336

Hence, in the contouring of a shape on a lathe, with the exception of straight cuts, different segments of the tool nose are in contact with the workpiece at different parts of the contour. If a certain point on the tool surface is programmed, then dimensional errors in the finished shape of the part will result. The problem is surmounted by programming the path of the *center of the tool radius*, rather than a point on the cutting surface. This practice is identical to programming an end mill, where again the center of the cutter is programmed. When one is contouring an arc such as a fillet, the arc followed by the cutter is the part radius R plus or minus the tool radius r (Fig. 337).

The part shape is produced on an NC lathe by allowing for a tool offset equal to the nose radius of the tool. The calculations for a tool path are cumbersome, involving much sine and cosine of the tool radius. A complete

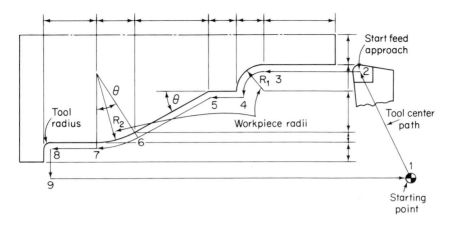

Fig. 337

discussion of tool path programming cannot be undertaken here. Nevertheless, simpler shapes can be worked out by simple trigonometry.

23.11 PREPARATORY FUNCTIONS FOR LATHES

Virtually all NC lathes use the following G or preparatory functions; some lathes may have more than these.

G01 Linear interpolation. To be coded when straight cuts parallel to either axis or a taper cut is programmed. G01 therefore is used when straight turning, facing, cutting off, or making plunge or taper cuts.

G02 Circular interpolation, for cutting a clockwise arc such as a fillet.

G03 Circular interpolation, for cutting a counterclockwise arc, such as a fillet.

Numerically controlled lathes are equipped with circular interpolation, which is the ability to contour up to 90 deg of arc. The lathe requires only three items of information in the tape for this purpose: the start point of the arc, the end point of the arc, and the center of curvature. The arc is not cut by the method of incrementing in X and Y as discussed in the previous chapter.

The lathe operating manual must be consulted to find out which rotational direction is clockwise and which is counterclockwise.

G04 A dwell or idle time. This is required for rotating a new tool into cutting position on the tool turret, for accelerating up to required speed, and other machine delays.

G33   Threading operation with a constant lead. G34 and G35 functions
      produce threads of decreasing and increasing pitch, respectively.

23.12 A SIMPLE LATHE PROGRAM

A reverse shaft for machining on an NC lathe is illustrated in Fig. 338. In
the program to follow, it will not be parted off and no chamfers will be cut.
Tool 1 will turn the $1\frac{1}{4}$ diameter, then face the shoulder, then turn the $1\frac{3}{4}$
diameter. The tool turret will then be retracted, and tool 3 will be indexed
into position for plunge-cutting the O-ring groove. The turret will then be
finally retracted.

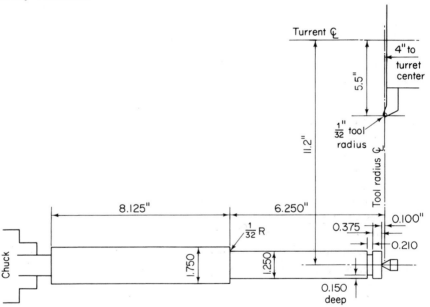

Fig. 338

The location of the plunge tool in the turret is not shown in the figure.
Assume that it projects 5.5 in. from the turret center line to the cutting edge
of the tool, and that when indexed into position, its left-hand corner would
occupy the position of the center of the nose radius of tool 1.

The tool turret is shown in the figure in the fully retracted position
in X. The turret may be set up in any "home" position in the Z direction.
In this example it is set up 0.100 in. to the right of the workpiece, as measured
from the center of the tool radius.

The program for this operation is given in Fig. 339. In the Tool No.

Seq. no.	Prep. func.	Incremental distance		Distance to arc center		Feed function	Spin speed	Tool no.	Misc. func.	Operation, tool holder, and tool holder location
		Transverse	Longitudinal	Parallel to X	Parallel to Z					
n	g	x ±	z ±	i	k	f	s	t	m	
001	04	02					57	11	03	Index tool, spindle CW
002	01	-05044				39651			08	Rapid to work
003			-06319			02057				Turn $1\frac{1}{4}$ dia
004		0025				400	54			Face shoulder
005			-08256			01211				Turn $1\frac{3}{4}$ dia
006		03	1389			14075				Retract for plunge
007	04	02					39	34		Speed change
008	01	-03181				5				Rapid to work
009		-0025				064				Groove
010		05225	00685			38469			09	Retract in X
011						5	57	11		Position in Z
012	04	02								Speed change
013									05	
014									02	

Fig. 339

column, note that tools are designated by two digits. The first of the two digits is the tool number (the second digit is the tool offset, which is not explained here). Feed function, spindle speed, and miscellaneous functions are not explained. The X and Y values are incremental distances from the previous position.

Block 001

A 2-second dwell (G04 X02) is programmed to index T1 into position and to engage and accelerate the spindle.

Block 002

The tool makes a rapid advance to cutting position at the required workpiece diameter, moving only in the −X direction. The X departure (increment) is given by

$$11.2 - 5.5 - 0.625 - 0.031 = 5.044, \text{ coded X–05044}$$

where 11.2 = distance from turret center to workpiece center line.
5.5 = tool offset in turret.
0.625 = radius of finished shaft.
0.031 = tool nose radius.

Block 003

The G01 function for straight-line movements still holds and is not repeated. The tool moves only in −Z a distance equal to

$$6.250 + 0.100 - 0.031 = 6.319$$

Block 004

The shoulder is next faced, going 0.250 in +X.

Block 005

The −Z departure is

$$8.120 + 0.031 + 0.100 = 8.256$$

The 0.100 distance is sufficient for the tool to pass clear of the workpiece.

Block 006

In this block the tool will be retracted from the workpiece in order to position it for the plunge cut and also so that a gear shift can be programmed in the following block. The retraction in $+X$ is decided as 3 in. and in $+Z$ to the position that places the plunge cutter opposite the groove it is to cut. The Z departure is

$$0.100 + 8.125 + 6.250 - 0.210 - 0.375 = 13.890$$

Block 007

Tool change and spindle speed change during a two-second dwell.

Block 008

The tool cutting edge is now positioned vertically above the groove to be cut, at a distance of 3.906 in. above the spindle axis. The tool is rapidly advanced to 0.100 in. from the work surface, that is, to a distance of 0.275 in. from the spindle axis.

Block 009

This is the plunge cut. The depth of cut of $-X$ departure is 0.250 in.

Block 010

The tool will be retracted to the X position from which this lathe program began. The X departure is 5.225 in.

Block 011

The tool turret is shifted in $+Z$ to its initial position from which this lathe program began.

Block 012

Tool 1 is indexed into position ready for the next part to be produced.

Block 013

Spindle off.

23.13 ARC OFFSETS I AND K

In circular interpolation, G02 or G03, the NC machine can produce the circular arc if given the start and end positions of the arc and the center point of the curvature. The start and end positions of the arc are programmed as XZ positions if the machine is a lathe. The information block providing the end position must include also an I and K word to locate the center of curvature.

The I arc center offset is the X distance from the starting point of the arc to the center of the arc. See Fig. 340. For most NC machines any minus

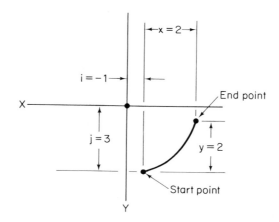

Fig. 340

sign is ignored for I, J, and K words. The K center offset is the Z distance from the starting point of the arc to the center of the arc. In the case of a milling machine with two-axis control and circular interpolation, arc center offsets would be given in I for X and J for Y dimensions.

23.14 THREAD CUTTING

The lead of a thread is programmed in a numerically controlled operation. Lead is, of course, the inches per thread, or the reciprocal of threads per inch. A thread of 20 per inch has a lead of 0.050 in.

To program a thread of constant pitch, the length of the thread on the bar is programmed as the Z increment. The thread lead is programmed as a K word.

Suppose a thread 4 in. long must have 10 threads per inch. If we assume five-digit words with four decimal places, this thread would be programmed

$$Z40000 \quad K01000$$

Trailing zeros would probably be omitted.

If a thread 2.6 in. long has 18 threads per inch, the words are

Z26000   K00556

The depth of cut for a thread is programmed as an X dimension, and as usual in thread cutting, the full depth may require more than one pass of the cutter.

Note that an 18-pitch thread has a lead of 0.0555555. When programming to four decimal places only, the lead error is 0.000045. In an inch of threading this error is accumulated 18 times, for a total error of about 0.0008 in. per inch of thread, or almost a thousandth. In 12 in. of thread, the accumulated error is 0.0096 in. or almost 0.01 in.

Although a complete development of the methods of programming NC lathes has not been provided here, the basic methods outlined apply to all NC lathes.

QUESTIONS

1. Counterboring with a dwell of two revolutions is required in a Cintimatic operation. Spindle speed is 600 rpm. Dwell time is provided by punching sufficient DELETE codes into the tape to provide the required dwell. If the Cintimatic mill reads 60 characters per second, how many DELETE codes must be punched for this dwell?

2. A slot is to be milled parallel to the Y axis at X06600, from Y03500 to Y07500.
   a. Since only a light cut is to be taken in aluminum alloy, the quill will not be clamped. Write the program for a Cintimatic mill.
   b. Write the program for a Quill Clamp and Quill Unclamp (Cintimatic mill).
   c. Write the program for a Slo-Syn. Select your own parking position.

3. Program the drilling of the bolt-circle holes in Fig. 331 for a Cintimatic mill.

4. Explain the principles of programming the tool path for an NC lathe for the usual case of a cutter with a nose radius.

5. Write the G, Z, and K words for NC cutting of a thread 6 in. long, 8 tpi.

6. Program a short arc of a circle of your choice, using the method of Sec. 23.5. A tolerance of ± 0.003 is suggested to reduce the amount of computation. Cut the arc you have computed with a $\frac{1}{4}$-in. end mill. Check that the curve is actually a circle, and note the effect of tolerance on surface finish.

7. Discuss the seriousness of the following tape-punching errors, and where

applicable, how the NC machine will react and how the error may be corrected:

a. Lowercase L typed for 1.

b. Capital O typed for zero.

c. Omission of one TAB in a tab sequential format.

d. Omission of one TAB from a word address tab-ignore format.

e. M6 for M06.

f. G78 for G79.

g. G79 for G78.

h. G81 in the storage register, no new G function as the spindle is sent to a parking position.

i. Omission of a whole block of information in a drilling program for a bolt-hole circle.

j. Interchange of two blocks of information in a sequence of hole drilling on a flat plate, all holes the same diameter.

k. Y word typed before X word in a word address format.

l. Y word typed before X word in a tab sequential format.

m. Omission of the sequence number from an information block.

n. Omission of the tape leader.

o. Omission of the cam M word for a series of holes to be drilled on a Cintimatic vertical-spindle mill.

Chapter 24

Chipless Machining

24.1 NEW HORIZONS IN MACHINING

Metal removal by standard machining methods may range from the $\frac{3}{4}$ in. thick chips removed from locomotive wheels to the fine finishing chips of finish-turning and finish-milling. Still smaller chips are removed in finish-grinding operations. The machining methods of more recent development discussed in this chapter generally remove metal by other methods than that of shearing with a sharp cutter. One of these methods, chemical milling, removes material atom by atom, the atom being the ultimate limit in chip size. In some of these methods there is no physical contact between the cutting tool and the workpiece, or there may be no cutting tool at all.

In general, the machining methods of this chapter date from the years of World War II and after. They must not be regarded as exotic methods, since some of them are extensively used and will be increasingly used in the future. The methods to be discussed are these, listed in order from most extensively used to least:

1. Electric discharge machining (EDM)
2. Electrochemical milling (ECM)
3. Chemical milling
4. Ultrasonic machining
5. Electron beam machining (EBM)
6. Laser beam machining

Except for chemical milling, which is a kind of corrosion, these methods are dependent on electrical and electronic circuitry for their machining effects.

Both EBM and laser machining are outstandingly useful for producing holes of very small diameter of any shape. Neither method uses a cutting tool. None of the methods of this chapter are restricted by reason of the hardness of the workpiece.

24.2 ELECTRIC DISCHARGE MACHINING

When a weldor accidentally strikes an arc in the wrong place, he removes a small crater of metal at the point where the arc was struck. In the EDM process, a continuous series of electrical discharges between the electrode and the workpiece removes material in the same manner as the "arc burn." The material is melted out in small craters.

The amount of metal removed by a single electrical discharge is proportional to the product of the discharge voltage, the current, and the time of discharge, though the magnitude of the electric current is the most important factor. Large currents are, therefore, used for roughing cuts and smaller currents for finishing cuts when an improved finish is desirable. The higher the frequency of discharge, the higher the metal removal rate will be also.

The machining rate is also influenced by the melting point of the metal. Aluminum alloys with melting points approximately 1000°F can be machined more rapidly than metals with high melting points, such as molybdenum and tungsten.

A dielectric fluid is pumped between the electrode and the workpiece. The word "dielectric" means an electrical insulator. This dielectric fluid breaks down under the electrical voltage to a conductive condition. Between discharges it acts as an electrical insulator, its other functions being to serve as a coolant and a means of chip removal. Several fluids are suitable for the EDM process, including petroleum oils and solutions of various glycols in water. The choice of dielectric fluid influences the process in a number of ways, including electrode wear and machining rate.

The electrical power supply is some type of electric oscillator circuit that charges a capacitor, the capacitor then discharging to the gap between workpiece and electrode.

The EDM process requires a constant arc distance between work and electrode. As in arc welding, the arc voltage is proportional to arc length. To maintain a constant arc length as the material is spark-eroded and the electrode advances, a servomechanism driving a leadscrew or a hydraulic cylinder is usually employed. (A servomechanism is a position-control device.) The voltage across the gap is measured, and a corrective electric signal is

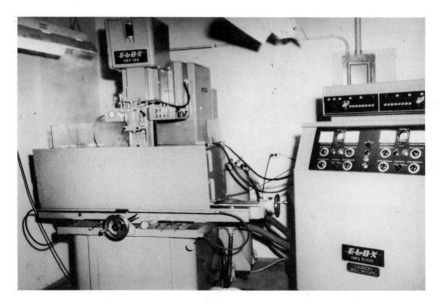

Fig. 341 Elox electric discharge machine.

sent to the servovalve, which then meters oil to the cylinder or drives the leadscrew to move the electrode the required distance. When the required depth of cut is reached, a limit switch is tripped. This shuts down the electrode movement and the discharge power supply.

The choice of electrode is determined by a number of factors, including the type of power supply, the ease of machining the electrode to the shape of the cavity to be cut, and the rate of wear of the electrode. The spark discharges erode the electrode as well as the workpiece. Brass and copper are easy to machine, but may erode almost as fast as the workpiece. Graphite, tungsten carbide, silver-tungsten, and nickel wear very slowly. Steel is generally used only for stamping and blanking dies, where the punch is used to machine its own die. Metal removal rates are low for steel, because this metal cannot employ high currents. The end wear of the electrode material is measured by relative wear ratio:

$$\text{Loss ratio} = \frac{\text{workpiece thickness removed}}{\text{loss of electrode length}}$$

In addition to end wear, the electrode will also tend to wear out of shape.

The cavity machined in the workpiece will slightly exceed the dimensions of the electrode. This overcut, as it is called, is proportional to the current, but is reduced by higher frequencies. Hence, if a punch is used to erode its own matching die, the overcut must be so controlled as to produce the required clearance between punch and die.

Since metal is removed by arc heat, some heat treatment of the workpiece usually results from this process. An extremely hard surface of Rc 68 is possible for a depth of a few tenths of a thousandth. Beyond this hardened layer there will be an annealed layer a few thousandths deep.

Any electrically conductive workpiece may be machined by this method, whether it is hard or soft, including carbides. The process is used to remove broken taps from holes, to drill holes in hard materials, or to sink various types of dies and cavities for stamping, extruding, forging, and other metal and plastic forming operations, with the advantage that the die may be sunk after heat treatment. Most extrusion dies are perforated by EDM.

Fig. 342 Louvre dies sunk by the EDM method.

Figure 342 shows a louver die for a car warmer produced by the EDM method from graphite electrodes.

24.3 SETTING UP THE EDM WORK

The workpiece must be machined to finished thickness, and may be previously heat-treated. If it is heavy enough to be immobile, it may simply be set down on the work plate of the EDM machine at a suitable location. If it may move, it can be held with clamps or a magnetic chuck.

Various methods are used to hold the electrode in the quill. Sometimes a chuck is used. A difficult tool to hold or one that is off square may be held in a ball-joint collet. The electrode must be checked that it is parallel or perpendicular to the work.

The depth setting for the full length of cut must be set up so that the machine will shut off automatically. Other controls vary from machine to machine. The capacitance setting usually controls the finish. On some machines an oscilloscope is used to check the charging pattern of the circuit, and capacitance and resistance values are adjusted to give a suitable charging pattern.

The work must be well irrigated by the dielectric fluid. If the chips are not cleared away as fast as they are generated, then they accumulate in the cut and short-circuit the tool to the work. This will cause the servo to raise the electrode to clear the short circuit, and time will be lost. The fluid is frequently introduced through a small hole in the electrode.

The overcut is determined usually from a chart, and depends on current and electrode material.

The depth of cut and the required length of electrode are both governed by the loss ratio. For example, consider a brass electrode with a loss ratio of 4:3; that is, 4 in. of workpiece will be penetrated for a loss of 3 in. of electrode. Suppose also that a hexagonal-shaped hole is to be cut to a depth of 0.750 in.

If the quill and electrode advance 0.750 in., then a depth of hole of 0.750 in. will not be cut, because the electrode will have eroded three-quarters as much as the workpiece. The actual hole depth eroded will be $\frac{3}{4} \times 0.750$, or $\frac{9}{16}$ in. To cut a hole 0.750 in. deep, the electrode must move $0.750 \times \frac{4}{3}$ or 1.000 in. Therefore, 1.000 in. would be the depth setting for a cut of 0.750 in. The depth setting thus depends on the loss ratio of the electrode material.

This is a hexagonal hole, and let us also assume that the bottom of the hole must have sharp corners. By the time the electrode has eroded to the bottom of the hole, its sharp corners will have become worn. Therefore, a second finishing electrode will be required to finish-cut the hole. In the case of a complex forging die, as many as five electrodes may be required to obtain the accurate die contours required.

24.4 ULTRASONIC MACHINING

Ultrasonic machining is more successful with hard and brittle materials than with soft and ductile materials. It is not limited to metals, but is equally successful with ceramic materials such as glass.

Ultrasonic machining was developed from the principles of SONAR used in hunting submarines in World War II. The basic scientific principle is that of *magnetostriction*. The highly magnetic metals iron, steel, nickel, and cobalt exhibit small changes in length if their state of magnetism is changed. This change in length is called magnetostriction. Cobalt has a number of disadvantages as a magnetostrictive material, and iron and steel rust; therefore, nickel is the preferred material for magnetostrictive devices.

In Fig. 343 a solenoid coil is wound around a nickel core or armature. If an alternating current is passed through the electric coil, then the magnetic

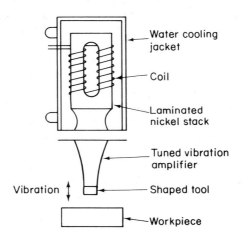

Fig. 343

field in the nickel armature will alternate also, in the same pattern as the current in the coil. If the magnetic field varies, then the length of the armature will likewise fluctuate, though the total variation in length will be less than 0.001 in. This small variation in length, or strain, is sufficient to allow the use of such an armature for machining purposes.

Suppose that the requirement is to machine a hole in a piece of glass. A steel tool with the required shape of the hole is attached to the end of the armature and thus is vibrated vertically at a frequency of about 20,000 cycles per second. Abrasive grit in a liquid lies in the gap between the tool and the workpiece. The impact of the abrasive driven by the magnetostrictive armature wears away the workpiece material.

The usual abrasives aluminum oxide and silicon carbide are used in ultrasonic machining, but boron carbide cuts faster than either and is preferred. The abrasive also wears the tool, but at a slower rate than the workpiece.

Figure 344 shows an application of ultrasonic machining. The part is

Fig. 344 Ultrasonic machining produced 2,176 square holes in this 3-in. by 4-in. carbon block in 10 minutes. (Courtesy of the Sheffield Corp.)

Fig. 345 Ultrasonic machining operation. The operator is cutting 2,176 square holes simultaneously in a 3-in. by 4-in. carbon plate. The operation will be completed in less than 10 minutes. (Courtesy of the Bendix Automation and Measurement Div.)

a carbon plate in which 2176 square holes measuring 0.040×0.040 were machined in 10 minutes.

Tool wear has an influence on the accuracy of the cut. The tool shortens as it is abraded, though this is less serious than the wearing of the side of the tool to a slight taper. The tapered end may have to be cut off to resharpen the tool. When the tool penetrates the bottom of the part, tool force and tool amplitude must be reduced so that the bottom of the hole is not broken out roughly.

This machining method is not called magnetostrictive, but *ultrasonic*. The magnetostrictive device generates a sound of high intensity, and if operated in the audible range up to 15,000 cycles per second, would be a most unpleasant machine to be near. The operating frequency is about 20,000 cycles, which is beyond the audible range, or *ultrasonic*. Ultrasonics is also applied to the welding of metal sheet and plastics, while ultrasonic cleaning is probably the most effective method of cleaning parts.

24.5 ELECTROCHEMICAL MILLING

In any electrical process, including arc welding, the two poles or terminals, one positive and one negative, that take electric current into and out of the process are termed *electrodes*. In the usual arc welding circuit, the workpiece is one electrode and the welding rod is the other. Usually in direct-current welding reverse polarity is used. This condition means that the workpiece is the negative electrode and the welding rod is the positive electrode. The electrical terms *anode* and *cathode* are sometimes used in welding: The anode is the positive electrode, positive meaning a higher voltage with respect to the other electrode, and the negative or lower-voltage electrode is the cathode. See Fig. 346.

Two electrodes are required in electroplating. Suppose that hard chromium must be plated on a worn shaft to build up the diameter. An anode

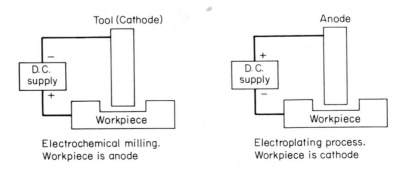

Electrochemical milling.
Workpiece is anode

Electroplating process.
Workpiece is cathode

Fig. 346

(positive) of chromium and the shaft to be plated (cathode) are immersed in a liquid solution that conducts electricity between the two electrodes. Such a conductive liquid is called an *electrolyte*. When current flows through the electrolyte from one electrode to the other, chromium is removed from the anode and deposited or plated on the negative cathode, which in this example is a shaft.

In electroplating the intent is to plate the part that is the cathode. In electrochemical milling, the intent is to remove metal from the anode, which is the workpiece, in order to shape it. The process is represented in Fig. 347, which shows the electrochemical milling of a hole or pocket. A

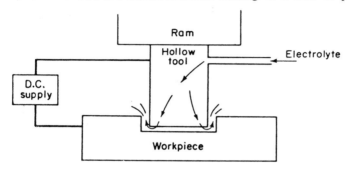

Fig. 347 Electrochemical milling.

cathode tool must first be prepared with the required shape for the electric machining operation. The electrolyte, usually sodium chloride in water, is pumped between the tool and the work. As in virtually all electrical processes in the manufacturing field, very high currents are used. The power supply is direct current, since alternating current reverses the polarity in each cycle. The gap between tool and workpiece must be a very short and controlled distance, except perhaps in chemical deburring operations.

The amount of metal removed is proportional to the product of current and time. Very large currents are used for maximum metal removal rates, often exceeding 100 amps per square inch of machined surface. Metal removal rates range between 0.10 and 0.14 cu in. per ampere-minute. ECM, therefore, can compete in speed of execution with standard cutting tools.

Sodium chloride in water is the preferred electrolyte. This is a highly corrosive liquid, and the ECM machine must be designed to resist such corrosion. Both the temperature and the concentration of the electrolyte must be controlled, since both these factors influence the electrical resistance across the electrodes.

The accuracy of machining is, of course, dependent on the accuracy with which the tool electrode is made. The tool for drilling a hole must obviously be slightly smaller than the hole in order to allow the electrolyte to flow in and out. The electrolyte may be introduced through the center of the tool. The control of the amount of this oversize or overcut is a matter of experience. The overcut is influenced quite markedly by the machining voltage, higher voltage producing a greater overcut. Control of voltage, therefore, controls the size of the hole or pocket being machined.

An important advantage of the ECM method is the absence of burrs, and it is used for many difficult deburring problems. In deburring, an electrode is positioned close to the surface to be deburred.

The first application of ECM was electrochemical grinding. This grinding method, used for grinding hard materials such as carbides, uses a grinding wheel with a conductive bonding material. The work being ground is positive. The dimensional accuracy of conventional grinding methods is not obtainable by this method.

24.6 CHEMICAL MILLING

No electric current is used in chemical milling; therefore, this method is not restricted to conductive materials. Chemical milling machines by controlled corrosion of the material, and is best suited to intricate designs on flat thin stock. The material to be milled is exposed to an acid or alkaline solution; the areas that are not to be milled are protected by a masking material. The tooling for the chemical milling process is, therefore, unusual; it consists of masking artwork prepared by photographic, silk screen, or other printing or artwork processes. For improved accuracy, such artwork is drawn to a large scale and then reduced to proper size.

The possibilities of chemical milling are displayed by the chemically blanked part of Fig. 348. The material is beryllium bronze, one of the hardest of all nonferrous alloys. The rectangle of the part measures $1 \times 1\frac{1}{4}$ in., and some of the metal bridges of the lettering and the symbol are only 15

Fig. 348 A chemically blanked small part.

thousandths in width. This is an impossible part to produce on a punch press. An additional advantage is that the part is burr-free.

The maskant or masking material that is to protect the areas not to be milled must be selected with some care, since a failure of the maskant ruins the part. The maskant must resist the etching solution for the period of time required to mill the part, which is several minutes to several hours, depending on thickness of material. It must provide the detail or resolution required in the part. The maskant must bond to the workpiece so that the etching solution does not penetrate the interface between part and maskant. It must be thick enough to provide sufficient protection to the workpiece. It must not chip or flake.

The etching liquid must be selected primarily for the material to be chemically corroded. In addition, it must not remove the maskant and must provide a suitable surface finish. It must remove the material to a uniform depth without developing deep pits or simply attacking the grain boundaries of the workpiece material. It must not penetrate under the maskant and lift it. The rate of etching must usually be restricted to one or two thousandths of an inch per minute. Faster rates produce such undesirable effects as serious undercutting of the mask and uneven surface.

The usual sequence of operations in chemical milling is the following:

1. Cleaning of the part surface.
2. Application of the mask by dipping, spraying, or other methods, in at least two coats.
3. Curing of the maskant with or without heat.
4. Scribing or otherwise producing the required shape of the mask. In the photoresist method, ultraviolet light is used to cure the mask areas that are to remain in place. The mask areas to be removed are protected from this radiation and washed away.
5. Etching, usually by dipping the part into the solution.
6. Removal of the mask.

Chemical milling to depths exceeding 0.250 in. is unusual. Tolerances as fine as 0.001 in. are possible on small work, but not on large areas. Thickness variations and scratches are generally reproduced in the chemical milling operation, and welded areas usually etch irregularly. The etch will undercut

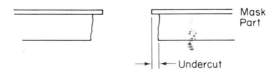

Fig. 349

the mask as shown in Fig. 349. Such undercut will vary from one-third to one-half the depth of etching and must be allowed for in the design of the artwork. "Etch factor" is the term applied to this characteristic: An etch factor of 3:1 means that for every 0.003 in. of etch depth, the undercut will be 0.001 in.

The edges of the sheet to be chemically milled are not usually protected from the etching solution, but are cropped after milling.

Instrument panels such as are found on the front of oscilloscopes contain a great deal of detail. They can be engraved, but often it is more economical to mill such detail chemically.

24.7 ELECTRON BEAM MACHINING

Almost all welding methods can be converted to metal-cutting operations. Flame-cutting and arc-cutting, for example, may be viewed as rough-machining operations. The electron beam welder also will cut or machine by suitable adaptation of the process. Electron beam machining, however, is somewhat limited in its applications, like laser machining, which is next to be discussed.

In EB machining, a stream of high-velocity electrons impact upon the workpiece material and vaporize it, either to drill a hole or to cut a slot in the material. The process concentrates a very large quantity of energy on a very small area of the workpiece, sufficient to vaporize any material, metallic or nonmetallic.

The electrons that carry the energy to the workpiece are generated in an electron gun with a very high voltage across it. Since electrons are negatively charged, they must be accelerated by a positive voltage on the anode in the gun. A voltage of 100,000 accelerates them to a speed of approximately half the speed of light, or to about 100,000 miles per second; a voltage of 150,000 gives the electrons a speed of about 140,000 miles/sec. On reaching this speed at the anode of the electron gun, the electrons then pass through a small hole in the anode and proceed at a constant speed to the workpiece. The beam of electrons can be focused by a magnetic field just as a beam of light can be focused by a lens, and is concentrated to an extremely small spot on the work. When the electrons are stopped by the workpiece, their kinetic energy is transformed into heat. The process must be carried out in a vacuum; otherwise the high speed and energy of the electrons would be lost in collisions with gas molecules, though some types of EB welding are carried out in a gas atmosphere.

Voltages in the range of 100,000 to 150,000 are used for machining, with currents usually less than 100 microamps (millionths of an ampere) in pulses persisting for less than 100 microseconds. A pulse frequency of 50 per second is usual. Holes and slots a few thousandths of an inch across are machined by this method. When used for welding, the electron beam is operated at lower voltages, with currents in the milliamp range, and usually continuous current rather than pulses. Only micromachining operations are possible by the EB method.

24.8 LASER MACHINING

Instead of a beam of high-velocity electrons, the laser machining process uses a high-energy beam of light. The operating principles of the laser have been well explained in a number of books and will not be discussed here. In brief, a high-power lamp filled with xenon gas stimulates the laser, usually a ruby crystal if the purpose is machining or welding, to emit a pulse of focused red light of unusual intensity. Laser machining competes with the electron beam in micromachining applications, and has some strong advantages over the electron beam. Electron beam equipment costs about $100,000, whereas a laser installation costs about a tenth as much and does not require a vacuum and the delay of pumping down a vacuum. Though at the present time laser machining has only limited uses, its techniques should be greatly expanded in the near future.

The EDM method is now a standard machining method very widely used. Chemical and electrochemical milling are unusual in that they call upon skills beyond those of the machine shop, notably in the tooling or artwork, which calls for the skills of art, drafting, and photography. The operation of electron and laser beams is beyond the skills of the machinist, though less difficult.

It should be clear from the discussions of this chapter that electrical technology is slowly invading the machine shop techniques. To put all these methods in proper perspective, a historical trend should be noted: namely, that manufacturing and machining are progressively concerned with lighter and smaller workpieces. A hundred years ago the skilled machinist bored out the big cylinders of steam engines, whereas now he may work on small mechanical parts for electronic computers and office equipment or the small spools of hydraulic valves. As parts become progressively smaller, the applications for micromachining processes are certain to expand as the decades go by. Heavy machining will persist, but it no longer dominates the techniques of machine tool technology.

QUESTIONS

1. What purposes does the dielectric fluid serve in the EDM process?
2. If the electrode-to-work distance were allowed gradually to increase in EDM, what would be the effect on surface finish?

3. What effect does the loss ratio have on the number of electrodes that may be required to produce a complex die by EDM?

4. What similarities do you find in the effect of both arc welding and EDM on the heat-affected zone?

5. Do any of the methods of this chapter
   a. Involve tool forces?
   b. Produce burrs?

6. Explain how the loss ratio in EDM affects the setting for depth of cut.

7. Explain the magnetostrictive effect.

8. What is the meaning of (a) anode; (b) cathode; (c) electrolyte?

9. Explain etch factor in chemical milling.

10. Why can deep cuts not be made by chemical milling?

11. How is it that a beam of electrons can produce a hole in a metal or a ceramic?

25.3 THE SURFACE PLATE

In practice, virtually all dimensions must be gaged from a reference plane, such as the anvil of a micrometer. The basic measuring plane is the surface plate (Fig. 352). A surface plate is a reference plane for measurements provided by a slab of granite or cast iron, and ground to a true plane with an error of less than 0.0002 in. Granite is preferred, because it is dimensionally more stable and more wear-resistant than cast iron.

Fig. 352 Surface plate measurements.

Grade AA surface plates are guaranteed to a tolerance of ± 0.000025 in. over any two square feet of area; grade A plates are ± 0.000050 in. over any two square feet; grade B plates have a flatness of ± 0.0001 in. over any two square feet.

A surface is no better than its condition. Dirt, grease, and oil deposits on a surface plate could exceed a thousandth of an inch in thickness. Scratches and burrs compromise the accurate surface of the plate. Unnecessary and unwarranted use of the surface plate leads to wear of the surface.

The vernier height gage is the most useful of the measuring devices in association with a surface plate. Checking two opposite surfaces of a part for parallelism, as must be done when one is checking a parallel for a milling vise, may be done with a surface plate, readings being taken on the top surface of the part at several points. The electronic height gage of Fig. 353 is more convenient for this purpose, however, since the contact point of this gage

Fig. 353 Trans-Chek electronic gage. (Courtesy of DoA11 Canada Ltd.)

can be slid along the surface as the operator watches the readings on the indicating scale.

Heights or scribed lines may be accurately set by reference to an assembly of gage blocks that give the required height. The measurement may be transferred to the part by means of an electronic or a dial indicator, or a height gage. If an electronic gage is used, it must be positioned as shown in Fig. 354, so that any movement of the contact will be vertical, since vertical distances are being read. In the wrong position shown in the figure, movement of the contact is at an angle to the vertical, and movements that are read out are not vertical movements.

Roundness is measured by rotating the part in precision vee blocks and reading an electronic height gage or a dial indicator. Roundness and runout may also be checked by holding the part between precision end centers, Fig. 355. In this method the accuracy will be influenced by the condition of the center holes in the part and the condition of the centers.

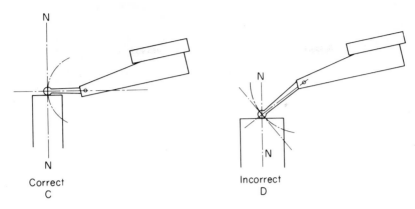

N

N

Correct
C

N

N

Incorrect
D

Fig. 354

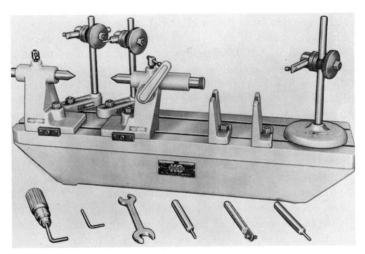

Fig. 355 BC3 bench center and surface plate. (Courtesy of K. O. Lee Co.)

25.4 GAGES

Measurement refers to finding a length. Gaging compares dimensions to a standard.

Conformity to tolerance specification in a production run is usually tested by fixed limit gages, often termed GO and NOT GO gages, such as the one of Fig. 356. Such limit gages represent the upper or the lower limit of size of the workpiece and are particularly suited to a system of limits and fits. For a hole on which diameter limits are specified, the GO gage should be a cylinder of diameter equal to the minimum hole size, and the NOT GO

Fig. 356 A thread gage with GO and NOT GO ends.

gage a cylinder of diameter equal to the maximum hole size. However, the 10 per cent tolerance rule for gages mentioned earlier applies, leaving a small area of uncertainty in the gaging. If the gage tolerance decreases the size of the NOT GO gage or increases the size of the GO gage, the gages can cause holes actually within tolerance to be rejected. If the gage tolerances are in the opposite directions, then holes will be accepted that are slightly outside the specified limits.

The dial indicator uses a mechanical system to amplify small movements. Electronic gages of the type shown in Fig. 353 are capable of amplifications of as much as 100,000, using a small pickup head to measure small movements. These movements produce some type of change in an electronic circuit, which in turn produces a change in current that is amplified and displayed on a meter graduated in increments of length. The change in electrical characteristic may be resistance, inductance, or capacitance. Graduations as small as 0.00001 of an inch are used, so that readings close to millionths are possible with the electronic gage.

Air gages use a pneumatic circuit for gaging. A diagram of a typical back-pressure pneumatic gage is given in Fig. 357. Air is fed through a restriction into a chamber and exhausted through an orifice against the surface to be gaged. The back pressure developed in the chamber is dependent on the distance between the nozzle and the workpiece, the pressure falling as this distance increases. This pressure is indicated on a pressure gage or is read out as a dimension. Measurements as fine as a millionth of an inch have been made by pneumatic methods. The pneumatic gage has the important advantage that contact of the gage with the workpiece is absent, so that there is no wear of the gage.

A second type of pneumatic gage measures the velocity of air flow through the orifice. As the distance of the work surface from the orifice increases, this velocity increases, and the difference in velocities is read out as a distance.

25.5 MEASUREMENT OF LARGE EXTERNAL RADII

The angular gage of Fig. 358 is fitted with a micrometer. The angle between

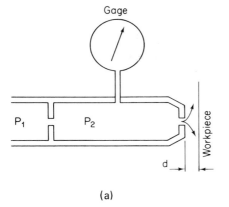

Gage

P_1　　P_2

d

Workpiece

(a)

(b)

Fig. 357 (a) Diagram of a typical back-pressure pneumatic gage. (b) Pneumatic gaging on a cylindrical grinder. (Courtesy of Federal Products Corp.)

the two arms of the gage must be known accurately. The angle A is the half angle between gage faces. From the figure,

$$\cos(90-A) = \frac{AB}{AC} = \frac{R}{R+H}$$

$$(R+H)\cos(90-A) = R$$

$$H\cos(90-A) = R - R\cos(90-A)$$
$$= R[1-\cos(90-A)]$$

$$R = \frac{H\cos(90-A)}{[1-\cos(90-A)]}$$

For any such gage, cos $(90-A)$ is a constant K; hence,

$$R = \frac{HK}{1-K}$$

But $H = h + K_1$

so that finally

$$R = (h+K_1)\frac{K}{1-K}$$

K_1 is the distance from the intersection of the faces to the datum surface, and h is the height from the radius to the datum face, h being read on the micrometer. A dial indicator can be substituted for a micrometer.

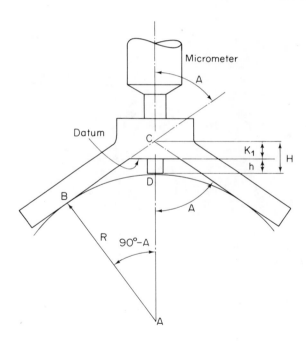

Fig. 358

25.6 THE OPTICAL COMPARATOR

The optical comparator has many applications in inspection, examination, tool setting, tool sharpening, and other operations, especially when complex contours must be examined. A magnified image of the part is projected onto a viewing screen by a powerful light source and a lens system. Hence, the optical comparator is a large measuring microscope. The usual screen size is 14 in. in diameter, though larger sizes are in use. A set of lenses provides magnifications of $10\times$, $20\times$, $25\times$, $50\times$, and $100\times$. With the 100-power lens, measurements can be made to the half-thousandth, though at this magnification a part width of only 0.14 in. can be examined at one time, if the screen size is 14 in.

Fig. 359 Jones and Lamson optical comparator with 14-in. screen.

The part to be examined is set up on the worktable in front of the screen, and can be positioned in two dimensions by leadscrews. An elevating motor moves the worktable vertically up or down. The worktable can also be rotated to an angle about a vertical axis.

Special charts for gaging specific shapes may be drawn on dimensionally stable clear plastic and mounted over the screen. If, for example, a special tool must be sharpened for making an O-ring groove, the required shape is drawn in black ink to the proper magnified size on plastic, and the sharpened tool is compared with the chart for accuracy of profile. A wide range of standard charts is available in all magnifications, including the following:

1. Radius and circular charts.
2. Grid charts, ruled for direct measurement.
3. Fillet charts.
4. Protractor charts for measuring angles.
5. Screw thread charts. For examining screw threads, the worktable must be rotated to the proper helix angle for the thread being examined.
6. Gear tooth charts.

Figure 360 is a photograph taken on an optical comparator with a 14-in. screen. The strange profile is that of a wheel puller screw that was not adequately induction-hardened.

Fig. 360 Examination of a ¾-in. NC thread on an optical comparator.

25.7 SURFACE FINISH

The planetary pin of Fig. 4 has a roughness specification of 16 microinches. Surface roughness numbers, such as this, mean millionths of an inch, in this case 16 millionths. This is, of course, the maximum roughness allowed.

The quality of surface finish is commonly specified. The ways of machine tools must not be too smooth if they are to retain a film of lubricating oil. On the other hand, surfaces that must have the best possible corrosion resistance should be as smooth and polished as possible.

Surface finish is measured over a very short distance of a fraction of an inch, in order to exclude larger effects that could be interpreted as surface roughness. Thus in the case of a saw blade the surface roughness measurement would not include the repetitive tooth form. Instead, the surface roughness would be the roughness of an individual tooth surface.

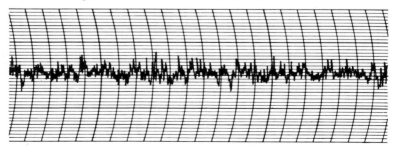

Fig. 361 A surface roughness record.

Figure 361 shows a graphical record of the roughness of a surface ground with a 60-grit wheel. The smallest chart division represents 10 micro-inches (millionths of an inch). A microinch is usually abbreviated as 1μ, the Greek letter μ often being used to signify "one-millionth." On the chart the maximum distance from a peak roughness to a valley is of the order of 100μ. This represents a smooth, but not a polished, surface, typical of a grinding operation. Since only the vertical scale of surface roughness is of interest, the longitudinal scale is greatly compressed on the chart.

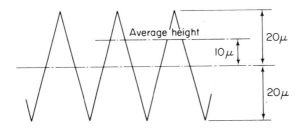

Fig. 362

Surface roughness is defined as the average height of roughness from the mean surface of the roughness. This definition is best explained from the idealized roughness diagram of Fig. 362. This is an idealized surface; actually, no machined or ground surface has the regularity shown in the figure. In the figure, all the peaks measure 20μ and all the valleys measure 20μ. If a number of measurements of roughness are made at random points along this profile, the measurements will range from zero to a maximum of 20, and therefore the average measurement will be 10μ, either for valleys, or peaks, or both together. Therefore, the maximum range from a valley to a peak will be about four times the average roughness. In the case of the planetary pin, with a roughness specification of 16, the maximum range would be about 64μ, which is 0.00006 in. Finish grinding can give results of 30μ (maximum range about 120) or even better.

Fine tolerances clearly require fine finishes. The finish should be 10 per cent of the tolerance; otherwise, the surface finish will have a powerful influence on the dimension. If, for example, a diameter must be controlled to 0.0002 in., a surface roughness specification of 125μ, with a peak-to-valley measurement of 500μ or 0.0005 in., would be a little odd.

One of the surface roughness measuring and recording devices, the Brush surface analyzer and recorder, is shown in Fig. 363. The finish is measured by moving a conical diamond stylus with a tip radius of 0.0005 in. over the surface. An electrical signal is generated by the movements of the stylus, then amplified, and either recorded on a strip chart or indicated on

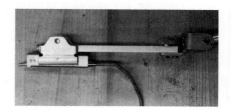

Fig. 363 (a) The Brush surface roughness indicator. The measuring pickup is reading the roughness of a small silicon bronze bar in the foreground. The roughness is read on the meter scale on the left. The larger instrument on the right is a chart recorder for roughness measurements. (b) The stylus that reads the surface roughness as it slowly traverses the surface.

a meter. The stylus movement must, of course, be across the lay or texture pattern of the surface.

QUESTIONS

1. The distance A for the cylindrical part of Fig. 364 is required, to the nearest 0.001 in. Set up a procedure using surface plate and vernier height gage for obtaining this distance. Accurate pins are available to insert into the holes in the part.

2. A taper is being measured with two precision balls as shown in Fig. 365. State how you would obtain the dimensions indicated in the figure.

3. For Fig. 365, $d = 0.5000$, $D = 0.7500$, $b = 0.6100$, $c = 1.3622$.
   a. What is dimension d_2?
   b. What is the taper per foot?

4. Design, sketch, and dimension a gage for measuring large diameters,

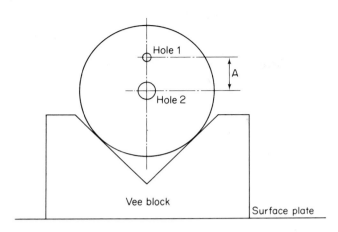

Fig. 364

similar to the one of Fig. 358. Use a 90-deg included angle between the arms. Devise a formula for part radius *R* based on your design.

5. What would be your choice of gaging device for checking the diameter of centerless ground pins produced at the rate of 1200 per hour?

6. What is meant by calibration?

7. On what principle does the back-pressure pneumatic gage operate?

8. A $\frac{3}{4}$-10 NC thread must be examined on an optical comparator. The screen must display at least three full threads. What is the maximum magnification that can be used on a 14-in. screen: 10, 20, 25, 50, or 100?

9. What is the meaning of a surface finish of 32 microinches?

10. What would be a reasonable surface finish to specify for a tolerance specification of 0.0005 in. for a pin?

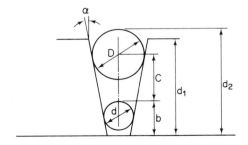

Fig. 365

The following two questions require the selection of gage blocks. It is assumed that a DoAll gage block set no. 86R is available. This set contains the following blocks:

0.0001 series	*0.001 series*			*0.050 series*		*1.000 series*
0.1001	0.101	0.117	0.134	0.050	0.550	1.000
0.1002	0.102	0.118	0.135	0.100	0.600	2.000
0.1003	0.103	0.119	0.136	0.150	0.650	3.000
0.1004	0.104	0.120	0.137	0.200	0.700	4.000
0.1005	0.105	0.121	0.138	0.250	0.750	
0.1006	0.106	0.122	0.139	0.300	0.800	
0.1007	0.107	0.123	0.140	0.350	0.850	
0.1008	0.108	0.124	0.141	0.400	0.900	
0.1009	0.109	0.125	0.142	0.450	0.950	
	0.110	0.126	0.143	0.500		
	0.111	0.127	0.144			
	0.112	0.128	0.145			
	0.113	0.129	0.146			
	0.114	0.130	0.147			
	0.115	0.131	0.148			
	0.116	0.132	0.149			
		0.133				

11. Select gage blocks to obtain the following heights: (a) 3.0106; (b) 4.4437; (c) 5.7103.

12. The center distance between two pins on a sine bar (Fig. 351) is 5.0000 in. Select gage blocks from the DoAll set to give the following angles on the sine bar: (a) 12 deg; (b) 16 deg 31 min; (c) 35 deg 35 min; (d) 42 deg 30 min.

Glossary

abrasive	a material in the form of hard grains that wear down softer materials
arbor	a shaft designed to carry a cutting tool
blind hole	a hole only part way through a workpiece
bore	to enlarge a hole
burr	a small rough elevated ridge produced by a machining operation
chamfer	a small bevel at a corner or shoulder
chatter	a heavy vibration set up between cutter and workpiece on a machine tool
chuck	a holding device for gripping workpieces or cutters that must be rotated as they are held
collet	a ring-type or tube-type chuck
coolant	a liquid used to cool and lubricate the cutting tool
critical	of first importance, as a critical dimension or a critical surface

flute	a groove in the side of a drill or reamer to provide chip space
gage	thickness
heat-treating	altering the characteristics of a metal, usually its hardness, by a heating and cooling operation
ipm	inches per minute
ipr	inches per revolution of the cutter or work
jig	a device for holding a workpiece in a drilling operation
kerf	the slot made by cutting with a saw or other narrow cutting tool
knurling	embossing the surface of the work with a diamond pattern or other pattern
land	the narrow peripheral surface of a tooth, between grooves or flutes
leadscrew	a power screw for driving a table or a tool carriage
mandrel	a tapered bar on which a workpiece is mounted
metallurgy	the science of metals
NC or N/C	numerical control
numerical control	the operation of a machine by a code of holes punched into continuous tape, which the machine can read and execute
parting	cutting off of a piece from a bar with a parting tool in the lathe
periphery	the outside surface of a cylinder
pitch	number of teeth per inch or distance between teeth; also has other meanings
plastics	solid materials usually manufactured from oil or gas by chemical processes
plunge cut	a movement of the cutter straight into the part at right angles to the spindle of the machine
reamer	a cutter for slightly enlarging a hole to accurate final diameter

recess	an internal groove in a hole
rpm	revolutions of a shaft per minute
set	the sideways adjustment of saw teeth so that the kerf is wider than the saw blade thickness
surface finish	the degree of smoothness of a machined surface
swing	the largest diameter of part that can be rotated on a lathe
tap	a cutting tool that cuts threads in a hole
tap drill	a drill that gives the required hole size for a threading tap
tolerance	the allowable range of error on a measurement
torque	a turning or twisting effect produced by a force
turret	a toolholder that can hold more than one tool and can rotate each tool into cutting position as required.
vernier	a small auxiliary scale that slides along a main scale to obtain greater accuracy of measurement
woodpecker drilling	a sequence of drilling and withdrawing the drill to allow escape of drilling chips

Appendix

TRIGONOMETRIC FUNCTIONS

The following summary of the trigonometric functions applicable to machining calculations applies only to right triangles. A right triangle is any triangle that has one right angle (90-deg angle). The other two angles of a right triangle will sum to 90 deg.

Each side of a right triangle can be considered to be opposite one of the angles of the triangle. The longest side of the triangle, called the *hypotenuse*, is the side opposite the 90-deg angle (the largest angle). Here capital letters will be used to designate angles, *A*, *B*, and *C*, *C* being used to designate the right angle. Lowercase letters are used to designate the sides of the triangle.

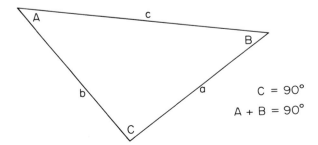

$$C = 90°$$
$$A + B = 90°$$

c is hypotenuse.
b is opposite B.
a is adjacent to B.

Also,

a is opposite to A.
b is adjacent to A.

Therefore, with reference to any angle of the right triangle, c is the hypotenuse, one side is opposite the angle, and the third side is adjacent to the angle.

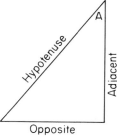 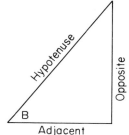

There are six trigonometric functions (ratios), defined by the lengths of the sides of the right triangle:

1. sine = sin = $\dfrac{\text{opposite side}}{\text{hypotenuse}}$

2. cosine = cos = $\dfrac{\text{adjacent}}{\text{hypotenuse}}$

3. tangent = tan = $\dfrac{\text{opposite}}{\text{adjacent}}$

4. cosecant = csc = $\dfrac{\text{hypotenuse}}{\text{opposite}}$

5. secant = sec = $\dfrac{\text{hypotenuse}}{\text{adjacent}}$

6. cotangent = cot = $\dfrac{\text{adjacent}}{\text{opposite}}$

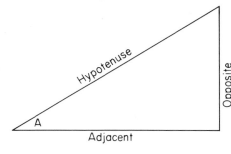

$$\tan A = \frac{\text{opposite}}{\text{adjacent}}$$

$$\cos A = \frac{\text{adjacent}}{\text{hypotenuse}}$$

etc

Values of these trig functions can be found in tables, to five decimal places. If one side and one angle of the right triangle are known, all angles and lengths of all sides can be found by these formulas, by looking up trig functions for the known angle.

Some useful values:

$\cos \ 0° = \sin 90° = 1$ $\cos 45° = \sin 45° = 0.707$

$\cos 90° = \sin \ 0° = \tan 0° = 0$ $\cos 60° = \sin 30° = 0.500$

$\cos 30° = \sin 60° = 0.866$ $\tan 45° = 1.000$

Answers to More Difficult or Doubtful Questions in the Text

CHAPTER 4

2. Pressure too low; the blade will wear out by rubbing.
   Pressure too high; teeth will be overloaded and heated.
3. Low speed does no harm.
   High speed greatly shortens the life of any cutter.
4. Abrasive cutoff wheel.
6. If there are too many teeth cutting, the pressure per tooth will be too low.
8. The faster the feed, the fewer revolutions to sever the piece and the less the rubbing and heating effects on the blade.
9. a. 2160 rpm.
   b. 2400 rpm.

CHAPTER 5

1. Metal is being removed over the area of the hole.

6. a. Shallow hole, large diameter.
   b. Hole to be enlarged.
   c. Long, slim hole to be made straight.
7. a. 360 rpm.
   b. 300 rpm.

CHAPTER 7

1. a. The bar can move away from the cutter.
   b. Dead center will be burned.
3. Dead center is easily overheated.
4. Cutting force and cutting heat are distributed over a larger area.

CHAPTER 8

7. Cutting edge is brittle and needs support, that .is, more material to support it.
8. Large back rakes exert less tool force. Soft materials are easily deformed by pressure.
13. 800 rpm.
14. 1000 rpm.
15. Rough bar size is 4 in.; finished bar size is $2\frac{1}{2}$ in.
   Area of 4-in. bar $= 12$ sq in.
   Area of $2\frac{1}{2}$-in. bar $= 4.7$ sq in.
   Bar area removed $= 12 - 4.7 = 7.3$ sq in.
   Rpm $= 600$, and tool travels 9 in. along the bar in 1 minute.
   Volume of bar removed in 1 minute $= 65.7$ cu in.

CHAPTER 9

1. For #3 M.T., diameter of plug at end of socket (dimension A) $= 0.938$
   Diameter at small end (dimension D) $= 0.778$.
   Standard plug depth (dimension P) $= 3.1875$.
   Taper in 3.1875 in. $= 0.938 - 0.778$.
   Taper per foot $= 0.565$ in.
   The slope of the taper is 0.080 in. in 3.1875 in.
   $\tan A = 0.080/3.1875 = 0.0251$; Angle $A = 1$ deg 26 min.

CHAPTER 11

9. 320 rpm, 5.12 ipm.
13. 1 turn plus $\frac{13}{27}$ turn.
16. 1 minute $= \frac{1}{60} \times \frac{1}{9}$ turn $= \frac{1}{540}$ turn.
   $\frac{1}{20} - \frac{1}{27} = \frac{7}{540}$.

CHAPTER 14

1. Bigger motor allows heavier feed and fewer revolutions and less time to complete the cut. Less rubbing and heating effects.

CHAPTER 16

Questions on stainless steels, after Sec. 16.8.
2. Due to magnetic effects. The 304 is nonmagnetic.
3. a. 410   g. 305
   b. 420   h. 305
   c. 420, 440   i. 304
   d. 410 or 420   j. 301, 410
   e. 410   k. 316
   f. 303   l. 410
5. Not much improvement in corrosion resistance until chromium is increased to 12 per cent.
6. Rockwell C 40 is not hard enough to hold a sharp edge for very long.

Questions at end of chapter.
1. The first steel forms chromium carbides and is a tool steel. The second steel is a low-carbon type with chromium, therefore stainless.
3. Too much carbon; brittle.
4. Not enough carbon; not hard enough.
5. So that the weld deposit will not harden.
9. a. Toughness.
   b. Resistance to softening at high temperatures.
10. Graphite flakes interrupt the metal chip.
11. Graphite in the iron serves as a lubricant.

13. W—no alloy additions
    O—low alloy
    A—higher alloy
14. b. A
    e. O
16. Test with a magnet.
18. Heat concentrates in the cutting area.
19. To exert less pressure against the work, since the workpiece deforms easily.

CHAPTER 17

1. Rockwell C 55.
3. Go about 50–75 deg above the critical temperature.
4. Delay in moving from furnace to quench.
   Too large a piece to cool quickly.
   Piece blanketed by steam when in the water.
   Water too hot.
5. Decarburizing and severe scale formation.
6. a. 55–60
   b. 65–67
   c. 65–67
8. Annealing is the dead-soft condition. Tempering reduces hardness slightly from maximum. Annealing requires heating above the critical temperature; tempering is done below critical temperature.
9. a. Hardest condition in steels.
   b. Nonmagnetic condition above the critical temperature.
10. There is a smaller temperature range in which to complete the transformation.
16. Delays grain growth at high temperatures.
17. No. Not enough carbon.
19. Heating below the critical temperature; no distortion, no scaling.
20. If the bar is not tempered, it is too brittle to bend. If induction-hardened, the core is soft and the bar can be straightened.
21. 0.005 in. is usually acceptable.
22. a. about 1000°.
    b. No.
23. b. Too much spread in the plotted results.

CHAPTER 18

7. Faster cooling rate.
8. Carbon 0.16 per cent, chromium 10 per cent, nickel 5 per cent.
   There is enough carbon to form chromium carbides, so that there will
   be some hardening effect.
11. Four times.
12. a. 6010 or 6011.
    b. 6024, 6027.
    c. 6013.
15. Other metals produce oxides with very high melting points that cannot
    be blown out of the cut.
18. Impossible to control hardness in the repaired shaft.

CHAPTER 19

8. a. Class 1 fit.
   b. Class 7 or 8.
   c. Class 4.
   d. Class 2.

CHAPTER 20

1. 0.1 HP = 254 Btu per hour. 1 Btu = 778 ft-lb.
2. 1 HP = 33000 ft-lb/minute.
12. More, because softer steel would indent under the pressure.
16. Too loose a chain.
24. Different tooth shapes that do not match.

CHAPTER 21

5. Setup operations consume more time on engine lathes, and less time is
   spent machining.
7. Several automatics can be managed by a single operator.
8. No. NC lathes are used for short runs on complicated shapes.

CHAPTER 22

1. Parity check requirements.

2. Zero is a piece of information; it is not nothing.

9. 0011, 0111, 00010000, 00010011, etc.

10. 3 × 3:   11   3 × 4:   11

          × 11   100

           —   —

           11   00

           11   00

          —   11

     1001 = 9   —

                           1100 = 12

11. EOB—hole in 8th track—10000000 binary and 128 decimal.

12. No.

CHAPTER 23

2. a. Go to start of cut with G80. Cut with G79.

7. a. Tape reader stops reading.
   b. Tape reader stops reading.
   c. Information will be used for the wrong purpose.
   d. Unimportant.
   e. Tape reader stops reading.
   h. Hole drilled at parking position.
   i. Drill the missing hole on manual operation.
   m. Unimportant.

Index

500